# Women Are Dreaming The Future

*The work of a woman visionary*
*is to know the past*
*dream the future*
*and take powerful action in the present.*
Shiloh Sophia McCloud

# Is this book for me?

*This book is for women*
*who have an idea and*
*a desire to make it happen!*

## This book is for women who:

- would like to live their dream and create vital lifework
- have a fabulous idea which they think will make some money
- are starting or thinking about launching a new project or business
- are visionaries who want to take their project to the next level
- want to treat their college education like a business-to-be
- finished college and wonder how to apply their degree to livelihood
- are thinking of leaving their current job to start a new life
- are in a corporate job and want to create a side business
- are budding entrepreneurs interested in turning ideas into income
- are in business and want to improve systems and profitability
- want to create a business plan with vision and heart
- desire to create a lifework in alignment with their values
- need to make a plan so they can quit their day job
- have always known there was a "greater work" for them
- want to spend their precious time doing something meaningful
- are rebellious and wild and cannot bear a traditional model
- know that they are called and have a divine purpose to fulfill!

***If you answered "That's me!" to any of the above...***

This book is for you!

# Heart of the Visionary

## A Workbook for Women's Work

**Created By Author and Artist Shiloh Sophia McCloud**

**AND**

**Co-Authors and Co-Editors:**

**Mary MacDonald, elizaBeth Benson-Udom,**
**Shannon McCloud, Caron McCloud,**

WITH

**Artist Sue Hoya Sellars and Contributing Authors:**

Nancy Ballard, Jean Shinoda Bolen, Alisa Franzone-Davis, Dori Etter,
Kelly Takunda Orphan Martinez, Jenett Miller, Sherri Morris, Gennifer Mountain,
Marilyn Nyborg, Caterina Rando, Nikiah Seeds, Julie Lampros Trad,
Alice Walker, Ananda Wildflower and Ama Zenya

**Foreword by SARK: Susan Ariel Rainbow Kennedy**

a project from the palm of her hand

**COSMIC COWGIRLS INK, LLC ™**

***A Woman and Girl Powered Publishing and Production House***

**www.cosmiccowgirls.com**

**0-9674214-5-4** 

*Created with Love in the United States and Printed with Care in Hong Kong*

# This Work of Women

Shiloh Sophia McCloud

This is the work of women!
Yes. It is time for a revolution of women and path,
women and money, women and business,
women and art, women and marketplace.
We do not choose to give
our works away for nothing.
We are not starving artists. We are not frivolous.
We are creators whose creations
save lives, mend wounds, change the world.
This work of priestesses and practitioners
of every kind is
VISIONARY WORK.
Our work is vital. Essential. Needed.
This work of women
must include creating livelihood.
This is not easy, quick, fun, or likely.
This may not be accepted or encouraged.
But this is what we must do.
Create an abundance revolution!
We are creating our own path.
We are creating our own marketplace.
We are creating our own money.
We create art.
We work from the heart.

We deserve to be compensated.
We are creating our own
mystical cosmic luminous overflowing BANK.
A bank that does not cause, contribute to or condone
the suffering of others for profit.
A Women's Bank. Believe it. Create it.
Deposit into it. Draw from it.
Invite other women into it.
Enter the income stream in your little golden boat
and dream and work and pray and play and prosper.
Do not stop. Keep going.
It will almost always seem impossible.
But we make miracles. Believe in you. In us.
Miracles are organizing themselves right now
around our dreams, our work, our visions.
Let us go out, armed with what matters

And with the prayers of our Grandmothers, shining!

# Dedicated To The Grandmothers

*This project is dedicated to the women who made our lives possible:*

**Our Mothers, Grandmothers, Great Grandmothers and all the way back to our very first Grandmother. The legend of their hard work, vision, wisdom and commitment to life is being honored in this book. Our visionary women ancestors have lit the torch so that we can find our way. Let us go forward celebrating, dreaming and creating a beautiful world together!**

We are our grandmothers' prayers.
We are our grandfathers' dreamings.
We are the breath of our ancestors.
W.M. Barnwell

# *We Honor Our Grandmothers*

*Nancy Ballard:* **Marie Louise Allaire,** born in Barcelona, Spain
**Annie Murphy**, from Ireland and San Francisco
*elizaBeth Benson-Udom:* **Ida Erickson Benson**, born in Kansas
**Mary Hazel Brouyette Fitzgerald**, born in Kansas
*Alisa Franzone-Davis*: **Jenny Franzone**, born in Brooklyn, N.Y.
**Marianne Giardina**, born in New York City, N.Y.
*Dori Etter:* **Dorothy Waterfill Corman,** born in Paris, Kentucky
*Ananda Wildflower Fong*: **Grandma Fong** born in Toi Shan Mountain, China
**Tam Quai Choy**, born in Canton, China
*Susan Ariel Rainbow Kennedy (aka) SARK:* **Luella Lee Anderson**; **Jessie Kennedy**
*Mary Stella MacDonald:* **Elizabeth Ann Kelly**, born in Aberdeen, Scotland;
**Mary Estelle MacDonald**, born in Prince Edward Island, Canada
*Kelly Takunda Orphan Martinez:* **Josephine Jenanyan Orphan**, born in Armenia
*Caron McCloud:* **Ethyl (Quier) Kenney**, born by a river in Oklahoma;
Paternal: **Selma Johanna (Selander) Grant**, born in Gamla Karlaby Finland,
The Kingdom of Sweden, Daughter of Charlotta, daughter of Brita Johanna Frahnholm.
*Shannon Johnson McCloud:* **Eden (Kenney) McCloud**, born in Crane, Oregon;
**Gladys (Allen) Johnson**, born in Los Angeles, California
*Shiloh Sophia McCloud:* **Eden (Kenney) McCloud,** born in Crane, Oregon;
**Helen Yarosh Davis**, born in Lopez, Pennsylvania, originally from Russia
*Jenett Miller:* **Ada Carl,** born in California
*Sherri Morris:* **Hallie Mae Thomas Harrison**, born in Edmondson County, Kentucky;
**Golden Philpott Hayes**, born in Hart County, Kentucky;
Step-Grandmother: **Mae Belle Smith McGrew**, born in Kentucky
*Gennifer Weaver Mountain:* **Mildred Mary Segale** "Mama" born in Angels Camp, California;
**Shirley (Krueger) Weaver** "Grandma", born in Berkeley, California
*Marilyn Nyborg*: **Anna Carlson Veghte**, born in Chicago, Illinois;
**Margaret Rosenbrock**, born in Baltimore, Maryland
*Caterina Rando*: **Caterina Asselta**, born in Southern Italy; Paternal: Born in Sicily
*Nikiah Seeds:* **Pearl Judges**, who was the daughter of **Mabelle Sutherland**;
**Dorothy Seeds**, daughter of Dorothy Willis, daughter of Selena Breakspear
*Sue Hoya Sellars:* **Daisy Conger**, born in Arkansas; **Grandma Sellars**, born in Kentucky
*Julie Lampros-Trad:* **Kathleen Hallis** "Little Grams", Tacoma, Washington;
**Violet Lampros** "Yia Yia", Chehalis, Washington
*Ama Zenya:* **Margaret Jackman Spencer**, born in Illinois;
**Esther Hopcraft**, born in Devon, England

Thank you also for the grandmothers of all of the other women quoted in this book. And for all the mothers and fathers, and all the grandfathers and grandmothers...

YOUR GRANDMOTHERS:

## Dedication To My Grandmothers from Shiloh

***This Little Grandma Goes to Market...***

### *Grandma Eden*

I have wanted to create this book all of my life. I was raised with women who "went to market." My Grandmother Eden and my mama Caron were in business together since before I was born. I learned my do-it-yourself and anything-can-be-done attitude from them. Sometimes they were up all night filling an order for dresses to be shipped to stores in the morning. I have found myself doing the same thing, only with artwork!

My Grandmother Eden was a dressmaker, a pattern maker, a fine art embroiderer, and could shoot a bow and arrow and a gun. She lived on a farm and her Auntie Mabel was a cowgirl who rode in the Pendleton Round-Up. Her life growing up in Oregon was tough from the start, but she brought all that tough girl wisdom to the women in our family. YAHOO!

She could fix or mend anything. She made me dresses. Her house was a jungle of plants. She encouraged me to be who and what I wanted. She is a living legend and has helped to make me who I am.

In the care center where she lives, she has a view of the lagoon where wild birds visit daily. She sits with her best friend Ruth, gossiping and, as always, creating quite a stir. My mom has created her room or "apartment" as Grandma calls it, all in royal and baby blue and paisley and white lace. Grandmother's artwork hangs all around her.

She works in a lost art, Thread Painting, and dyes her thread by hand. My mom continues to rotate her "show" so it is fresh. Grandma loves to show her work off to passersby and guests. It is our work—and I don't mean job, but our true work—that identifies us.And it is glorious the pride, the joy, the context, the purpose that having her work around her creates. Artist is her identity and reminds her of who she is as other memories slip away. Therefore, her spunk and passion live in a very real way.
She will continue to live through her art, her poetry and her legend.

When I was little I would spend the night at her house often and we would spend the whole evening hanging out together. She would make me her special chicken and sweet potatoes—we would knit, play cards, watch TV, listen to Elvis, and set my hair in rollers, all in the same night. This is for you Gran!

*Note: When this was written, my Grandma Eden was still with us.*

Eden McCloud

October 8, 1911—May 2, 2008

# *Grandma Davis*

My Grandmother once told me that when she was a young woman she decided she was going to love herself no matter what. I was amazed, as that seemed so progressive for her generation. Then she said that the more she loved herself, the more others seemed to love her. She made a decision and then backed it up with consistent action all her life. I wish you could have met her. She often wore a leopard silk shirt, rhinestone crusted cat glasses and hot pink lipstick. Her hair was as white as dove feathers

She died a few years ago. She did not need to, but she was ready. When we asked her to go to the hospital, as we all knew she could be renewed that way, she refused to go. I said, "But Grandma! You can stay alive!" She said, "For what? For you? For all of you? No way! I have had a full and lovely life! I have experienced what I was here to experience. I love you and I am at peace. And now I am going home. I want to see your Grandpa and my Lord."

Years before, when Grandpa died, Grandma put money in his pocket before he went up in flames at the cremation. When I asked what for, she said it was for a drink at the bar and grill in the sky. I think she sort of imagined him, sitting there, on the Far Side Banks of Jordan Tavern, waiting for her. After she passed, we found some erotic letters written between them, but that is a story for another day! They were married, and will be, forever, and their Anniversary is my birthday!

Right before she died, though she had not spoken or eaten for days, she sat up and asked our family to get dressed in white. Then she asked me for her lipstick and I put it on her soft full lips. She asked us to gather around to have our picture taken. I put lilies and roses on her lap and she seemed happy and peaceful. We felt the request unusual, but someone said: 'It's so Russian.'

Her parents came from Russia and were shopkeepers, so I've got it in my blood to be a merchant! Grandma Davis worked at the College of Marin most of her life and she used to take me to work with her and "register" me for classes when I was a little girl. Later, I did go to school there!

I saw her choose love, joy, hope and forgiveness at every turn. And I witnessed her service to her community up until the day she decided to lay down and did not get up again. I saw a woman at home in herself. I have learned from her peaceful and generous ways.

Our times together were always filled with yummy food I did not get to eat at home like instant mashed potatoes and kielbasa sausages. And, there were many many questions. She wanted to know everything. It was so wonderful having someone who was truly interested in me! And of course, I asked her about every detail of her very busy social and church life too.

Some of the most delicious times of my life were spent with my Grandmothers. So it is with my Grandmothers in mind and all the Grandmothers in my heart, that *Heart of the Visionary* is dedicated. I look forward to being with all of them in Paradise, and celebrating our legendary lives!

*Note: When I started this book, many years ago, Grandma Davis was still with us.*

Helen Yarosh Davis

July 24, 1921—May 5, 2004

# HEART OF THE VISIONARY
# TABLE of CONTENTS

## A WARNING!

**This book is an organic work in progress like a wild garden—so if you are a critic or perfectionist, you might have to turn back, or look the other way! There may still be typos and blunders, so surrender your critic now! If you dare continue, watch for spontaneous bursts of genius and unexplainable acts of passion! Beware of the impact of expanding consciousness! Make room for the outrageous blessings that come as you awaken your visionary heart!**

**If you still chose to continue, We Welcome YOU!**

## Heart of The Visionary

*is a creation between many women whose hearts, minds, bodies and resources went into action to make this book possible. I give thanks for these brave souls working with me on this dream which I have been cultivating for over eight years which includes this workbook and the workshop. Thank you to all the Cosmic Cowgirls for being my tribe of wild women who make miracles happen! May we be the mothers to many more collaborative creations!*

## Gratitude for Movement Foremothers

*I would like to thank Jean Shinoda Bolen, Marilyn Nyborg and Alice Walker for their transformative work in the world and for their generous contribution to this creation. Each of them has blessed my life in many ways!I would like to thank Susan Kennedy, aka: SARK, for being such a powerful catalytic agent in the realm of creativity and visionary business. From making a decision as a little girl to bless the world, to becoming a bestselling author many times over, Susan forges pathways that benefit all of us. We love Susan! Here, she shares the story of her own journey as a visionary entrepreneur!*

# for·word

BY SARK

I've Admired SHILOH's work since I first saw it, and was lucky to have it appear on the front cover of my planet SARK magazine in 2000. Her art, words and vision are deeply moving to me, and to all kindred spirits everywhere.

Heart of the Visionary is the perfect descriptive title for this book, and it's exactly the kind of heart-centered non-linear and immensely practical resource that I've been searching for. This work takes a quantum leap for women and for business.

My creative work in this world began at birth, and became a physical reality in 1964 when I was 10 years old and announced to my mother that I was meant to write books and be a beacon of hope to the world. She told me to eat my peanut butter sandwich. She also assured me that I could do whatever I wanted.

I wrote my first book that summer, and I'm always glad to say that the art in it isn't very different from the art I do now.

My best friend at the time was an 80 year-old man named Mr. Boggs. He became quite ill and went into the hospital, and my mom told me that he probably wouldn't come back out. I resolved to write and create something for him every day, which I did for a month.

Mr. Boggs did get out of the hospital, and said to me; "I think you saved my life. Nobody else called or wrote, and I had to get out to see you."

I immediately knew that if I could do that for one person, I could do it for the world, and that became my dream and vision.

That dream waited for me until 1988, when I started being actively creative each day. I created a poster called "How to be an Artist" that is my statement about how we are all artists of life.

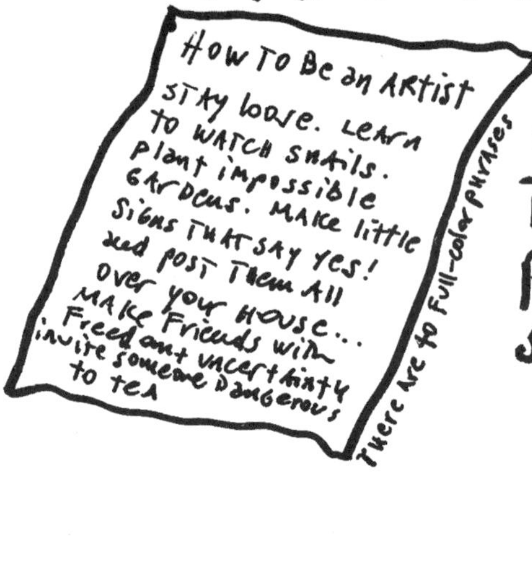


I made 11,000 of these posters by hand, and then created 18 other posters, on 18 other subjects.

I then entered into business with a store and catalog, and my art and words began traveling around the world.

This led to my first book being published in 1990, A Creative Companion.

I then formalized my company in 1993 and named it Camp SARK. In order to learn more about business, I studied and worked with a business mentor. I learned a lot about being a creative business person, becoming a brand and forming a team. I continued writing and creating a book per year.

In 1997, I wrote and published a book called Succulent Wild Woman, which is my statement of self-liberation.

i found etched into the cement on a sidewalk in San Francisco

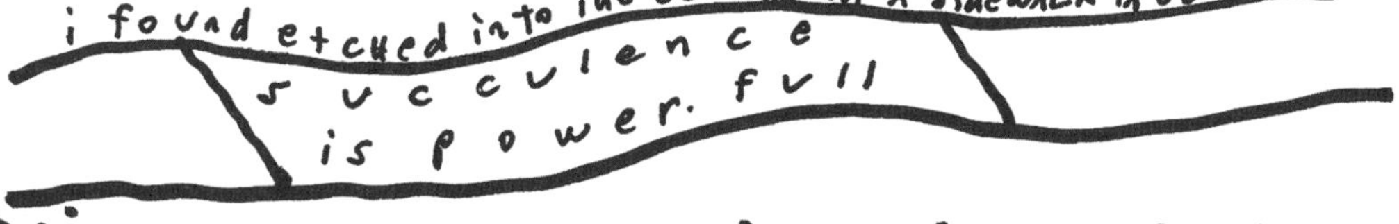


This book became an immediate national bestseller, optioned for a movie and I went on 25 city book and media tours.

In 1998, I launched the licensing division of Camp SARK, and with the help of a small creative team, created 250 products with my art and words.

The products were a huge success, and the SARK brand traveled around the world, connecting with people everywhere and generating millions of dollars in revenue. The growth of my little company was enormous, and I made lots of mistakes as it grew larger. One of the biggest mistakes was that it was actually costing more to have a team and produce the products than I was earning from the licensing fees.

One of the greatest blessings was being able to recognize that, and make adjustments to the business plan. I was also so glad to utilize my brand to support causes and charities close to my heart.

By 2001, I'd disbanded the team, and retreated from the licensing portion of my business, to help take care of my Mom who had begun her dying process.

I then focused my energy on writing and speaking, and created 4 more books, and taught many creative workshops.

In 2003, I launched a new websight called planet SARK, dedicated to my Mom "Marvelous Marjorie" who died that year.

I think I've made just about every business mistake possible, and enjoyed most business successes in the past 20 years.

When I read Heart of the Visionary, those "mistakes" don't feel like mistakes anymore—just paths I've walked on my marvelous visionary journey. it's an endless PATH

Now I can imagine even greater successes, because I am restructuring my business and rebuilding it from the "inside out," to support Susan Ariel Rainbow Kennedy, who is so happy to share the SARK spirit with the world. My 15th book is called Juicy Pens, Thirsty Paper: Gifting the World with Your Words and Stories, and Creating the Time and Energy to Actually Do it.

Heart of the Visionary supports my new vision for SARK beautifully, and I can feel the tremendous groundswell of all the visionaries crawling, walking, running, dancing and FLYING right along with me!

# Invitation

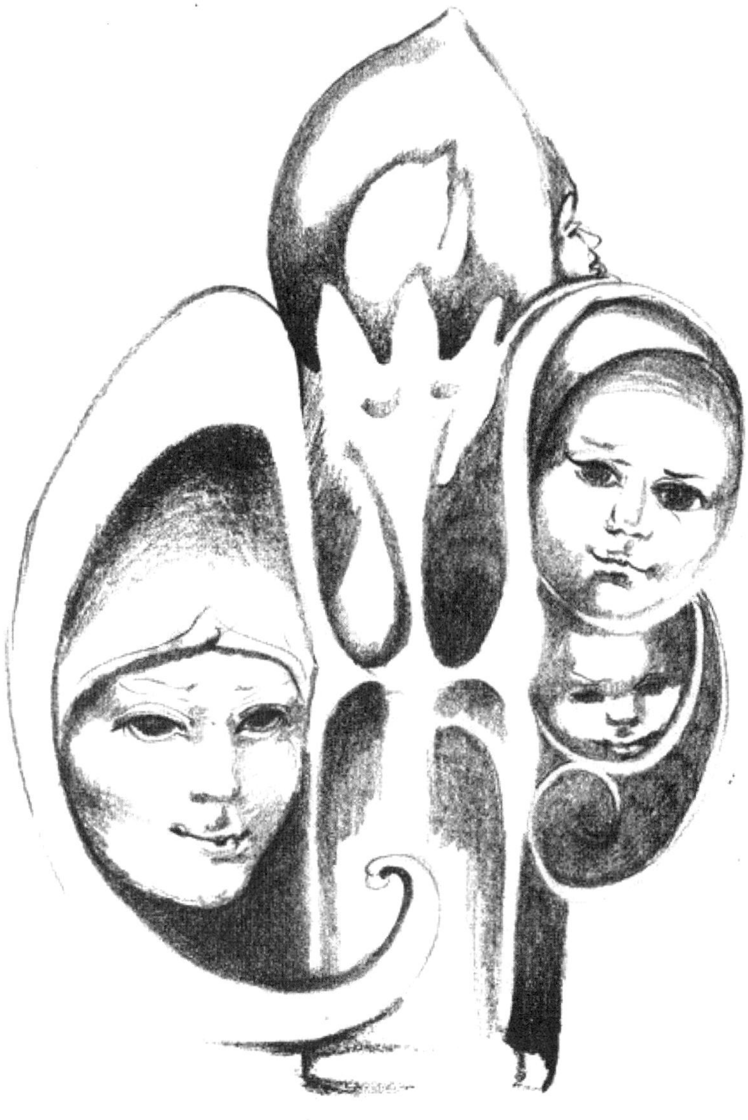

## The Power of Love

***Welcome Into The Heart of the Visionary***

**Author and Artist Shiloh Sophia McCloud**

**Illustration by Sue Hoya Sellars**

# Shiloh's Invitation

## The Burning Questions = The Awakened Heart

*Dear One,*

I want to write you a letter as if we are old friends. So, this would be a good time to make yourself a cup of tea. If we were together right now, as I wish, I would make you a cup like the one I am having. Lots of cream and honey, with cinnamon sprinkled on top. Candles are lit on my kitchen table, and we have red velvet pillows behind our backs. We suck slices of Summer's last watermelon from glistening pink layers on crystal plates. As you settle in, with your head resting on your hand, you are so lovely there next to that vase of blue hydrangeas. I tell you that they are the last from that tree you can see through my kitchen window.

We are here together because we want to ask the burning questions of life. Why do the questions burn? Because when they are asked, whether or not they get answered, they set our hearts on fire! Hearts flaming with life! With love! With possibility! With hope! With passion!

Tell me everything. Because I want to know. What are your favorite colors these days? And your favorite things to eat. What animal would you be if you could be any animal? What work are you into? Projects. Of course I want to know all about your mother, your father, your kids, your cat, your dog, and your job. Deaths, births and obstacles overcome. And we will eventually get to all that. But right now I want to talk about something else.

Tell me, what is on your mind the first thing in the morning, right before your eyes are open, when your thoughts have just begun to shake off the night? If regrets are what you find, then cast them into the morning fire and let them crackle and die there amongst the red ash of yesterday. If there is joy at the dawning of this new day, tell of all the deliciousness of your joy!

Are you happy? Are you doing work that you enjoy? What are you working on that is thrilling you? I want to know. I want to know what dream keeps coming back that is yet to be fulfilled. I remind you of your wild ways, and you remind me of mine. I remind you of who you were before everything else happened. You remind me of who I was. I ask if you have let go of your little girl's desire to be loved fully for who you are. Do you still have one foot out the door? The one that kicks ass?! Do you remember what was important to you when you were a very young woman? When you were just a little girl? Before everything got too too busy. Did you grow up to be who you wanted to be? What are you doing that you are proud of?

Are you doing your life work—not just a work life? Did you give up too much of yourself to others? Have you let go of too many dreams? Is there a dream you are nursing in quiet? There in the corner, feeding it the occasional dark chocolate to keep it from roaring too loudly? Can we bring it into the light right now? Can I be midwife to the reawakening of your hope for yourself? If you start to cry now, then I know you need this time together even more. And if you don't, then it is about me needing to share myself with you. And, of course, it is both.

Do you have a project, a vision, a plan? Some unreasonable desire? Some wild hair that just knows you are born to touch a lot of lives. Do you dream of having enough money to spend your time doing what you want to do? Have you let go of thinking you don't deserve to be well taken care of? Do you know that, for some of us, having regular pedicures is just as important as going to the dentist or the therapist?

We can save the world and have fun and look good doing it. Come on! Admit it! You want to create something juicy! I believe in the beauty of your dreams! If you do not admit to having a dream, then I am not done with you yet. Because I know you do!

If you confess to having let too much of who you are go, I will challenge you. Maybe you do not want this conversation and you would rather e-mail me next week, and speak of everyday things. But I won't give in to your protests. Maybe you will challenge me back. I hope you always will. Maybe you won't let me forget what is possible if I believe in myself. And I will tell you boldly, I believe in me and I believe in you!

You might laugh nervously because you do not want to answer these uncomfortable questions. I know this makes us feel vulnerable, exposed. And I am sorry. And I am not. Where else but here? When else but now? Who else, but us? The burning questions will never go away. They insist upon being courted like an eternally new lover. They must be sought and sung to, nurtured and adorned. Ani Di Franco says, "If you don't ask the right question, every answer sounds wrong." We must do as Clarrissa Pinkola Estes suggests in *Women Who Run With the Wolves* and seek the river beneath the river. We must call aloud upon the name of the door that opens it. "Otocar alla puerta!" Let's build an altar for our questions and pray for guidance to see the path more clearly. To hear the call! And answer it with our "Yahoo! Here I AM!"

I am not just trying to get you to answer these questions. I am trying to get you to ask them with me and of me. If I am not living my questions, living my way into the answers, how can I ask you if you are living yours? And I want to ask, must ask, cannot help but ask. And, of course, I want to explore, how do we live into the answers!?

I want to know, if you could do anything, what would it be? What does your perfect day look and feel like? From beginning to end. As you speak, I will bring a listening that creates a safe space for you to speak into. A listening that searches for clues to what is needed. If your day includes two naps, I will know you need to rest more. If your day does not include any art, I will know you have forgotten how much you liked to draw and color when you were little, and it was late, and you did not want to put your crayons down. If your day does not include a lover, I will ask you about your heart's desire. If you LOVE being alone, I will congratulate you on this great victory that many struggle with!

If you say you hate your job, I will continue to talk with you about change. Life IS too short to spend our days at something we hate. Period.

This letter is about having a life you choose. Some women cannot choose. Some live in situations and environments where there aren't choices like the ones we get to make. Those who can make our dreams come true, must give it a try! The rest of the world needs us to RISE to the occasion of our own lives! There are choices even when we no longer see them! Choices are here with us in this moment!

Right now I wish I could take you out and buy you some brand new red cowgirl boots! You are going to need them! It is time to kick ass again! All women should have a pair of red boots. You look damn fine in cowgirl boots. I want us to take off on an adventure! Today! If we risk, we may be in jeopardy of one kind or another for a while, but we can make it. We have moved mountains before. We have a bold faith that keeps us from giving up no matter what!

If we feel we don't have a powerful circle of friends, allies, and associates we can trust right now, then we should try to make one or join one! We all have a vision of some kind, don't you think? And some folks have a big vision. Something so big that we are embarrassed to speak it aloud because it sounds too grand. Like wanting to end world hunger, or start an orphanage, or plant an organic garden for our town, or start a business, or write a book, or become a painter. I think many of us have big visions, but there is a strange feeling that comes along with them. Although the big visions are about blessing others we often feel alone in them. That is because we need to talk about them. And find others of like soul to vision with.

Most of the women I know have a save-the-world-complex just like I do. It is not so uncommon as we think. But we must have the courage to share and act on our grand desires! Alice Walker says that one of the things we can do for the world is to be in conversation about what is going on, personally, collectively, cosmically. Our big visions can give us clues to what we truly care about. If we do not know what we truly care about how can we know our purpose here on earth? How can we know what to manifest? To attract?

Alice Walker also says that "No one can end suffering except through dance." What does this mean, really? For me it means to create no matter what! It means that my vision, my love for you, and for others, is contributing to the great goodness of the world. It says that art is medicine. **Our dancing, our knitting, our singing - like our prayers - lift one another up**. It says that our dancing does not fall on empty streets, nor our visions on empty ears. We do not have to become whole first, or suffer more, or do a better job before we contribute. We start by choosing a way to participate and then we act on it! And we don't stop - over time, it, and we, will grow. We have to commit art, with intention, says my art teacher and mentor, Sue Hoya Sellars. And as my mother Caron McCloud always says, "It's about creativity!" Creativity is not just something for artists, it is something for all of us.

And we have to choose a life path and do it no matter what!!!! We have to do it even when we don't feel like it is possible. Even when there does not appear to be enough money. Even when the odds seem against us. We have to work on it even if we are doing other work. We cannot go on without living some part of our vision. And I know you have one. Please, with me, take action on your behalf. The time is now. There is no other perfect time to begin.

I am not afraid to tell you of my unreasonable desires. *I want to do what I can to end suffering in the world*. It isn't something one just makes up one day, it is something that comes

alive in you. Your heart awakens, with a little flame on top that won't go out. You cannot help it. And sometimes it is so unreasonable it sounds ridiculous in sentence form – but we must form it into sentences and images that articulate our visions! Yes! And it is my vision that leads me to create – to be in business – to follow my visions – to be in conversations like this one! It is my experience that my Vision is informed by prayerful, consistent seeking of the purpose for which I am born. I have worked with thousands of women in the creation arts now, and I have to say, purpose and passion are found on the journey itself. Not some remote destination in the distance somewhere. Destiny is found along the way. Caring about people I do not even know is what keeps my projects moving. I cannot understand how I can feel so much pain for my brothers and sisters that I slump and cry and scream. And then, I go to the canvas or to the classroom or to my computer and my worries are transformed into more prayer, peace, sharing of insights, wisdom, and even, bliss. Yes, Bliss. The suffering, my own and that of others, informs me, opens me, awakens me to my love for the Divine, for you, and for myself. I attempt to touch and soothe the suffering, and express the love, by creating what beauty I can in response to the tragedies of life. I can respond with more sadness and anger, or I can respond with a healing remedy, whenever I am able.

I also say, as I often do: **The work of a woman visionary is to know the past, dream the future and take powerful action in the present.** I say that we must celebrate, and create art, make love, create abundance, share in beauty, spread joy and hope and information however, wherever, and whenever we are able. Ready for another cup of tea? Or how about some fresh squeezed juice? (Imagine me getting it for you - and giving you a hug on the way.) And isn't it amazing how hard it is to practice self care? While we know sometimes that it is in caring for others that we find peace, we often neglect caring for ourselves. There are some of us who serve and serve, but never serve ourselves or allow ourselves to be served by others. Some of us just serve our own interests and don't serve others. But if we are to find peace we must honor both serving and being served. To know the suffering in the world, and to be sick from it, to be overburdened and overwhelmed by it, to be too sensitive, to become hopeless or let suffering make us mean, does not do anyone any good. Well, maybe it helps at first! We have a right to be mad. There are a lot of terrible things happening, while at the same time, so many good things! How to hold it all in context? Contrary to popular belief, it is not "all good." The next big question is: How do we find and practice self love? If we could do just that, transformation would become our rhythm, instead of like a goal we keep striving to reach.

We know there is more we can experience than what is perceived on the surface of things. We are vaguely aware of an ever widening landscape of bounty, which we sense, hear in the distance, smell. Oh, how we long for it! And we buy books and tapes and workshops that promise to give it to us! But really, where is it!? We try and try and then feel bad about our failures. Have you noticed that if you don't pull off your latest self help plan, you feel worse?

Let's go out on a treasure hunt for our bountiful vision! It's time we rid ourselves of those wounds that poke us in the eye when we are gazing at the horizon. We have to let those harmful stories about ourselves go. We have spent enough time tending them and licking them. We must do whatever we can do to get them out of our immediate sphere. RIGHT NOW! We can store them for later if we're so attached to them, but for now, we release them, we send them out to be dissolved, we compost them, bury them, burn them up! Do it Now!

We honor the spaces that are created by choosing things that delight us and serve our greater purpose. Let's begin things that are so inspiring that our old wounds haven't the room to surface. Only through creating our lives as powerfully as we can, will we be able to move beyond the wounding. Let's pray right now that wounds no longer keep us from our highest good. (Did you do it?) Clear the path! We are breaking on through. A tribe of folks who love themselves enough to create miracles is moving in!

I am closing this very long letter to you with a few more of the burning questions I ask myself. The ones that seem to provide me with—if not always answers—the vitality that comes with the awakened heart! What stories no longer serve me? What guilt can I surrender? What project can I begin that inspires me? How can I deepen my spiritual practice? What am I excited about, I mean, thrilled about? Have I let too much of the "bad girl" go and replaced her with too much of the "good girl?" How do I "self medicate" and is it working? What is healing for me? What do I really long for? What infuriates me? What do I find the most beautiful? What scares me? What good message can I tell myself when I start to think harmful thoughts? What would need to happen in my life for it to feel like a visionary life, a life well led? Needless to say this can go on and on, as good conversations want to. Through our explorations information and inspiration break forth like a hummingbird flying out of a fuchsia shaft, drunk with flower honey but ready for the next hit. YUM! The more we inquire, the funner it becomes to look within for answers! To seek the Divine for inspiration, guidance and clarity. And to offer up our gratitude.

The first thing this morning I stood in the dark, in the rain. Enclosed in this letter to you is a maple leaf that was on the wet grass. And a seagull feather I found at the beach a few blocks from my house. I am going to kiss your letter now. Wait, I have to go put on some lipstick first.... Okay, I'm back. SWACK! Did you hear that? If you like the color—it would go great with your new boots—write back and I'll tell you where to get it, the color is called, Strength. And that is what I send you right now. Strength. I hope you write back!

***With Bright Blessings and Love, Sparkling in Hot-Pink Flames,***
***Your Visionary Ally and Friend***

Shiloh

BE PATIENT
TOWARD ALL THAT IS UNSOLVED IN YOUR HEART
AND TO TRY TO LOVE THE QUESTIONS THEMSELVES
AS IF THEY WERE LOCKED ROOMS
OR BOOKS WRITTEN IN A VERY FOREIGN LANGUAGE.
DON'T SEARCH FOR THE ANSWERS,
WHICH COULD NOT BE GIVEN TO YOU NOW,
YOU WOULD NOT BE ABLE TO LIVE THEM.
AND THE POINT IS, TO LIVE EVERYTHING.
LIVE THE QUESTIONS NOW.
PERHAPS THEN, SOMEDAY FAR IN THE FUTURE,
YOU WILL GRADUALLY, WITHOUT EVEN NOTICING IT,
LIVE YOUR WAY INTO THE ANSWER.

RAINER MARIA RILKE
LETTERS TO A YOUNG POET

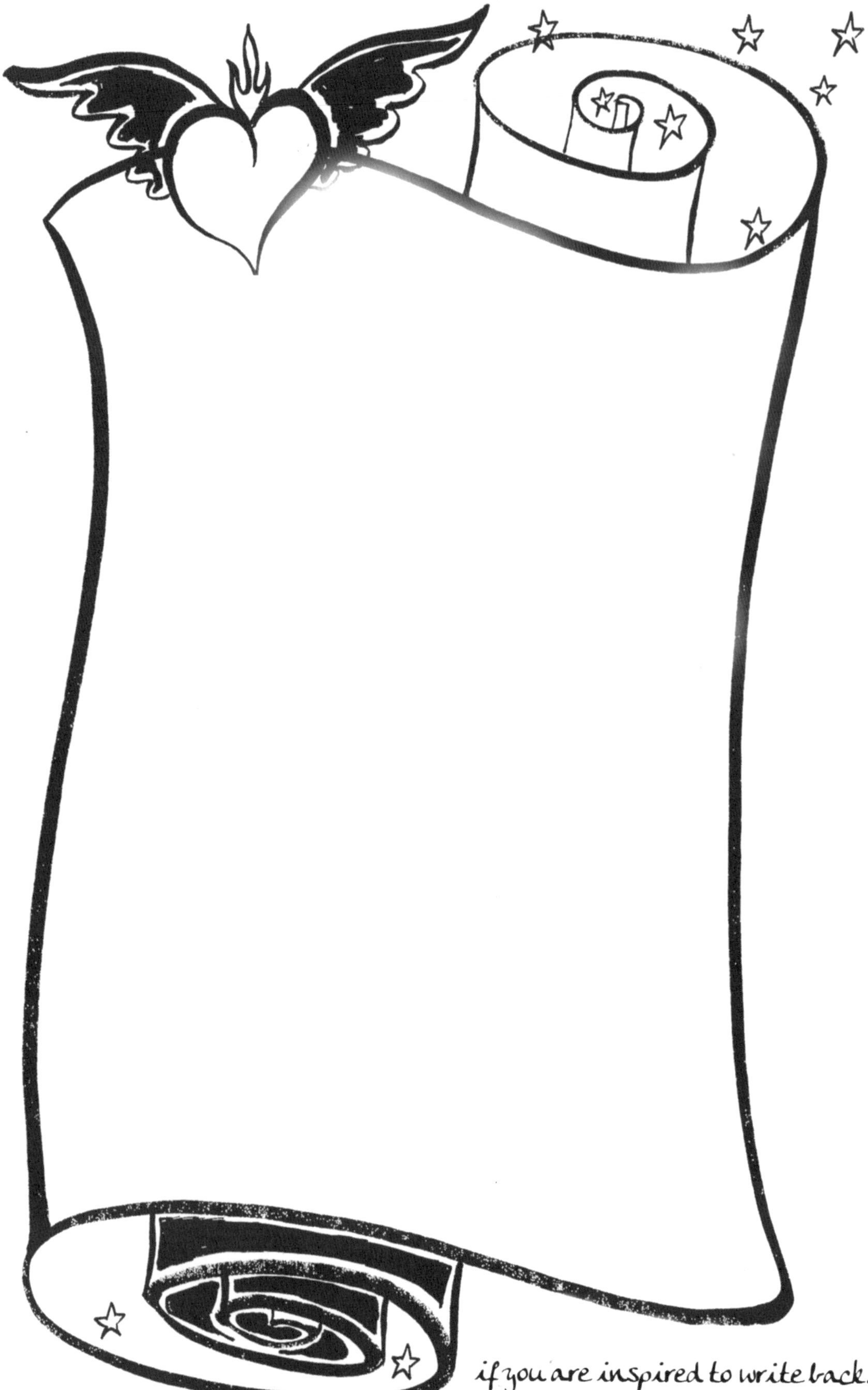

*if you are inspired to write back...*

# Introduction—Welcome to the Journey

## What is this Journal About?

Imagine living your life with vision, purpose, and possibility. What does it look like? How would it feel like to say: I am living life in a way that I choose. That reflects who I am. Well I believe it is possible. This may seem like an unreachable dream. Many are not living their dream and when we look around it can be discouraging. But if it is possible, wouldn't we give it everything we've got to try? And guess what—the trying part is the journey itself and it contains much joy and fulfillment along the way.

This workbook will serve as your own personal project sanctuary and guidebook for your visionary endeavors, projects and plans. This is an invitation to take action on your behalf, be unreasonable about your plans for your life and manifest your dreams! Trust that YOU have a purpose for being here on this planet and it might just be fulfilled through your own ideas!

No one can dispute the fact that a clearly defined plan will help our ideas become real. Writing down a plan is putting all of your ideas into an energetic garden so they can grow. Once the garden is planted it continues to grow all the time. That does not mean you have to be working on it every second. Once you have created the context in which you are going to live your vision, everything you do either makes a contribution to that, or it takes away from it. The overall goal is to lead a visionary life, no matter what we are doing or how close we might be to it now. Choose to lead a visionary life right now! View everything from within that context.

Each time I have looked at a traditional business plan I have gotten really excited. And frustrated. Excited about the possibility of getting my plans and ideas THAT organized and articulated. And of having something to SHOW others—see what I am doing!? I am playing with the big kids now! But a few pages into it I start to get overwhelmed and realize that I don't relate to the language. And somehow after these eleven years of business the 'traditional plan' never feels like it quite fits me! But I see the value in the process, and that is a big inspiration for designing this workbook in a way that women can really use it and identify with the presentation.

In this workbook, concepts of creativity, personal identity, manifestation and belief systems are explored as tools for designing your life work. An extensive VISION Plan Process introduces concepts that will prepare you for the Business Plan further on in the book. First, let's get as clear as possible about what you really want to create, which will guide the entire process towards the trajectory that will best facilitate your plan. The women authors in this book have made and manifested some amazing plans in their lives, and are generous in sharing their wisdom! Our perspectives, stories, and ideas are all diverse, and offered in great love. I had a vision to work with other women to create a visionary workbook based around the values of women's work that takes into consideration what we personally cherish.

A plan that looks at impact and footprint. That uses language that has feminine perspectives (example: the term *focus* instead of *target.*) I am inspired to introduce a plan that is visionary. A plan that has heart and care and giving and compassion built into the structure—where the actual form is built around life giving principles—as well as profitability. Just because we want to do something good and humanitarian, does not mean we don't want to make a profit. We are women of abundance—our resources empower us!

I am committed to creating and teaching a plan that shows the power of VISION to create and sustain abundance. If you are reading this and you don't know how you will fund your project, just keep reading—this workbook is a Start Where You Are Journal. Why should women get into business for themselves, or join other business projects? Mostly because it brings us vitality. Purpose. Meaning. A feeling of worth. A sense of participating in the gift of life. Somewhere to share our richness and wisdom. Something to be proud of. A path to follow. A plan to make. A dream to unfold. A story to be told. A legend to become. I also want to say that for the sake of this book "business" does not always mean what we traditionally think. It could be a project that you need a plan for. A book you want to write. A design you want to put in place. OR organizing your personal life and finances in a very real way. Throughout the book we sometimes call business "project" because to start working on something does not require it BE a business yet. My business IS formed from a series of ongoing projects. This is the way it works!

I believe business is a spiritual practice and path when we choose for it to be. It is a remarkable medium for learning and growth. And indeed it encompasses most of the things we need to learn anyway. Balance, boundaries, management, community, time, money, relationships, integrity. So much has to be learned on the spot, it is our personal transformation school! And we are choosing the textbooks, the courses, the learning outcomes.

My business is a HUGE part of my spiritual path. It is where my ministry is expressed. Almost any medium can be chosen through which to "practice" our life. Everything is an opportunity to grow. But when we focus it in a project or business it truly becomes a medium and context through which our lessons and transformations can occur. And it is truly cool that while we are learning all this, money is being made, systems are being established, goals are being met. So our "AH HA's" and our breakdowns all occur in an arena we have defined.

This does not just "happen." We have to choose it and choose it powerfully and profoundly. We have to CHOOSE to make our business an area where personal work will be done so we can celebrate the challenges as breakthroughs instead of "if only's." I have made short sighted choices along the way, but my work continues to thrive. It is true that we learn from our mistakes. Some say there are no mistakes, but I take exception. There is too much tragedy out there for it all to be on purpose. Let us not fear failure, as failing is a part of beginning. Let's take the charge off of failure and let hope be our guide. Continuing to do the work is easier if you love what you do or are inspired by the vision for the work. I do love what I do, and yes, that helps a lot. But even more than that, I will not do anything else. Call me stubborn. I just don't want to go back now that I have experienced the freedom of being an entrepreneur! (Not that it is less work). A business can be the extension of our soul work. Our life work can be a flowing forth from within our visionary heart. A blessing for others through our offerings, and a blessing for us through living a life of vitality, in which we are the leaders of our destiny! Sound good?

# The Inspiration—How This Book Came to Be

About five years ago I was teaching a college course in San Francisco. It was an inspiring class for my students and myself. I felt so blessed to be teaching women how to access their own inner creative expression through painting—no experience required! Towards the end of the semester the students and I were talking about their plans after graduation. And it was one of those moments—holy fire breathing instants—when everything shifts.

As they were speaking it became clear that they did not know what they were going to do once they graduated. They felt that what they wanted to do would not pay them enough, and student loans were about to kick in. They weren't sure how to apply their degrees to real life and money making, and they had upwards of $55,000 in debt! I could not believe my ears. Not because I thought they should know what to do, but because they didn't know, and were so far from knowing! Years and years of school, and no business card. No portfolio. No business plan. When one of them jokingly mentioned working at Starbucks, I felt I would come unglued.

A fire in my heart was ignited that day and has not stopped burning since. And it is because of them and that day that this book was born. The predicament startled me awake to this great need. Women must be empowered to do their work, and I must do whatever I can do to help make it happen. And so I am. This book is my action, and the action of the entire community of Cosmic Cowgirls. Every entrepreneur starts with an idea. A visionary entrepreneur starts with an idea that they believe is transformational. A woman visionary entrepreneur starts with a transformational idea that is in alignment with her values and dreams as a woman. And it is through awakening to our life work, our life path, and our life purpose that sets our hearts a flamin'!

How does a woman do business differently? Well, whenever I have brought up this conversation with women in a workshop, I am often met with opposition. "What about the men? Why do we have to exclude them? Why does it have to be called a feminine business paradigm?" I bet men don't hear this in their groups! But as soon as we get talking, the women realize the distinction that they too have been making, either consciously or unconsciously.

The conversation in this book provides a lens through which to view and consider the distinctions. So that we can move towards a more integrated model of doing business overall. We are not suggesting moving completely out of the existing paradigm—but working around it and within it—and still finding a way to do it in integrity with who we are. And being CONSCIOUS! As women visionaries we are informed by principles that are based in sustainable, healthy growth, giving back, and in the values of knowing "what is enough."

We are committed to a path of creativity and inquiry so that all decisions are based in ethical and sustainable business practices as a whole. We want abundance for ourselves, and for everyone.

*I was gravely warned by some of my female acquaintances*
*that no woman could expect to be regarded as a lady after she had written a book.*
*Lydia M. Child*

# Creating Art and Books Is My Ministry

I am an artist who has made a living selling my work for over ten years. I have a gallery, a wholesale line, and a series of workshops that make up the multiple income streams of the entrepreneurial business woman that I am. Thankfully, I have a product people want because my work is designed to meet a need and a want. So I have been relatively successful in pursuing my visions. It has taken tons of diligence, support from my beloved husband Isaiah, my family and friends, and an unreasonable love in my heart to do this work on behalf of all people. Other than help from family, we have had no outside funding, but have managed to make our living and enjoy our lives in a most miraculous way. If I had to say why the business has been able to continue and thrive, I would pick two reasons: My constant passionate determination that there is nothing else for me to do but this work which was given to me by Creator, and Isaiah's continuous and persistent insistence on business education and personal development. I am by nature a worker bee, and it is his guidance that put me in the mindset to think about implementing business systems and not just doing all the work by myself. If you have studied business at all, you know what it means when you do everything yourself. Instead of working on the business, you are working in the business. I am beyond grateful for a wise partner, of fourteen years, whom I adore.

So, it is with the spirit of loving doing my own work that I offer this book to the women of the world. When you get "called" you just get called. Sometimes you don't know why you are so crazy about something that you have just got to do. That is how I am about women and business. No, I am not a millionaire selling millionaire tricks. I am an artist and entrepreneur who has sold close to two million dollars of my work. I am a woman in business, who has lived a life that includes so much bliss and peace and abundance and love, that to share it is the natural outpouring. And so, I make art and books that I feel are healing tools for the blessing and transformation of all the folks I can reach. And I have a GOOD time doing it!

I founded a woman and girl powered company, Cosmic Cowgirls Ink on January 23, 2006 with 25 Founding Mamas. This work is my legacy, and is becoming the legacy of many others. As of today we have 97 Cosmic Cowgirl Member Owners and we are going for 5000! This book is our first offering in a list of hundreds that we plan to co-create and publish together. Do we think we can save the world? Well, we do think that if one has the inclination to become part of that process, what better way to spend ones days than to create beauty, and healing tools designed to bring transformation to a suffering people and planet. Blessings and Gratitude goes out to all the Cosmic Cowgirls who have helped to midwife this book especially my Mama Caron who has stood by me, this work, and this book with unfailing wisdom and support.

So she set out one day on her journey.
She didn't look back and she didn't rush.
She just kept taking one step at a time.
And opening her heart to the possibilities.

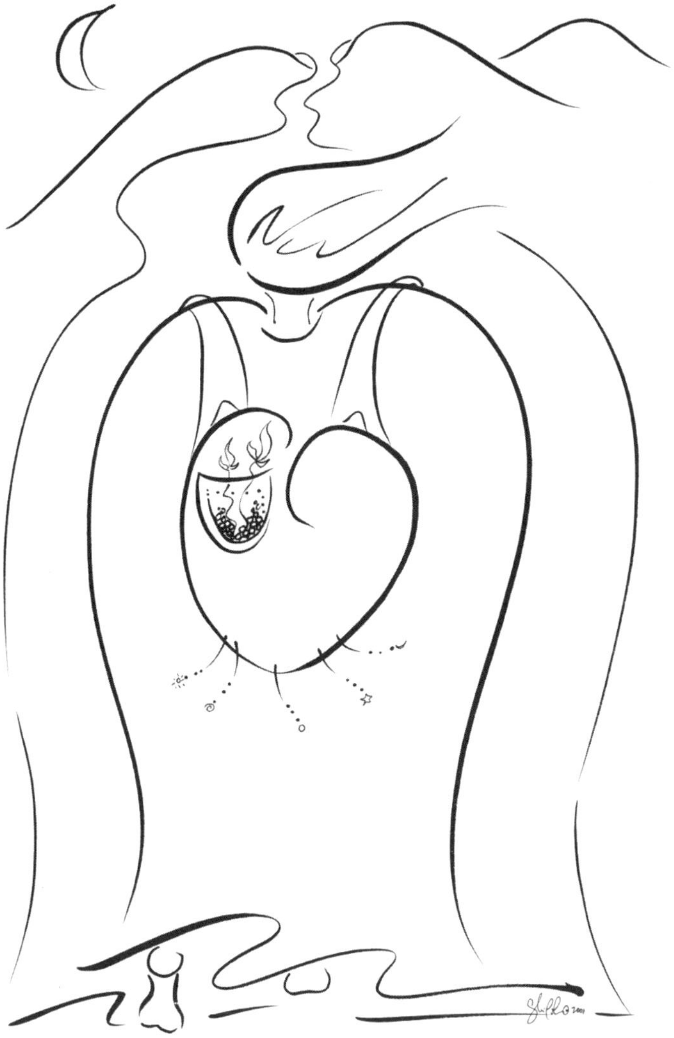

# Gratitude for the Primary Authors

***With Great Enthusiasm I would like to introduce the women who made this book possible, my incredible tribe of women visionaries! If you have ever had a team of women around you that you love, that love you, and that have your back, then you know how grateful I am for the women I have been working with at Cosmic Cowgirls. ~ Shiloh***

## Caron McCloud

When people ask how I got this way - the first thing that comes into my mind is: my mother made it possible for me to be who I am. I have been blessed with a Mama Bear who is my best friend, greatest supporter, closest ally and absolute gift in my life. We have always been close, and now more than ever. We do everything together. She has always been the most beautiful woman in the world to me - I used to send her cards of Grace Kelly and say I thought it was a postcard of her. She is so brilliant, her mind is like a fine design, just like in her beautifully sewn tapestries. She is a poet, a scholar, and a mystic, and an inspiration to all who know her. My mama taught me about perspective, and about being conscious - tools I use ALL the time. What a profound gift it is to be able to work with her on this book! I love my Mommmmmiieeee!

## Sue Hoya Sellars

Sue is my mentor and Co-Madre with my mother Caron since she was with us even before I was born. It is because of her that I stuck with my art and became a painter. Her work is the cosmic star stuff that informed my journey to become an artist. She always made sure I had a notebook and pens and pencils to work with and she brought me to the museum from the time I was little. Her artwork is genius and in her own words, she "illustrates the intelligent heart." One of my most dramatic shifts happened from a teaching she gave me - I was complaining about wedging clay - and she said for me to work my intention into the clay itself. This was a breakthrough on how to bring meaning to our work! We have worked together on a weekly basis for over seven years, and her illustrations for this book bring to life the spiritual concept of the visionary woman. Her way of being in strength and grace continues to teach and mentor me all the time.

(Note: For those of you who are not familiar with the difference in our work, Sue's illustrations which head each chapter should give you an idea!)

## Shannon McCloud

My big sister. My first Sheroe. I thought of her kind of like a movie star when we were growing up, with her cowgirl boots, dark sunglasses, red fingernails and rides in convertible cars with good looking sophisticated men. She is the one who started the phrase in our family, 'bad but good at it.' We have always been close and she taught me about being cool and about being tough. She is such a gentle being, but with such a kick ass attitude that she has always been an inspiration to me. She showed me that there was a different way of going about business, by doing it in a way that reflects who we are as women. She was VERY successful in the business world and now she has tossed her lot in with Cosmic Cowgirls, for which I am most grateful! Her work in this book served as the "irreverent" wild woman nature that we embrace at Cosmic Cowgirls! If it was up to her the book would have a sound track from Sister Sledge: "We are Family, I got all my Sisters with Me!" The Cinnamon Cowgirl makes my heart sing!

## Mary Stella MacDonald

I have been working with Mary for a year and a half and I have to say, I have experienced profound laughter, celebration, creativity, friendship, support and wisdom in working with her on an almost daily basis. That is a BIG deal. She is absolutely gracious to me and to all of our community - and an absolutely brilliant conversationalist! When Sue, Mary and I went out to dinner with SARK, Sue and I just sat back and listened as the two of them in their wild woman wisdom dissected the universe on everything from sex to drugs to art and a few other unmentionables. I love a woman who cannot only hold up her end of the conversation, but actually be GENERATIVE. Mary is a dear friend and ally and I hope to work with her forever. I recently discovered her name means Star of the Sea, and certainly that is what she has been for me. A bright jewel in the midst of a vast expanse. Her experience working in business, marketing and not-for-profits has made an incredible contribution to our projects! And to my life!

## elizaBeth Benson-Udom

I have known and worked with the amazing elizaBeth for several years. Her enthusiasm and willingness to play always gets me inspired and motivated. She is also in publishing, elizaPress, and has published many books. Her contribution to the Cosmic Cowgirl team and to this book has been such a blessing for numerous reasons, but most of all because her wisdom regarding getting paid, media, and the press in general has been a gift. Her guidance in launching the e-book in December 2007 made the adventure so much fun. I am grateful for her friendship and for her support in bringing our book to market. She is the one who got us going on our Sheroes!

## More Thanks!

Much gratitude goes out to the Contributing Authors who have shared their time and wisdom in this book and in my life. Thank you for being a part of the Cosmic Cowgirl dream!
To learn about the rest of the Contributing Authors, go to Chapter 13 to read their BIOS and while you're there, see the Sheroe listings of the primary authors!
I also thank Dori Etter for her generosity and enthusiasm in getting this project to market!
Thanks to Michelle Noe who has worked with me on design projects for many years.
Thank you to Jill Peden for her eleventh hour editing magic.
Special thanks to my sweetie Isaiah who sat with me in the final hours to design the inside cover, and who assists me with technical difficulties, and who so beautifully holds space and love for me every time I am working on a book or painting.

### The Book Cover image: The Heart of the Visionary Holds the Prayers of the World

This book is named after the painting of the visionary woman we used on the front cover. She has the winged eye, flowers in her hair, a messenger bird, and doves on her cheeks. She has cosmic stardust wisdom coming into her mind and an awakened flaming heart to hold all the prayers. The prayers are from the prayer bowl I started in our Mendocino gallery after 9/11. Folks would write their prayers, wishes, and dreams on little ribbons of paper and put them in the prayer bowl. In the beginning I performed a ritual where I would read them all and then burn them. I continued to ask what else I might do to truly honor the prayers. Then one day, I took a huge canvas outside and began to pray the prayers as I varnished them directly onto it, dancing around as I went. For me the painting represents the beauty, the power, the mystery, the majesty, the possibility, the sweetness, the love, and the wisdom that lives in the heart of every visionary human being.

Note: Prints and cards are available at: www.shilohsophia.com or 1-888-385-6866

# The Feminine Business Paradigm

### Why We Designed This Workbook For Women

### Shiloh Sophia McCloud

The fact that a very small percentage of women artists have their art in museums today is representative of the status of women's work in the world. Within the Female Business Paradigm, women's art must be identified by the word 'women' in order to define the work, and to define an arena in which we are free to explore our work without competing in a predominantly male marketplace.

We desired to create a Visionary Business Plan designed with life affirming principles. The Feminine Business Paradigm is being defined as a lens through which to view our work as women in the business world. A way of being, seeing, and working in alignment with who we are as women. Our work is to create an arena in which women have access to business tools that are designed for the way we want to work as visionary women. We utilize the wisdom of the existing paradigm, transform aspects of it to meet important ideals, and create a business model in alignment with life-affirming and life-sustaining values.

The Feminine Business Paradigm movement that we are introducing embraces and encourages women to embody all aspects of female life, from nurturer to warrior, from birth-giver to athlete, from lover to leader, from homemaker to business woman. We believe that we can live a vital life doing work that does not compromise who we are and still make a living. This is not a utopian ideal in which we just do what we love and expect money to follow. Rather, it is the introduction of a system and of tools we can use to transform what we love into a business with a product or service that is needed and wanted by others at this time.

Although our actions can be inspired by it, our work is not in reaction to the existing corporate model. We are creating a vision in which all aspects of our work are in alignment with the highest good for all, at all times. We understand business as more than a destination, but a journey, and a lifestyle. Therefore we strive not to put the rest of our lives on hold while we "work." We seek to create a structure of balance, that leaves room for who we are becoming.

The reason we feel inspired to define the movement as feminine is to draw a distinction between the current paradigm and the one we are creating. Women's work does not need to be in opposition to male's in order to be pro-female. If we are being who we are destined to be, this will serve all beings, and men will be blessed through our living empowering, fruitful lives. The word 'feminine' can also be used by men or women, just like the word 'masculine.'

Four of the key elements to living this movement are: We interpret success for ourselves, we choose life affirming principles for operating our businesses, we celebrate our wins every step of the journey, and we work towards the betterment of life for ourselves, and all beings.

## The Feminine Business Paradigm  Ten Decision Making Questions

1. Does this decision excite, nurture, and sustain me?
2. What and who is being served and blessed by this offering?
3. What is the impact of this on me, others, and the environment?
4. Where is the main source of profit, and is it accomplished by ethical means?
5. What will the impact be on my family, community, the earth?
6. Do I feel that I MUST do this, even if I do not know all the reasons why?
7. Is this fulfilling my purpose—a deep place of truth within myself?
8. What and who do I need in order to make this work without overworking?
9. Is love at the center of my motivation?
10. When I see this project at its highest point, is it in integrity with these points?

## The Feminine Business Paradigm  Ten Self Value Questions

1. Have I defined reachable and frequent journey points and goals?
2. Do I know what reaching success looks like for me?
3. Have I clearly articulated what resources I personally need for this to work?
4. How and in what ways do I want to give back?
5. Am I willing to let go of limiting beliefs and self sabotaging behaviors?
6. Do I have ideas in place for celebrating myself and team members?
7. Have I established a self value practice, including pricing for my services?
8. Do I have a plan of action that supports and sustains growth?
9. Have I made a commitment to value my project enough to seek counsel?
10. Do I allow my on-going accomplishments to affirm that I am enough?

A few percentages for the presence of women's art: MOMA permanent collection: 5%,
The Whitney, permanent collection: 19%, New York galleries, 23% solo exhibitions
From Jerry Saltz, The Village Voice  2006

# Intention for This Workbook

# Goals, Ideas, and HeartStorming

# Heart of the Visionary Workbook Instructions

This book is not linear. You have to move around to get the fruits you want. You can go in order or work ahead. But I want you to stop right now, and browse through all the material first so you know what is in here. You might think of it as a series of interconnecting circles. Just look through the whole thing so you have an overview of the material and how it relates to you.

There are many sections that have recurring themes particularly with regard to vision, which is at the heart of the workbook. The reason for this is to get you to continue to dig, to explore, to re-write, and to get clear. You may have to write something many times to get it to be not only clear but compelling. Just keep working it. The process of repetition teaches us and illuminates new things when we least expect it.

There is no set order to the steps of creating a business and several options are presented in this book. But just like each child has a different learning style, each woman has a different style of doing business. So go along as you like— but don't overlook key points or steps. If you are dreaming about money, don't skip the abundance work. If you are dreaming about getting recognized, don't skip the press release. Keep cross-referencing your information, answers and guiding lists—ours and the ones you make, as it is easy to get caught up in the day to day and miss the big picture as you are going along.

Through doing the digging work of discovery, using your spade of creativity to reveal the treasures, you will find what you are looking for. First there is a lot of dust. Then you see a shining shard. It may be the one hundredth hole but you will find it. Each treasure reveals to you how close the next one might be and provides insight as to the whole of your search.

Some of the material in this book may also be found in other books. And a lot of it cannot. Some information is very basic, but has been adjusted to a feminine lens. There are tons of connections and ideas to be made on the Internet, so we have not gone into too much depth about things that you can study and research as you go along. We hope you will use the Internet as a supplemental study guide. One of the reasons for writing your work into the book and not doing it on the computer is so that your creative self will has permission to flourish! Others may choose to write it on the computer and paste it in your journal. We hope you write in the margins, color, use sticky notes and tabs and make this book your own. We encourage the use of images, doodles, colored pens, collage, different hand-writing styles. DECORATE IT! Write all over it! Claim your territory!

There will be tons of information to draw from. If one section does not speak to you at this time, move to the next. Different women's perspectives have been offered here so that you can hear their stories and angles and find something to spark YOU. It is not about perfection —and while we are on that subject: There will be errors in this book. Perfectionism can be one of the biggest obstacles to creativity you will encounter. More important than our endlessly counting commas and spaces, was to have you holding this book in your hands in this moment! We are continuing to refine it as we go along!

## Workbook Process

There are activities, exercises and processes throughout the book. There are writing, drawing, visioning, dreaming, reading, listing, researching and fill in the blank sections. You can make it up, use extra paper, draw, collage, write poetry, songs, lists, notes, whatever inspires you. If you feel you lack enough instructions, make up your own! The words at the top of the page are just prompts. You can color the illustrations or journal inside of them. Use the margins of the book to doodle and develop your curves, signs, symbols and totems. This will be work and play! We hope that your heart and mind will be filled with brilliant ideas!

We invite you to use a blank journal for extra writings, notes, articles, and photos.

Many things WILL come up as you read and work and there will not always be space when something comes to mind. Pick a journal and stick with it throughout this process. BUT try not to write rough drafts in it to copy into here. If a space is provided, be spontaneous - juicier material comes out that way. You can re-write it in your other journal. Whatever you do, don't "save" the pages for when you get things worked out. We have tried to cover as much as we can and hold your hand throughout the process. If you don't understand something then stop and research it on your own. For example, if you come to a place that asks for you to write your mission statement go to the Internet and search for mission statements. This book would be twice as long if we covered everything and provided enough paper for every single part.

## Creative Uses and Activities and Materials

Crayons, felt pens, sparkle, gel and milky pens, colored pencils, pastels (not oil), metallic pens, glitter, glue, stickers, photos, letters, magazines, catalogs, scissors, greeting cards, fortune cookie fortunes, ticket stubs, lipstick kisses, coffee and red wine stains, feathers, and whatever else will fit.

By the time you have filled it up it will be twice the size it is now and "REAL" according to the Skin Horse in conversation with the Velveteen Rabbit.

Real isn't how you're made. It's a thing that happens to you. When a child loves you for a long long time, not just to play with, but REALLY loves you, then you become real. It doesn't happen all at once. You become. It takes a long time. Generally by the time you are real, most of your hair has been loved off, and your eyes drop out and you get loose in the joints and very shabby. But these things don't matter at all, because once you are real you can't be ugly, except to people who don't understand.
Margery Williams ~ "The Velveteen Rabbit"

# GO-GIRL-GO ACTION PLAN CHECK LIST

## Sherri Morris

***This is towards the beginning of the book as it has some important starting stages. You may want to keep coming back to it and fill it in as you go along.***

Decide on Your Business Type and Name - do research based on the design you have in mind.

Business Name: ______________________________

Business slogan/motto/tag line: ______________________________

Theme colors/symbol/image/brand: ______________________________

Domain Name for Your Website: ______________________________

Get a Business License, File For a Fictitious Name or whatever is required in your county.

______________________________

Describe Product or Service: ______________________________

______________________________

Set Up a Business Checking Account - Where & When: ______________________________

Get a Resale License/Sales Tax Permit if your product or service is taxable: ______________

Mailing Address - This will be your permanent business address, a P.O. Box is good.

______________________________

Set up a toll free number or a permanent line: ______________________________

Get Business Cards, Letterhead and Related Printed Items. Goal Date: ______________

Ideas and who can help: ______________________________

Find a Mentor, Allies and women who inspire you! Having a team is good all the time!

Name a few: ______________________________

Network with Other Businesses and Women Entrepreneurs

Where? Who can you connect with? ______________________________

I will call: ______________________ By Date: ______________________

Research Business Groups and Professional Organizations in your field.

Name a few: ______________________________

Get Funding - Credit Cards - What are your money sources? How much is there to start?

______________________________

Trademark Your Name/Copyright (Recommended but not required) and Register a Brand.

______________________________

Set up a Computer and Record Keeping System - Have a trail for everything.

Plans for Records:________________________________________

What do you need to set up your workspace:______________________________

Create a Work Schedule and a Vision Schedule - even if it is very part time, what are your hours?

____________________________________________________________

Marketing Action Step One:_____________________________________

Step Two:_________________________Step Three:___________________

How will monies be paid? Do you need to process Credit Cards/Pay Pal?_____________

E-Commerce Website Goals/Ideas:___________________________________

E-Mail Address:_______________________Blog Address:______________________

Hire or Team Up with The Right People - the ones who can balance out your learning curves.

Who do you need?______________________________________________

Immediate Resources Needed:______________________________________

What supplies are needed to deliver on your offering:___________________________

What is YOUR title?______________________________________________

**Action List - What's Next:**

**A few other ideas**: Review goals with dates, order supplies and stock, sufficient to get started but do not overstock, market, advertise and sell. How do you initially want to launch the business? If you have the funds, it may be helpful to hire a marketing firm. Buy Insurance, damage or liability-determined by your type of business. Establish working systems and keep a personal eye on quality control - don't hand over too much stuff that you need to manage. Work with a great tax accountant to learn how to maximize your entrepreneur status.

***Wax Your Brows, Get a Manicure, A Good Lipstick and GO GIRL GO!***

# How This Book Is Designed

*Each Chapter creates the context for the next one. While this book is guided and best used in order, you can go where you want to based on what your needs are at the moment. As you work through each process, the next one should begin to make sense to you. Find a way to make the template work for you! Go to the place that is natural and exciting based on where you are in your journey.*

**Note: Primary Authors are mentioned below. Refer to the Table Of Contents for a full listing.**

**<u>Chapter One: Invitation—The Power of Love</u>**

**Author and Artist Shiloh McCloud invites you to the journey of your life work!**

We lead with the Invitation, the WHY of this book, and then Invite you to become enrolled in living a life that's inspiring. We hope this will spark and encourage you to take this journey!

**<u>Chapter Two: Creation—The Power of Insight</u>**

**Discover and deepen into how creativity informs and awakens your process.**

This chapter is written by Shiloh McCloud who believes that by activating your creativity you will have greater access to your internal wisdom. Every woman has a deep well of profound knowledge within her that she can apply to any endeavor. This is a warm up for the VISION!

**<u>Chapter Three: The Vision—The Power of Passion</u>**

**Create a Vision Plan using creative visualization for articulating aspects of your work.**

The Vision Plan section is at the heart of the workbook. This is the place where Shiloh McCloud guides you to vision and journal about the different aspects of your blossoming project. You have the opportunity to explore and manifest each part—moving from the idea to the reality.

**<u>Chapter Four: Abundance—The Power of Giving and Receiving</u>**

**Explore your relationship to abundance, self value, giving/receiving and beliefs.**

This section is an invitation for you to consider abundance as a way of being - and to define what that means for you. Many of our beliefs about this subject are affecting our ability to create not just income, but also, to create a life that feels abundant no matter what is going on!

**<u>Chapter Five: Perspective—The Power of Originality</u>**

**Hear from Shannon McCloud who worked in corporate America for many years and learned to survive and thrive doing it her own way**. This chapter is an inspiration for women entrepreneurs to not give up who they are as they pursue their goals - and to continue to choose themselves along the way. As you move on through the rest of the book, women's stories will serve as catalytic tools to create your path in a way that aligns with your personal legend.

**<u>Chapter Six: Wisdom—The Power of Experience</u>**

**Learn from poet Caron McCloud who has been in business for herself most of her life and shares her experiences in the form of parable-like stories and poetry.** This chapter demonstrates how we find our teachers, even in the most unusual of circumstances, and how to achieve success in business through looking at both the bottom line and all the lines in between.

**Chapter Seven: Money—The Power of Enough**

**Spend time working on your money beliefs and get clear on getting paid.**

This chapter is an exploration of your patterns around money, value and having. We take a look at how our money stuff affects the rest of our lives - and how to transform it. We also provide tools and templates for looking at how much you want and need to get paid to do your work.

**Chapter Eight: Market — The Power of Presence**

**Define what it means to get your work into the marketplace and make an action plan.**

This is a very exciting section because it is about exploring the time and place where you offer your goods/services. Mary MacDonald guides you through many step-by-step actions towards the creation of your marketing plan. We hope this section decodes some of the marketing mystery that makes it challenging for us to "market" our stuff!

**Chapter Nine: Communication—The Power of Action**

**Get clear on the basic steps for getting the word out about you to the press and the world.**

Everyone knows you can have a great idea, but if you don't get out there no one will find out about your idea. In this chapter elizaBeth Benson-Udom demystifies the process of sharing your work using point-by-point plans of action to get you motivated to take the next steps in the right direction. Being able to articulate what it is we do is going to help us form strong alliances!

**Chapter Ten: The Business —The Power of Strategy**

**Write the business plan basics and create what your successful business will look like!**

By now you will have prepared yourself very well for filling in this section which includes many of the traditional business basics, but with some feminine flavor added. Mary MacDonald has created a powerful starting place for taking your whole plan to the next level using both traditional and non-traditional business tools. You can take this to the bank!

**Chapter Eleven: Wellness—The Power of Awareness**

**When we choose ourselves as visionary women we also need to choose our self care!**

As you work through this chapter and hear other women's stories and ideas we hope you will be inspired to create a balance between the business of your life work and caring for yourself.
In our book, self care is a ritual that includes everything from laughter yoga to green smoothies!

**Chapter Twelve: Compassion—The Power of Caring**

**At the Heart of the Visionary is the heart of the world. Make a difference and have a good time doing it**! Learn from visionary women about working with other women, waking up to what is wanted and needed in the world and how feeling compassion inspires us to take action on behalf of ourselves, others and the planet. May our projects be informed by our caring hearts.

**Chapter Thirteen: Community—The Power of Legend**

Learn about our Sheroes, the women who inspire us! Write your own list! Find out more about the Cosmic Cowgirls who made this book learn about our projects in the making including things like from printing and design to websites and publishing to help launch your Vision.

# I Create My Possibilities!

*Before you go into the next section about creativity, take some time to journal and draw what is in your heart and on your mind right now! What has come up for you so far? What ideas, resistance, hopes, dreams, desires...*

# The Path Chooses You

Shiloh Sophia McCloud

Do you choose, or are you chosen?
Do you make the path
or has it been in you all along?
The soul's journey deepens at the crossroads.
There is nothing else to do. Say Yes.
All steps now are about staying on the path which has chosen you.
Your path will call upon everything you think you are.
And show you
day by day
moment by moment
the mystery of the great and bountiful self
you have always known is within.
Let her out.

# Creation

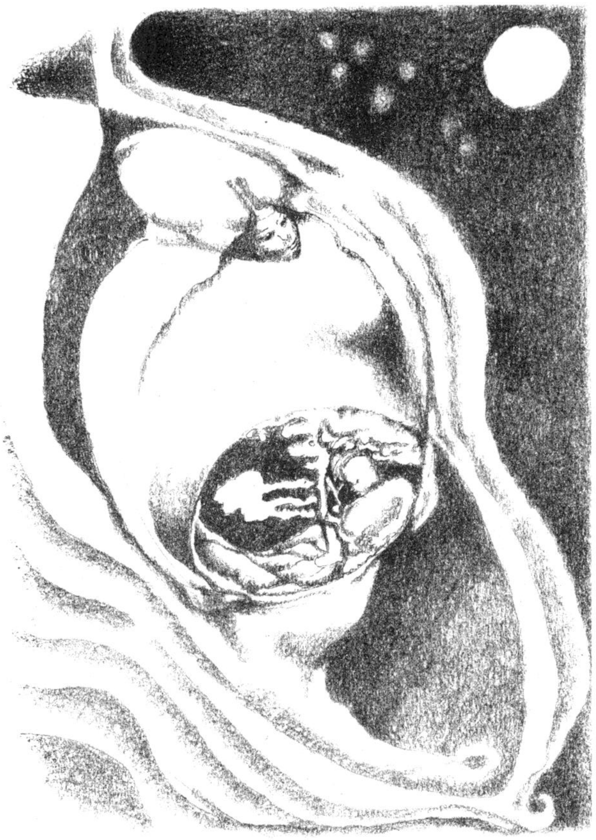

## The Power of Insight


**Author and Artist: Shiloh Sophia McCloud**

WITH

Mary MacDonald

Illustrations also by Sue Hoya Sellars

## *The Time is Now*

*Shiloh Sophia McCloud*

*It isn't too late*
*and you don't have to*
*get rid of your fear first*
*miracles are on their way*
*to you now*
*this isn't about hope*
*this is about unreasonable faith*
*don't let your track record stop you*
*this is not a test*
*you are not who you think you are*
*you are a mystery*
*in the soul of the universe*
*you are not here to figure out*
*what's going on*
*or what's going wrong*
*you are here to discover*
*the time is now to take a risk*
*not risking is the greatest risk*
*the time is now and now and now*
*you may have to start over again and again*
*shame and guilt may try to prevent you*
*don't listen to their stories about you*
*listen to honor possibility truth and love*
*don't listen to those around you who don't see you*
*listen to your ancestors who made*
*a way out of no way.*
*This is your time to shine!*

# The Power of Creativity

***Creating transports us through exterior veils into deep levels of knowing.***

When we know what we want we are always working towards it whether we are out dancing all night or at our desk. This is what is so powerful about the focused work in this book. By the time you are done, you will have a clearer idea about what you want to bring into your life and how to set about making it happen. You will be empowered to use the gifts and tools we have collected here and to access your intuitive feminine wisdom to bring your vision into form and real time.

Although sometimes we may not see or have access to the inner world, most women suspect that there is a deep, rich wisdom hidden somewhere within. Where and how can we access it? And on a continual basis? Sometimes we may be afraid to take a look because once we catch on to who we really are adjustments of time, energy, relationship and resources are required. Creativity inspires movement, but not up or over as in a linear, sequential, hierarchical, patriarchal way. We weave our way through matter that seems impermeable. Spiraling in and out and through and saturating our very cells with our own unique, self-designed revelation.

By our agreement to move, not as the world moves, but as *we* are so inclined, our body responds to our thoughts. Isn't that amazing? Our thoughts in turn are affected by the internal rhythms that begin to show up and must be heard. Our decisions inform our biology and our biology responds instead of reacting. While reacting unconsciously can be disabling, responding is generative and life giving in the here and now. We do not have to premeditate the next move.

We know what it is because we listen. It is in our bones and in our blood. It becomes the ground of being or Heartland out of which we operate. **In our Heartland, work is always being done on our behalf.** And even more so when we pay attention. Our heartaches don't go away easily, they often resurface throughout our lives. And so do our callings. We can create through them, using our passionate experience as guide and inspiration.

One of the phenomenal powers we have is in how we relate to the choices we make.
We can design our thinking with more gusto and passion for living a life that we are excited to live! It is possible!

When we can look, right now, at what is, and get it, then, instead of being the victim of it, we can take responsibility - this is the catalyst. Isn't this exciting? **Responsibility does not mean resignation—it means action can be taken from a pure place.** We can change from 'sorry for myself' into active participant, and we are mobilized to make a transition, or, if you're really ready to do the work, a transformation. This transformational work is a catalytic agent, that causes us to evolve. As we evolve our projects and relationships evolve.

For example, finding a mentor who is really right for you will be a more fruitful task if they see in you someone profoundly creative. And inspired. Mentor type folks are approached all the time. Who can you BE, that would make someone want to offer you their services? How are you going to be different?

**You are going to bring your creativity to it.**

When I have a breakthrough, I have the sense that I am helping others whom I do not even know to break through. This sense of interconnected transformation, which we visionaries speak of, is what informs all of my work. When you do good work, make things happen, make money—you make the pathway easier for other women to travel. Think about this rewarding transpersonal aspect of your work.

**Women's work is a many faceted jewel shining a prism of light into the world.**

And the thing is, to focus does not mean you just pick one thing - in the feminine paradigm, we include everything that makes sense, we 'stack it' and therefore our menu of services and products is diverse and bountiful. The initial challenge is just to discover and define the container, the context in which you are offering your work.

For example, if I see a business card that says Massage Therapist or Business Coach and then in the fine print it also says, nutritional supplements and/or real estate and/or ask me about _______. I automatically assess that they are doing too much in one container OR they do not know how to define their offering in a large enough container. I struggle with this myself. So the goal is to FIND or CREATE that which holds all of your work in one visionary context. And then to learn how to talk about it to others.

# Business as a Creative Practice

***Anything we choose can be made sacred through our attention and intention.***

We spend considerable time working. What if we could make that time more meaningful based on how we think about what we are doing? What if bringing our clear intention to any action could actually change how we feel about what we do, and the results that we create? Different results manifest on the physical plane in accordance with different kinds of thinking.

When I realized just how much work I was going to be doing as an artist entrepreneur I was both thrilled and somewhat overwhelmed. This was to be the most of my days and hours on planet earth. So how I design that time, and the quality of my experience in that time, is a primary focus for me. For example, when I am painting, I am praying for people *and* creating income with my work. When I am bookkeeping, I am grateful to get organized, joyfully explore numbers, and I also pray for other people's money needs. We can turn every response into a chosen one. We cannot always control our circumstances as you well know, but you can change how you respond by being prepared in advance for the challenges.

When I start to get grumpy or resentful about a part of my work, I move to another part for a while. The less desirable parts are actually like weeding and fertilizing a garden. All can be pleasurable throughout if we chose, as it is all necessary to make the garden flourish.

You might say, "Oh, easy for her to talk about her business as a creative or spiritual path —She gets to paint and make beautiful things." Well, while one of our Authors was writing her own book, and working on this one, she took a housekeeping job at a Bed and Breakfast. She described it as not only her way to pay her bills, but as part of her spiritual discipline. How did you do it? We wanted to know. She said: "When I am preparing the room I pray for the people that are coming I ask that they have a most wonderful and memorable time that is transformative for their relationship. I make the bed as though it were a gift I am wrapping for them. I give thanks for getting paid to get the exercise I need after sitting so much to write my book." Wow.

I don't expect the best of myself, or anyone else. I think this "winning mentality" is overrated. I do what I can and what is reasonable for that day. I try to navigate stress before it settles into my body by being alert to it's presence. When you are in business for yourself you invariably give way above average. I keep the sparkle in things by continually refining and upgrading my environment even in small ways. I light candles. I think what I would like to have happen. I pray to meet people I can bless, and who will bless me. I stay as present as possible. I sit in my beautiful creation chair that my friend Sherri gave me. I put on my writing shawl that is from my grandmother Helen, or my visionary necklace from Sue. Our work becomes sacred. We make it so. I choose some days are "result" days and some days as "process and play days."

When we operate our businesses and projects as an offering—a gift to the world—people respond to that energy. I am not talking about just positive thinking or creating your own reality. I am talking about a conscious way of being that you continually cultivate. In this way, our work can be creative and spiritual. It is our decision.

# The Big Dream

## *Meditating on the Vision*

This workbook will address MANY aspects of manifesting your visions and dreams. The list of meditation questions is an overview of some of the topics we will be exploring in this book. This will give you a warm up, a starting place, an idea of the kind of thinking and the kind of questions you are going to be answering with your work. Hopefully, it will create the context, the mental and intuitive environment, in which to RECEIVE the gift of the information which informs your plan.

Note: The BIG DREAM is excerpted from the process we use for the "Heart of The Visionary Workshop" and has been utilized by thousands of women to activate their plan!

***Instructions**: Sit in a quiet place with the book open to this page. Have a glass of water and quiet music playing with no words. You might want to light a candle or put a little flower in a vase next to you. Simple ritual creates space - if you have not tried it, do it now. If you have a special thinking cap, necklace or shawl, put it on. Ready? Ask yourself each question from The Big Dream, close your eyes and sit with it, seeing the answer in a visual way. Then go to the next question, creating a gold thread between each answer. If you don't get an "answer" but another question, that is your answer. This is not a problem solving activity, but an exploration to align your mind and heart. This is a mental exercise, but you can also use additional paper if you want to write it out.*

*After you have completed the process you can take some notes in the space below to summarize your BIG DREAM! The more concise you are able to be in your language, the more solid the foundation of the vision will be able to become. Use more paper and take some time to journal about what surprised you, what delighted you, excited you, scared you and of course, informed your dream!*

(Who are you serving + who is paying for that
(where the money comes from)

# THE BIG DREAM

Being blissfully in love + family
To be love done! Creator of dreams, creative hearts, creative communication - soul relations, love - in soul teaching, sharing that

THE BIG WHATS

WHAT IS YOUR BIG DREAM? What is at the heart of your idea?

WHAT IS YOUR VISION? What do you see and what are you going to create from your vision?
I see an entrepreneurial enterprise of Self love sovereignty

WHAT IS YOUR MISSION and PURPOSE? How will you define your work to the world?

WHAT IS YOUR BUSINESS? When you see yourself "doing" the work, what is it?

WHAT PRODUCT/SERVICES DO YOU OFFER? Describe with joy, what you are selling.
clothes, products of love - Creative cards - artwork - sessions spa retreat

WHAT IS YOUR LONG TERM BUSINESS PLAN? See your business at the highest point.

WHAT IS YOUR LONG TERM PERSONAL PLAN? See yourself living the life you want.

WHAT IS SUCCESS? Define what success looks like—so you will know when you get there!

THE BIG WHERES

WHERE IS YOUR PLACE OF BUSINESS? Where do you do your work?

WHERE IS YOUR MARKETPLACE? Where do you sell/offer your work?

THE BIG WHENS

WHEN ARE YOU GOING TO DO WHAT? Create the initial timeline projection.

WHEN WILL YOU ACTUALLY LAUNCH OR CELEBRATE? Open for business!

THE BIG WHOS

WHO ARE YOUR CLIENTS/RECEIVERS? Imagine the folks who are receivers/purchasers.

WHO IS YOUR DREAM TEAM? Imagine yourself surrounded by your team of support.

WHO ARE YOU AS A LEADER? Think of and develop language around you as the leader.

WHO BUT YOU IS GOING TO CARE FOR YOU? What does a self care regime look like?

THE BIG HOWS

HOW MUCH IS NEEDED TO START YOUR PROJECT? Start with the minimum range. $6,000.00 month

HOW MUCH DO YOU NEED FOR PERSONAL LIVELIHOOD? Be clear! $9000 — month

Helping heal love Reclamation
broken hearts by working w/ body, creativity, sensuality + erotic + humor (Wild Feminine) Wild Freedom of Love Loving
Loving the body - Self-image

# Vision Altar Project

*You have heard the saying, energy flows where attention goes? Well we are going to spend some time creating an Altar for your vision. This gets all aspects of YOU involved from mental to emotional and is a TOOL for you learn how to THINK about this work. Everything we do in this book is designed to facilitate your images and language being revealed to you. Being able to think and talk about your work is essential because it informs how you think about it, and the energy around it.*

**Materials:**

**15 Pieces of paper - nice card stock recommended**

**Scissors, Colored Pens, Glue, Glitter, Ribbon**

**A cardboard box or shoe box - or a nice box you already have and things to decorate the box with.**

**Instructions:**

Cut the paper in half and on the top of each piece of paper write the words below. Decorate the page with borders, flowers, stars, doodles and then answer each prompt with whatever comes to mind. Don't edit too much. There is no particular order. Come from the place of having it - desiring it - celebrating it:

**VISIONS—DREAMS—PASSIONS—PLEASURES—IDEAS—LEGEND—ABUNDANCE—POWER—GIVING—MY MONEY—FRIENDSHIP—LOVE RELATIONSHIP—VACATION—LOVE—CONNECTIONS—EVENTS—CELEBRATIONS—HOME—CLOSET—BODY—FOOD—LOCATION—WISHES—GRATITUDE—SPIRIT—INFLUENCE—CHANGES— DREAM SCHEDULE—HEALTH—SUCCESS**

**OBJECTIVE:** Create a VISION ALTAR Box to hold your Altar Cards. Cut out pieces of paper, decorate them, use wrapping paper, magazines or whatever you want and glue it onto the box. Once all your cards are created, even if you haven't written all of them - put them in the box and keep it tied with a beautiful bow. You can put it under your bed, on your desk, on your dresser and keep adding to it as you go. The final step is to glue another piece of paper on top with your AFFIRMATION INTENTION for your life work. Reference this box as often as possible! You will be amazed at what a blessing it is, and how powerful it is for holding your ideas in order!

Shiloh

# What I Love

*Write a list of all the things you love, from personal pleasures to business endeavors!*
*When we work from the heart, love is at the center of all choices.*

# Visionary Declaration

*Write a declaration for your lifework. Include your time commitment schedule. Make this as clear and as serious as possible. This will help you "stay the course" when you want to give up. Don't let anything make you give up! If you feel comfortable, you might even make it a contract between you and you! Hold yourself accountable for this project.*

# Making New Pathways

***Transforming Our Thinking, Transforming Our Lives***

**Shiloh Sophia McCloud**

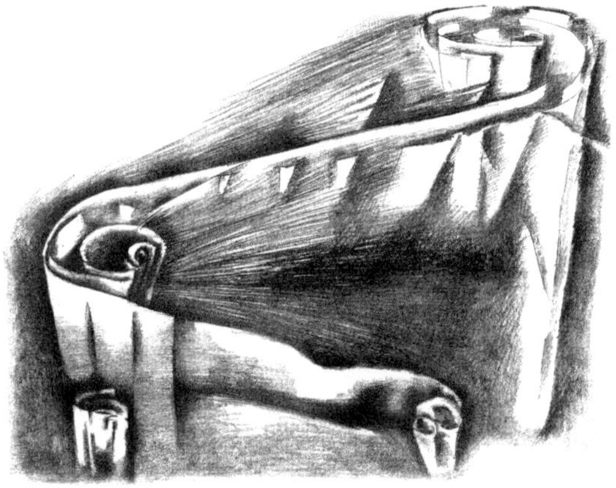

Neuroscientists have studied how our neuroassociations never cease to send electro-chemical messages all throughout our body. What does this mean? It means that action along the nerve pathways of your entire body is occurring on your behalf! AND we can influence these pathways to bring transformation to our emotional and physical patterns! This is a spiritual concept backed up by a science concept. What we have is the ability to change, not just mental, not just physical, not just spiritual, but literally all three. AND it takes OUR action to affect this powerful action that is already just happening. How often do we feel helpless to change?

At the same time that messages are traveling across your neural pathways, billions upon billions of other impulses are traveling in their own individual direction. This is the system within us that keeps us functioning. When we were children, once we learned how to walk we never forgot, or how ride a bike. It becomes natural. But if we do not practice it, like anything, our body can get out of sync.

When we learn something new, a physical path is created in our body at the same time a new mental path is being formed. A golden strand is formed from one place to another and our highly organized holy system of life knows where to connect what to where! Each time we do it, more strands are added and strengthened and eventually, over time, depending on what it is, we have a strong channel or path for that information to travel on and it takes little or no effort to conjure it up! In the instance of hurting yourself, like getting a burn or a stubbed toe, the connection is usually formed strong enough the first time, because pain is such a huge sensation that we don't need practice to strengthen that association! However, in emotional situations, this seems to not be true, because we cause ourselves undue pain and suffering over and over when we could choose not to. We can learn to choose joy and self honor instead. (Most of the time.)

Consider how this reality plays into our addictive or harmful behaviors. When people say, "I want to stop but I just can't," it may be because the connective pathways and tissues and emotional baggage are so keyed to that action that not to do it can literally make someone sick. It is also true in relationships, and negative self talk. Think of what you do in a fight with a loved one. Is the pattern similar each time? And so hard not to do, even if in your brain you want to scream out, "I love you! I am sorry!" but instead you leave the room and slam the door in an effort to punish them, while you are the one most punished by this behavior.

Then there is your view of yourself. Your actual attitude about you. For example: You want to set up an art space in your home and take an hour, a whole hour to just color and draw and dream but you feel guilty, there are dishes in the sink, and when you sit down you cannot get your mind off of what you need to do later, and you experience unworthiness, guilt, and all kinds of mental hoopla. OR even worse, you finally do choose to take time for yourself, and some of the terrible ways you have been treated start to flood your mind, immobilizing your enjoyment?

WOW! Do we all need some power tools to deal with this stuff or what?! What is it within us that causes such a punishment response to our taking pleasure?

How often do you feel guilty resting. Stopping work early? Even a long walk can spur anxiety. If you do not have this, I salute you! I struggle with it—but not as much as I used to. After years of doing this, I can see that "sharpening the saw" truly is a blessing to all the other work I do. The thing is, it is harder to do when someone else is around. Find your quiet time, alone, and TAKE IT!

So, what does this have to do with our project? Our business? Just Everything. Because we have to interrupt our patterns in order to do business in a healthy manner and not duplicate the same damaging behaviors over and over.

Our patterns can really play out in relation to the folks we work with. We will play out our behavior patterns which have not been dealt with, no matter what, unless, we change them or are conscious enough to stop them. And we do have the power to stop them. But like everything else in this book—which is called a workbook for a reason, there are challenges to transformation.

I appreciate the info that is all about ease—"It comes to me with ease." Well brilliant. But you know, it doesn't work that way for all of us, and there is nothing wrong with hard work. Nothing wrong with heart wrenching soul searching. With screaming out for answers. With breaking down to break through. Some things do come with ease, though usually not the things I think will. Anticipate and plan for the most clear and direct path. Then do what you need to do to make it happen. Whatever you do, keep going.

**Expect miracles in unexpected places.**

# I Am A Woman Entrepreneur

*Explore claiming yourself as a woman entrepreneur. What would it mean for how you value yourself? How do you want others to see you? Does being a visionary entrepreneur make you feel proud? What kind of title would you give yourself? List the qualities you value about being in business for yourself. You can also do this as a letter of invitation to your inner entrepreneur.*

The duty we are called to is precise and personal
—the fulfillment of our own authentic self expression—
even though we may carry it out imperfectly. The imperfection is our growing edge.
Reverend Ellen Grace O'Brian

# Design Your Own Visionary Meditations

*Meditation is a tool that helps you focus, think clearly, and take care of yourself. By making up your own creative visionary meditation you connect with the process in a personal way. It could be for just one minute. It could be to drink a glass of water while loving yourself. Don't worry about emptying your mind. Focus instead on creating clear visual spaces for ideas to emerge, so that vitality can come! You can start with a meadow, or the stars, or the trees, or the ocean as a visual space maker. Design a few and use them before you get to work on your projects!*

## Write a Letter to Your Inner Artist

*Invite her to come and play, to assist you, to open the doors that need opening.*
*To bring you wisdom from your soul garden within. Court her like a lover. Promise her rewards.*
*Write poetry to her....*

# Draw Your Vision

*Who cares if you know HOW to draw, draw from within. It could be you smiling and holding a bunch of money. Or a sanctuary where you work. Or you surrounded by a group of other leaders. If you are one of the people who says I cannot even draw a stick figure - draw one now, dancing. Just draw. It does not have to be good - don't listen to your inner critic! Be visionary!*

# Beliefs I Am Giving Up About Myself

*You probably don't need instructions for this one.*

A strong woman is a woman who loves strongly and weeps strongly
and is strongly terrified and has strong needs.
Marge Piercy

# Forming New Beliefs & Creating Your Legend

*Now is the time to choose how you will THINK during this process. You have acknowledged the patterns and beliefs that have limited you in the past. Now create a new set of beliefs about you, life, faith, ideals, goals, money, and all the parts that make up your life. You may not have it figured out yet—just play. It can be helpful to meditate on your ideal day and see what beliefs and realities are informing your decisions that day. You can always make a new one. Again, what beliefs would have to be alive within you, in order for you to create the story you want?*

# The Language of Women

**Mary MacDonald**

Words have the ability to cause our hearts to soar, they can cause immeasurable pain and they can define a culture. The language shaped by an economic model based on exclusion, entitlement and might makes right has defined our popular culture for 4,000 years. It has been a deeply ingrained conditioning that unfortunately continues to marginalize women and at the same time not allow men to explore different expressions of what success means to them.

Sojourner Truth said: "If I can't see it, I can't be it." If women only see ourselves portrayed in words, pictures or sounds as an adjunct to the work of men, how do we become all we are meant to be? Women are taught to define ourselves as the mother of, the wife of, the daughter of... These are all roles to value and be proud of but they become a limitation when we only see ourselves through the eyes of others, behaving in a way to avoid disapproval and to compete for male attention.

It is no wonder that women are making a mass exodus from corporate environments. In interviewing the women who are leaving to start their own businesses, women are say that we are leaving because we feel our contributions are not valued or recognized, we feel isolated and believe we are not taken seriously. We are generally excluded from training and informal networks and face an inhospitable culture. The corporate environment is often shaped by a language and culture foreign to women.

In studies done on the differences between how men and women behave in the workplace, women tend to be more persuasive, more inclusive,and lead with a team building style. We celebrate diversity and are more willing to learn from others, we collaborate and want to create sustainable structures. Women are less interested in power and hierarchical systems. Women emphasize creativity and mission, rather then being primarily profit driven.

The business world conversation and decision-making historically has been focused on the paradigms of aggression, sports and war analogies. We pitch a story, we ask for a ballpark figure, we say someone is out in left field, the other team has two strikes against him or her, we need to jockey for position, we gather intelligence, we respect the chain of command, and someone is a loose cannon. They used to hold workshops for women where we would learn how to speak "football" so we would understand what men were talking about in the boardrooms and around the water cooler.

As women create a new paradigm of business, what analogies shall we use to describe our goals, our assessments, our relationships? How can the language of women help to shape a culture that speaks to all?

It is time for us to stand in our own power! Without shame or confusion. We need to be a transformative force in creating a new consciousness in business. We need to bring our whole selves to the workplace and the marketplace. Diverse needs, ideas and dreams can come together when we deal with people with loving kindness and an open mind and heart. We can impact the lives of all people in the world through images that are healing and represent the fullness of who we are in our lives. We can offer our value, support, and guidance, and act as a catalyst for change.

One of the ways we can achieve this is by being aware of the language we are using and framing that language differently so it is inclusive for all. We can free ourselves from the need to please others first, to compete with other women, or to feel powerless in our relationship to men. We can acknowledge that women are still not being paid a fair wage in comparison to men and we can change that paradigm by paying men and women equally. We can join with men to take equal responsibility in making the world a better place for those who will follow us. When we bring our authentic language into the world of work and business, we create new pictures of what is possible. If we can see it, we can become it and if we speak it - and live it - others can see and become it too! We must free ourselves of the entrenched habits of being defined by others and instead begin to define ourselves. Women use language to create and maintain social connectivity. We want to integrate our work with our personal lives in a way that blends kindness and compassion with our desire to make money at something that lights up our soul. In so doing, we open up new spaces for women and men to be the change we long to see in our world
We can do it!

***Women, if the soul of the nation is to be saved, I believe that you must become its soul.***
***Coretta Scott King***

# Women Are Image Makers

**We are image-makers!**
**This is a call to create!**
**Listen now my friends!**
**Let us source our own images!**

When we claim our lineage as image-makers
we no longer allow ourselves
to be defined by the harmful symbols used
to interpret woman and her world.
By developing our own personal
iconography we create
our own legend of woman!
We connect with the greater wisdom
of the collective Woman Soul. We refuse to
accept the associations, interpretations, and
perceptions that do not acknowledge
who we know ourselves to be. We can create
our own way of seeing and being through
cultivating an identity defined by us. An
identity that encompasses the largeness of
who we are and who we are becoming.

We receive intuitive guidance from the existing global community—
the collective woman-soul who is right here with us asking these same questions.
Praying these same prayers in our own language of the heart.
The changes we are working so hard for *are* in full motion,
from the birth movement to the elders movement and all the wild-folk in between. We know that the act of creating art in all forms and mediums is a powerful vehicle for re-imaging woman in her full glory. And for re-claiming the images of lovers, and family, and our relationship to our garden earth.
Let us create together! Each woman has a story – an image – a song – a dance – a prayer - a poem - a movement to move within. The courage to create our own sacred images is right here, right now.

*Excerpted from "She Dances Between The Worlds" by Shiloh Sophia McCloud 2003*

***When women open the doors of their own lives and survey the carnage there in those out-of-the-way places, they most often find they have been allowing summary assassinations of their most crucial dreams, goals, and hopes.***

***I have heard all the excuses that any woman might knit up: I'm not talented. I'm not important. I'm not educated. I have no ideas. I don't know how. I don't know what. I don't know when. And the most scurrilous of all: I don't have time. I always want to shake them upside down until they repent and promise to never tell falsehoods again.***

***Excerpted From Women Who Run With The Wolves - Clarissa Pinkola Estes***

## The Anger Pages

On the front and back of this page go ahead and write what you are really pissed off about. Then you can rip it out. Anger is not popular these days - but anger is a healthy response to injustice, it is just a matter of what we DO with our anger. My anger MOTIVATES me profoundly to do good in the world. Express yourself. Admit it if you are mad as it will help you get through to the other side. Right after you rip it out is a plan for a day of painting which will help you to ground out the energy and use it for creation.

# A Painting Day

*Are you ready to paint and play? It doesn't matter if you are a painter or an artist. I don't even care if you feel like it. I want you to plan a day within the next month for a whole painting day. Turn off the phone. Tell your family you need space. Put paper on the floor. Fill up water jars. Get a big canvas and brushes. Get acrylic paint. If you don't like what you do, you can paint over it. This canvas will be your 'blank canvas.' I want you to paint your vision. Do it like you are a kid. Or a cave woman. Or a wild woman. Drink wine. Light candles. Turn on the rock-n-roll. You will discover things you did not know. I promise. Keep the critic out of it. No matter how she says she is just trying to protect you from making a fool of yourself, she is up to nothing good. On this page I want you to sketch out your vision. What does it look like? Is it a book? A jar of jam? A massage practice? A network marketing company? A daycare? A housekeeping business? A lawyer? An invention? A pottery business? Organic gardening? Green building? Draw it here as a preparation for your canvas. Don't try to save white space in this book.*

# Right Brain-Left Brain Activation

First of all, let's get our right brain and left brain engaged and communicating. Stand up. Think about crawling or a swimming pattern. It is this motion that develops and strengthens the connection between the hemispheres. Now do a cross pattern. Bring up your right arm and lift your left leg, then alternate for a minute or so. This can feel really good and because it stimulates the mind it well help if you do it each time you work in Heart of the Visionary.

This whole workbook is designed to stimulate right and left brain activity. There is only so much you can do with a typed page, but since you are filling in blanks and drawing and doodling while dreaming, you are using both sides. Many of the activities include both sides. A very left brain assignment will have instructions to be completed in a very right brain way.
**Left Brain** stimulation: verbal, systematic, problem solving, step by step, structure, outline, formulated, structured assignments.
**Right Brain** stimulation: visual, kinesthetic, intuitive problem solving, creativity, art, poetry, summary, abstract, open assignments.

So just think, if we put those two groups together we should have some genius going on 'up in here!' And then, if you add the awakened heart to the intelligence equation, we are really on fire! Having access to your inner wisdom, mental faculty, soul language, intuitive reasoning, and all that juicy girl stuff will help you design a better business. We are not just saying: Do this book. We are saying: Live this life! Make your work part of your spiritual practice.

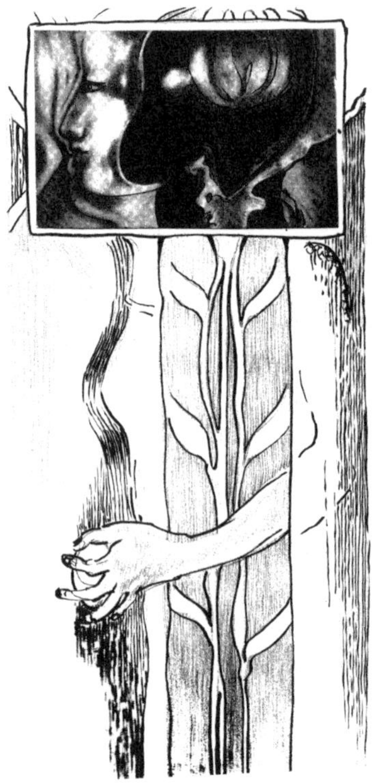

Work has gotten a dirty rap. I love the word "work" itself. My work is what I BE and DO in the world. Now, this is not the case if you are doing a job you don't like. So start a project you do like, and use this book to grow it. And eventually, we hope, you will LIVE INTO the LIFE you LOVE and WANT and DREAM about!

*Every so often we will recommend a research date—this is one of those. Please go to the internet and do some research on right brain left brain activation!*

## <u>Creative Exercises</u>

### Opening the Heart - Opening the Mind - Shared by Sue Hoya Sellars

*Draw a heart using both hands. Have a pen or pencil in each hand, start at the v at the top of the heart and draw out from there with both hands at the same time. Then draw wings on each side, still using both hands. Then, with one hand, write inside of it put your name or project name. Then write a manifestation affirmation that you can use to stay inspired during this journey!*

### Opening Your Visionary Screen

*Write an article as if you were a non-biased reporter who is viewing your business/project. What would they say? Try to think from their mind and write as free flow as possible. See what comes.*

# Name, Logo and Brand

*Take this page, and as much time as you need to work on your symbols, colors, shapes, totems and ideas for your company Logo, including your name and your tag line. Research Date: Go to a BIG bookstore and look in the business and design section. Look on-line, look in the grocery store, in your make-up drawer, tool chest or closet. A logo is a distillation of the image, look, symbol, brand, idea, concept that represents your work.*

# Dangerous Perfectionism

## Getting Focused In Your Project

Awakening to living our life vision is just about the most enlivening thing I can think of! The work in this book is about exploring and planning the possibilities for manifesting your vision. Whether that is a full time gig, or a side gig, at least you are doing something of the sacred work you feel called to do. The clearer you are about articulating your vision into words the closer to real it will become.

Business is quite a journey! It leads to destination after destination. And, it is utterly thrilling because you discover new things about you and your work all the time. Things that you did not understand before begin to fit into place. There will be many occasions throughout your process to continue to refine your work and words. So when you get started, just write what comes up as it flows. Don't think too much yet. Don't edit out your authentic voice through dangerous perfectionism. Just let it flow forth like a bright and powerful river!

The business plan model we have developed and included will be a summary of your vision in more professional terms. It is towards the end of the book after you have already done a lot of visioning and clarifying of your material. We feel that to create a business plan without the vision process is a missed opportunity to truly work out your ideas. We do all this preliminary visionary heart work so that our business plan is true, and real, and about the real work of us. Not some invented fill in form designed to impress investors while not based in the heart of the vision you are excited about!

**This workbook is designed to be a guide and an invitation for your work to come to life! The visionary business plan you develop will serve as a road map for your journey!**

# We Are Women Warriors

## Facing our limitations empowers us to move forward armed with wisdom.

We may feel trapped by our situation. Or we may not be able to play, or express joy or sensuality. We may hold back too much, not be able to celebrate. Or we might go over the top, giving too much exuberance and exhausting ourselves and others. In any case you can take time to get conscious and clear, you can shift the context and get some movement. And that little bit gets you onto the next situation.

If you use creativity and use this journal all along, eventually your lifework, your personal material and reason for being on the planet, your calling, will reveal itself. Seed by seed, miracles are born out of becoming present and shifting your context. What you have made something mean, it may not mean that. You are free to pick another view. Through that new view, you have greater access to your soul seeds. You begin to unfold as a bud to a flower.

Being able to choose is in and of itself a decision made by one who has the wherewithal to pick between one thing and another. There are many situations where it doesn't seem that choice is an option. It is important for those of us who are free to think our own thoughts to consider those who either do not have a choice or do not realize that they do. Over the past 11 years I painted and created as if my life depended it, as if the world would fall down around me if I didn't paint. I called out to the Creator, "How can I serve you and those in need in this world? Show me!" And out of that place, which is tired and tried, many bountiful blessings have been born. Our challenges are not negative—they just must be put to good use and not allowed to take too much space that is needed to make art. Do not think that you must be brilliant and funny to create and write. Your bluest moment and your darkest thoughts are compost that will serve the garden of your creativity very well indeed.

As much as the "New Thought" movement likes to affirm that you can have and create ANYTHING YOU WANT—I still don't believe it. Nor do I think it is good for us to have ANYTHING. We need to be able to articulate clearly what our offering is, and what is needed to continue to sustain and make that offering thrive. But if we do not know who we are and what we are doing here—how will we even know what we want and what is best? So often want lists are filled with things even before personal development lists. No matter what you believe about how manifestation happens, we will need to face our limitations, to know what they are. So as you move onto the Abundance chapter, remember to work with real and imposed limitations. Structure creates bounty.

*Invite the inner woman to speak in her language of poetry, bones, clouds, dreams, red shoes, fairy dust, ravens, and fissures of the heartland. She who dwells in the wild within will help to navigate the cliffs and valleys. She will show you the passage through - give you eyes to see in the dark. And then, when you are able, she will give you wings to fly out from that both nurturing and devastating abyss into divine light.*

*Blessed be that flight. - Shiloh*

# My Visionary Business

*Here we go! Describe your business. The who, what, when, where, and why of it.*

*Each time you do an exercise like this your vision becomes clearer and more embodied.*

# Declaration of Desire—What I Want!

*This is the place to express your passionate desire to the universe. Don't hold anything back.*

# Project Phases

*What items are in the first five phases of your project/business? If you are starting in your home with a desk, that might be phase one. Phase two might be to share an office with a friend or renting a small studio. Phase three might be to get an office downtown and so on. For each phase list what is present at that phase, starting with where you are now. Draw about five spheres moving down the page as if they are a winding path. In each one list where you hope and plan to be at the next phase. You could focus on money, location, staff, products or services, or whatever inspires you about each phase. These are about reasonable upgrades to make your business more profitable. A phase two might have one additional staff person and laptop computer and a catalog of the products you introduced in phase one. This is another process about starting right where you are, and ending up being able to SEE and FEEL your destination!*

# Preparing To Manifest Your Vision

*Write down a few notes after each of these prompts.*
*Develop your intuition to guide you in answering questions and coming up with ideas.*

**NURTURE** - Celebrate your process, tend the vision, open your mind and heart. Seek counsel, be creative, don't be interrupted, don't give up, research your topic. Commit to this book. Find mentors, create alliances, work on your project in some way at least four days a week.
Action: Invite a friend to tea and share your vision, ask her to help you articulate it. Note it here.

**FOCUS** – What is at the center of your project? At the heart of it. Make a mental picture of it – and see rays radiating out from it. There are many rays of light – that may be very diverse from each other – and jewel-like. To focus does not always mean one thing – just choose the animating principle or motivation to put at the center of your sun or jewel. Action: What is it?

**LOVE** – Bring your love to it, and let LOVE ultimately be at the center of all your choices. You know what? If you don't love it, at some level, maybe you should reconsider or do something else. How is your LOVE and heart being served and blessed by this focus? Action: How is the greater love in the world being served by your offering? Where is your love in this?

**PASSION** - What about your project gets your heart a thumpin'? It may even be something you are angry about, and want to bring healing to. Action: What is really motivating your decision? What fires you up? What do you find yourself wanting to talk to your friends about? What makes you want to live fully?

**THE FOLKS i.e. Your Client** - Who are you doing this for, in addition to yourself and your family? Who is being served? Why do you want to offer your product or service to them? Who is at the heart of the work? Imagine the recipients of your work in your mind - who are they?

## My Ideal Day

Take a few deep lovely breaths. Sit in a quiet place. Relax your whole body. Get as comfortable as you can. You are going to imagine a day when all is as you wish it to be. Start with waking up and go all the way to bed time. In this day you are doing your own career—spending time doing what you love and making the money you want doing it. You are happy. Write down the day.

## She Believes in Her Possibilities

**Shiloh Sophia McCloud**

she surrenders to change
she dances, chants, prays, seeks
she does what she knows to do
to bring healing to her temple body
to bring clarity to her sound mind
to bring joy to her soul
to awaken her heart to love's fire
to honor her relationships
to nurture her spirit
she moves beyond her limitations
she dares to create
she connects to her truth
she forgives what she can
she accepts what she must
she gives up shame
she reaches out, she reaches in
sometimes it feels like it isn't working
she falls down and cries and listens
she breathes, moves on
she rests when she needs to
she sets new boundaries
she releases old rules

she invites new experiences
she tends her garden
sometimes she feels that it is working
she leaps and shouts and grows new little sprouts
she is abundance, she is a tree of life
to those that embrace her
she evolves, she shines
she falls in love with herself
she is transforming, of that, she is sure
she celebrates her journey
she says yes to miracles
she heals and moves on
she grows orchards of fruit
in her flowering soul.

# VISION

## The Power of Passion

**Author and Artist Shiloh Sophia McCloud**

**WITH**

**Caterina Rando**

**Illustration by Sue Hoya Sellars**

# Remembering You

Shiloh Sophia McCloud

Remember that no one can do what you do, the way you do.
What you do is needed and wanted.
Remember that you have a unique purpose that has always lived within you.
And that it will continue to call on you until you say YES!
Remember that saying YES will call upon you to become more than you are.
And that this is part of the bliss of life, to become the most YOU that you can.
Remember that the key is to keep going no matter what.
And that you can start and stop as many times as you need to.
Remember that unless you do this you may always wonder "What If?"
And that to try to live a dream changes how we dream, even if we don't reach it.
Remember that living a dream, is the journey, is the process, is the dream itself.
And that we are not waiting for a destination, but living each moment truly.
Remember that it will sometimes seem as if forces are against you.
It is just that to get up enough speed to break through, we often encounter obstacles.
Remember that a true vision will have a combination of you and "them."
It is the "them" that you work with or serve, or both, that will inform your process.
Remember that each step leads to another step. So that is why we have to step up!
It is more important than we can even know, how each flow flows into the next.
When we move forward in our vision an energy flows towards us at that moment.
And it opens up the next action, the next door, the next opportunity.
When we take a leap of faith, new territory opens up that we did not see before.
And we have access to information that was not previously available.
When we risk believing in ourselves we will be amazed at the support that comes.
And we will recognize that doing this work is what we were born to do.
When we remember that a life not lived is not the life we want, then we choose.
And we choose powerfully not to turn back again.
We may fail. We may fall. We may even disgrace ourselves.
But what if we didn't? Remember to remember you and what you are all about.
Go Forward Now! And live the life you were born to live!

# The Path of QUESTIONS

## Shiloh Sophia McCloud

We are full of vital questions that lead and pull us along our path. Wandering, searching, ranting and raving, filled with unquenchable passion for our cause and that of other women and all people. We make our way through to the land of POSSIBILITIES. Throwing off skins and old baggage and unwanted boxes and perceptions as we go along. When we are willing to give up who we thought we were and consider who we are already becoming, we are inspired to make ideas into reality. And why not? Why not be wonderful, wild and outrageous?

We are spirits who live in beautiful bodies who must learn to live in the material realm. Sometimes this doesn't fit our pictures and we feel we have to compromise ourselves. Women Visionaries are the ones who create new pathways that balance the elements of mind, body, spirit, heart and soul with the material and financial realms. At the heart of the *Heart of the Visionary* is the desire to serve wellness, happiness for all and to be supported in the process. To take our Love into Action that actually "makes a difference."

In working with thousands of women I have found that there are several questions that beyond the basic how-tos of business. While this workbook may not answer all of them for you, it will give you a context to explore them for yourself and enable you to arrive at your own conclusions naturally. This workbook is essentially a discovery system.

### *Women Visionaries Want to Know*

How do I get from an idea to an action?

From the unmanifest to the manifest?

How do I create, as a spiritual woman, a path with heart that is sustainable financially?

How can profitable self-expression not commodify my work/product/myself?

Why is it so hard to value myself and what I have to offer?

If I am already financially challenged and have responsibilities, how can I justify starting a business?

Isn't it too big of a risk?

What can I give of myself and my ideas to others that is wanted and needed that people are willing to pay for, that doesn't compromise myself, other people, resources, or the environment?

How can I create a life for myself that is more in alignment with who I know myself to be?

A life work that is in alignment with my values. My ethics. My heart.

What are your questions? Don't let them stop you - just be clear on them and move on!

# VISION

*Share your vision as you understand it now. Just let it flow freely from your visionary heart!*

# Create Your Compelling Vision

## Caterina Rando

Congratulations on your decision to put attention on creating the life you desire! I am sure you know about the importance of goal setting. However, goals hold little power without a strong emotionally significant picture to drive you forward to their realization.

In the coming pages and throughout the *Heart of the Visionary* powerful information will be revealed to you. You will gain some inspiration, yet action is required! Commit yourself right now to not only reading, pondering and reflecting on the thoughts and ideas that come to you - commit to taking action. Knowledge is almost nothing without action when it comes to your life.

As you read these pages remember it is all up to you: you have to be willing to be uncomfortable and to take consistent action to create the vision you now only imagine.

Before we get started with lots of information, take a moment and write some ideas, without editing what comes to you.

- What do you want in your community and relationship life?

- What do you want in your creative and leisure life?

- What do you want in your business professional life?

- What do you want in your financial life?

- What do you want as you think about your home, your car and your wardrobe life?

*The important thing is not to stop questioning. Curiosity has its own reason for existing. One cannot help but be in awe when she contemplates the mysteries of the eternity, of life, of the marvelous structure of reality. It is enough if one tries merely to comprehend a little of this mystery every day. Never lose a holy curiosity.*
*Albert Einstein*

# Visions Are More Powerful Than Goals

## Caterina Rando

Now take what you have written and turn the ideas that are most appealing to you into a compelling vision—a Technicolor® snapshot in your mind of what you want and of what your ideal life looks like. A vision—not a goal, is what I want you to focus on; goals are beneficial and important, however alone they are not enough. Visions are more powerful than goals because visions have an emotional component. When you see a picture it evokes emotion—involving your heart, not just your head. This is far more powerful than just writing down an idea. You might say, "I want a bigger house," and that's a good goal. However, that simple statement by itself is not significant enough to get you to figure out everything you need to do to support you through sacrifice, to get you to take risks, to have you learn new skills, to overcome your "friends" telling you to forget about it, to overcome self-doubt and any other obstacles that get in your way.

If, instead, you create a compelling vision in which you see yourself standing in front of your yellow house with a two-car garage on a sunny street lined with trees, with a rose garden in front and a lemon tree and hammock in the back, a chef's kitchen and a master bedroom with a view of the ocean, you now have an idea that is not only in your head, it is in your emotions too. That is how motivation happens, that is how desire is created and that is why it is necessary to connect with your emotional power; the power to pull you through all the challenges you have to address to create your compelling vision.

In psychology there is a term S.E.E. - significant emotional event. This is a moment in your life that is imprinted on your psyche that shapes who you are. These occurrences can be positive or negative. Like your first day of school, your first date, your graduation or wedding day or the moment your child was born. You can create in your mind significant emotional events that I call a compelling vision - events that haven't even happened yet and they will influence your actions. Choose to use your compelling vision as a powerful tool to keep you focused and in action!

Let me explain why emotion is such a key component in creating your compelling vision. The human brain is actually made up of three separate brains. Your reptilian brain which is the oldest brain responsible for regulating your physiological functions like heartbeat and breathing. Your newest brain is called the Neocortex and is responsible for your higher function activities like understanding language and logical thinking. Then there is your third brain, your mammalian brain where your amygdula is, which is your emotional brain center. Unlike your Neocortex brain your amygdula does not understand language—so when you write down a goal you are not accessing the power of your emotion. You are not connecting with the place where your desire lives, your passion comes from, your joy flows.

In order to fully access your emotional power you have to take your goals and translate them into a language that your emotional brain understands. That language is the language of the senses: touch, taste, smell, sight and sound.

The easiest of these senses with which to consistently conjure up your compelling vision is sight. You want to start by creating a picture in your mind that is so powerful it will become your beacon to drive you toward the realization of that picture in your own life.

By evoking this compelling vision in your mind everyday you are in fact training your brain. Getting your conscious and subconscious mind used to the idea. In essence you are shifting your self-perception of who you are now to the person you will be when this vision is realized.

Consider a classic example: A high school teenager puts pictures of the hot rod she wants to buy up all over her room and on her bathroom mirror. She thinks about it every day, she focuses on it, she imagines how cool and fun it will be to drive this car. She sees herself driving around with her friends in the car, listening to music. She feels how great that feels. Soon she begins studying to get her license, she gets up extra early to go to drivers education class and takes a job after school to earn money. When her friends invite her to a concert she chooses not to go because she is saving as much of her paycheck as possible to get her dream car.
She researches the costs. She discusses her dream with her parents. They are impressed by her commitment and enthusiasm and tell her if she gets good grades and stays out of trouble they will give her a loan to make her down payment. She agrees and complies and soon she is driving down the street feeling exactly how she thought she would feel, not even realizing that her vision served as a powerful catalyst that had her align her whole life to get what she wanted.

# Compelling Vision

## Caterina Rando

- What is one of your compelling visions?

- What is another one of your compelling visions?

- What is one more of your compelling visions?

# Compelling Vision

## Caterina Rando

Make following these next eight steps important, make them a priority. Make creating your compelling vision a constant focus in your life. Another thing about your mammalian brain is that it has no sense of time. That is why if you run into someone you used to know 20 years ago you will feel the same way about them today as you did then. This is also why you can look at a picture from years ago and feel the same emotion you felt on the day the photo was taken.

How this benefits you in relation to your vision is that while your Neocortex brain knows a vision you see in your mind or a picture you put on the wall is not real today, your emotional brain does not. So, whether triggered by real or imagined images, your emotions can be as equally, powerfully triggered to realize your vision in your life.

By utilizing your compelling vision every day you will find that you are more in action, that you are happier working your business and you will begin to shift your self-perception from where you are now to where you will be when your compelling vision is present in your life.

**Follow these steps to create your compelling vision, keep it present in your life every day and watch it work for you.**

1. Get clear about your compelling vision. Write it down on paper; be specific, use visual language. See it in your mind.

2. Share it with someone else. Ask them if they can see the snapshot. If they cannot, you are being too vague.

3. Read your vision every day and continue to clarify it when new ideas come in.

4. Create a physical anchor: a drawing, a real photograph or a collage that represents your vision. Put that physical representation of your vision where you will see it every day. This is key because we are rarely more successful than we perceive we can be. That is why it is key to imagine you are where you want to be every day. Not only to imagine it but to also feel the positive feelings you will feel when you are living out that vision.

5. Take your vision with you in your purse or day planner as another physical representation of your vision that you will come across when you are out and about.

6. Put your vision at your bedside. Write it on a 3×5 card, read and reflect on it each night before you go to sleep and each day as you wake up. Tiger Woods had a 3X5 card that he read every night before retiring. That card said, "I am the greatest golfer in the world." While it was not true when he was a boy, he was training his brain for the man he would become.

7. Create an action plan to realize your vision and take even some small action every day.

8. Get the support you need. You do not have to do it alone. There will be good days and bad days. The way you get to your goal is by being able to bounce back from setbacks.

***Remind yourself every day and throughout the day to stay focused on your compelling vision!***

## *Define Your Compelling Vision*

*Once you have your vision, ask yourself: Are you more committed to your compelling vision, or are you more committed to your current situation? Our reality interferes with our vision because we see what is not ideal around us and that is far more vivid than a vision of what we desire that still lies only in our head and heart. That is why it is important to follow these steps and spend time with your vision every day, gradually bringing it more and more into focus and finally into reality. Do not let the busyness and immediate needs of your life prevent you from stopping to create what you want your life to look like at this time next year and the year after that. You are ready! Below please write concisely, the VISION for your life work. See yourself IN the work itself. What are you wearing? Where are you going? Who is with you? You may want to use an additional piece of paper to write or type out your vision to display it!*

Yet if a woman never lets herself go, how will she ever know how far she might have got? If she never takes off her high-heeled shoes, how will she ever know how far she could walk or how fast she could run?

Germaine Greer

# *I Am A Visionary Woman!*

*Write a declaration about yourself being a visionary empowered woman! Put it into the present. Even if there are things you have not manifested yet, write about it as if you already have!*

# Understanding WORK as the Journey

**Shiloh Sophia McCloud**

**We are moving from ideas into identity.**

**Moving from existing to designing a life that is in alignment with who we are.**

**Moving from exploring ourselves to creating ourselves.**

**Moving from our desires for our life to actualizing it in language and time.**

We are on a transition journey, alchemically moving from where we are to where we want to be. When we are aware of our visions we can learn to choose our next destination. We can begin creating the path in advance. In the Land of Possibilities, we are the ones who design the landscape and what goes into it. For this to work we have to build our own bridge between the worlds.

The spirit world and the material world are often treated as opposites. This perception can polarize our ability to move between them with grace. When we can create the BRIDGE ourselves that connects the two worlds in conscious union within us, the LAND of POSSIBILITIES comes into view. Having access to information from between the realms and from both realms helps us think.

This workbook addresses the process of moving from ideas to an identity. Sometimes this means we have to let go of our position and surrender into an unknown place. Well, not sometimes, more like, most of the time. But in this unknown place, genius shows up. WATCH and LISTEN for her VOICE. She is the one who shows up between the worlds. As Visionary Women - WE ARE MOVING! Manifesting! Awakening! Creating! Blooming!

**Congratulations on making it so far into this book! You are now about to embark on the brave and powerful journey at the heart of this book, The Vision Plan which explores the Who, What, Where, When, Why and How of your dream, project or business.**

***At the heart of the visionary is the heart of the world.***

Keep the channel open...

There is a vitality, a life force, an energy, a quickening that is translated through you into action, and because there is only one of you in all of time, this expression is unique. And if you block it, it will never exist through any other medium and it will be lost. The world will not have it. It is not your business to determine how good it is nor how valuable nor how it compares with other expressions. It is your business to keep it yours clearly and directly, to keep the channel open. You do not even have to believe in yourself or your work. You have to keep open and aware to the urges that motivate you. Keep the channel open...No artist is pleased. There is no satisfaction whatever at any time. There is only a queer divine dissatisfaction, a blessed unrest that keeps us marching and makes us more alive than the others.

Martha Graham

The Vision Plan
SHILOH
Created By Shiloh Sophia McCloud
To Empower Women's Work

# The Vision Plan Ideas and Instructions

## Fifteen Visionary Manifestation Initiations

The intention of The Vision Plan is to empower you to do your work by creating an emotional and physical bridge between your ideas and your ability to manifest them in real time. The structure is designed to guide you between the *thinking* and the *being* in your visionary plan. To activate your imagination, to spark and to inspire you to action. Besides the work of it, there is room for playfulness and thinking big. The information you input in The Vision Plan will inform the work you will do later. Starting with The Vision Plan is leading with the heart. By the time you get to The Business Plan you will be ready to write on a somewhat more linear level. **Give permission to your dreams and wild and wonderful ideas and hopes to be expressed!**

**DIG DEEP—DREAM BIG: Ideas for getting the most out of The Vision Plan**

**VERY IMPORTANT!** Each of the fifteen exercise topics is divided into two parts. The first half of the page is the idea part and the second half is the realization of the idea. From Idea to Reality. From concept-to emotion-to living it! Here is another way of thinking about it:

**1. Creating the path** – The first part is about naming the desire, the idea, the dream, the wish. Identifying the areas and aspects of the topic. This process is part-plan and part-reality based on where you are in your current project or business. You will have to adjust accordingly.

**2. Living the path** – The second part is about acting as if it is already in motion – VISIONING and Imagining what it would look and feel like if your Vision was REALIZED or being realized. You can use sentences, images, or a few words to describe the sections. It isn't important that it be understood by other people, only by you. This process is like gathering the seeds for the garden that you are planting. And then seeing them grow instantly. Be outrageous – this is the place for it. Expect what you don't expect to show up. DIG down deep beyond the limitation thinking. DREAM big so it goes beyond your world and into the world of others on planet earth.

**Take time to reflect before you start writing. Sit with the question. Each page has two words to work with. For example, Passion and Vision. Essentially, Passion is the unrealized part and Vision is the realized part. There is no need to rush or force it, allow words to bubble up like living water to nourish your new seedlings.**

## Examples

*Allow your words to just flow out. Don't worry about it being good or sequential. Below is a rambling example.*

Part One Example: My **Passion** is to work with women in the areas of creativity, with a specific focus on painting, writing and wellness. I am passionate about this because I feel that creativity is a transformative agent. I feel called to this work because I can see the results in women's lives and in my own happiness when I am doing the work. I was inspired by my anger at the way women have been treated, about how we don't value ourselves and so I committed a long time ago to do what I could to teach women to love themselves. I am totally passionate about doing whatever I can to bring wellness to women.

Part Two Example: The **Vision** for my work is a Wellness Center for women focused in creativity through art and education. The center is called Wild Wonder Women and we see upwards of one hundred women a day through our workshops, events, spa and offerings. My role is to design curriculum and to teach classes, as well as hire other instructors. Our center is the town hub for women, so clients come to us all the time for one thing and then end up connecting with us about something else. This Vision is bringing empowerment to women and girls in the community as well as providing work. This is the most amazing gift of life I can possibly be living!

Get the idea? Move into the **Vision Realized** and see what is in there! When you allow your creativity to flow, the ideas are harder to hide from yourself. And yes, we do that. Because we might be afraid of what it might mean to awaken to what we really love?! The great combination is when what we really love lines up with a need in such a way that there is money behind it. Heres another example:

Part One Example: My income **Need** for my business at the moment is $2500 per month. I would like to create $4500 within the next 3 months so that I can expand the services I am able to offer while making sure my bases are covered. My income comes from the three multiple streams including.......and.........

Part Two Example: My **Livelihood** is composed of the services I provide for women through the center, my private practice and a percentage of profits from the center partnership. My income is between $15,000-30,000 gross/net per month depending on which projects I chose to say yes to. The more I create for myself, the more the entire business is able to create.

Remember after you do the first one, sit with it. Then GET INTO the emotion of the realization part, SEE yourself in it – like when you worked with Caterina in the Compelling Vision section. SEE the details of your work fulfilled and write from that empowered feel good place.

# Guidance For Accessing Your Vision

### How to relate to the distinctions between sections:

As has been explained, for each of the sections in The Vision Plan you will be making a transition from one way of thinking to another. We are "projecting" our desire from where we are now, to where we want to be, so we can SEE it as happening! And the kind of thinking you will need to embody and practice will be expanding in order to create the next level of SEEING the vision. Stop now and read all the Vision Plan sections you will be working with. This will allow you to be mentally aware of the distinctions between sections - some do overlap but since it is so comprehensive try to stick with each one without doing too much of the next one. When you are working on Vision, try to stay with your Vision, don't move into Location or Need even if you see it in your visionary screen. For example, an image may come up of your client, but since you know there is a section for clients save up most of what you have to say about your client for that section. For each one you are, in essence, creating a powerful intention for manifesting that particular part of your plan.

### Instructions as you approach each of the Fifteen Processes:

In a comfortable place, breathe. Relax muscles, including your eyes and tummy and chest and toes and brain and all the space around you. Imagine light radiating from your heart. Smile. Invent or see a visionary screen behind your closed eyes. See a moving image, like a personal movie. Watch clouds move across the sky. See the sky colors. Watch for a little while as birds come, light changes, you see a moon - a butterfly - feel the temperature - take a breath - let it unfold - try not to force it - let it flow - gently introducing the moving images. Practice a bit and notice what comes up. Keep all negative or harmful voices at bay by just noticing them and gently dismissing them as if they mean nothing. Then imagine the first part of your vision plan, like Passion, and see that in action. Then when you have watched for a while, call in the next level, the manifested Vision—the place you want to go with your passion. See it and see yourself in it. See things like who and what and where and how much money. But then when you write, focus on the Vision, and save the other details for their sections. Take notes if you are afraid you are going to forget. You can always return to the sections if you have moved on.

If you are not able to WATCH the screen at first, kindly request your imagination to INVENT it. Or invoke your own personal muse to bring her voice to the process. In both cases, you can add your design as you go. What are you wearing? What is the space and place like? What color is the desk? The couch? What is your right hand woman wearing? What does her voice sound like? How much is in your bank account? What is on your calendar? Get into the details! Add more as they present themselves.

This is SUCH a powerful tool! Remember that your brain believes it is real at some level - and your heart wants it to be real! There is a great forward moving FORCE organizing on your behalf. When you are feeling ready, begin to fill in the sections. If you want a different sentence than the one provided, cross that one out and write your own as it will be different for different people. Most importantly, you are writing the legend of YOU! Let it be playful *and* serious!

Let it show your personal style. No one is watching, or is going to correct you, or tell you to calm down. There is no one to say you are not good enough or don't have enough money or education. This is between you and your visionary woman self. She is not wounded. She has no baggage. She is pure Wisdom in action. Let her do the talking. What is she saying to you?

**Moving between sections:**

When you have completed one, before moving onto the next one, stop and acknowledge the victory that you have created a LINK between your idea and your future reality. Let the knowledge of your action sink in, see the image continue to form. Get attached to it - but not so attached that it cannot shape shift. And have a good time visionary woman! You are CREATING your lifework!!

*You must do the thing you think you cannot do.*
*Eleanor Roosevelt*

<u>You will be journaling TWO worlds for each page.</u>

Please note the distinction of moving from one visionary world or realm to another. First you are in one world, NAMING, which is somewhat based in the NOW and in the planning. Then you move to the second world, LIVING, which is based in the feeling and possibility realm - it hasn't happened yet but it is what you want to have happen so you envision living it.

Allow yourself to be delighted and surprised by unexpected revelation!

| World One<br>NAMING THE VISION | World Two<br>LIVING THE VISION |
|---|---|
| The Un-Manifest | The Manifest |
| The Plan | The Success |
| The Idea | The Reality |
| The Concept | The Form |
| The Hope | The Possibility |
| Describe | Invent |
| Explain | Imagine |
| Explore | Actualize |
| Thinking | Dreaming |
| Knowing It | Feeling It |

## Vision Plan

Your Name

Date Started—Date Completed

# I. Why

## PASSION: Naming The Vision

Share your vision and your passion and why you feel compelled to create it.

## VISION: Living The Vision

Imagine what it will look like when you are living your vision. Describe it.

# II. What

## PRODUCT OR SERVICE: Naming The Vision

Create and explain your products or menu of services.

## SUCCESS: Living The Vision

Imagine your product or service being very successful, explain what it looks like and feels like. Come from a place of success when you write.

# III. Who

## CLIENT: Naming The Vision

Explain who you are serving. Who are your customer. What are their needs and wants. Most importantly, why it is important to you to reach them.

## COLLECTIVE: Living The Vision

See yourself fulfilling your greatest work for your clients. For the world. Share it.

# IV. How

## PURPOSE: Naming The Vision

Explain how and in what ways you will fulfill your life purpose with your vision.

## MISSION: Living The Vision

Imagine sharing your purpose as a mission statement with others. What is it?

# V. Where

## VENUE: Naming The Vision

Explain the environment in which your work is realized. The space it happens in. Where the work is delivered. There may be several locations.

## MARKETPLACE: Living The Vision

Envision your work in your favorite marketplace where your offering is appreciated, purchased and valued. See yourself there, representing it.

# VI. How Much

### NEED: Naming The Vision

Write down how much you are being compensated now. What you see in the next six months. In the next year. In the next five years.

### LIVELIHOOD: Living The Vision

Imagine the time when your livelihood and compensation is as you would like it to be. Share it here in detail. Explain what it gives you. And how long away is it?

# VII. Who I Am

## IDENTITY: Naming The Vision

Explain how who you are is suited for this work. Why it is in alignment with you. With your legend. Do you have a working title for your position?

## LEGEND: Living The Vision

Imagine yourself at the zenith of your career, respected and well known. Share your legend - how you want to be seen, what you want to be recognized for.

# VIII. Sales

## CUSTOMER SERVICE: Naming The Vision

Create your customer service standards. Your values. Your commitments.

## HAPPY CUSTOMERS: Living The Vision

Imagine a scenario where a customer has returned for a 'big deal.' It is the kind of deal you dream of in your kind of business - see it and tell it.

# IX. Wow

## GIFT: Naming The Vision

Describe the gift you bring to your work. Why this work makes use of your gifts. Your skills. Also share the gift you get back.

## GRATITUDE: Living The Vision

Imagine a time of utter gratitude and thanksgiving, a celebration regarding your Vision being acknowledged. See it and share it!

# X. The Woman

## PLEASURE: Naming The Vision

What is the personal pleasure and self value you feel you will experience through your creation? How does it add to you?

## PEACE: Living The Vision

Envision a time when all is well with your life work, things are smooth and good and balanced. A day when you have a peaceful sense of accomplishment.

# XI. Who Else

## FRIENDS AND FAMILY: Naming the Vision

Write down how you feel your friends and family will benefit, or how it may impact them. What will it bring? Take? Provide?

## COMMUNITY: Living The Vision

Imagine the new friends/connections/contacts you will be creating. Tell about it.

# <u>XII. Wisdom</u>

## KNOWLEDGE: Naming The Vision

Explain what you hope to gain from your work, in terms of personal development and growth. What is the education and transformation you will experience?

## EXPERIENCE: Living The Vision

Invent a scenario where you feel proud of yourself and what you have created. See yourself presenting on your work, you feel BRILLIANT! Radiant! Do Tell!

# XIII. Where You Live

## HOME: Naming The Vision

Describe how where you live will facilitate your work journey. Your rest time.

## HOME: Living The Vision

Travel to your future homestead, yes, the home of your dreams. Write it here!

# XIV. Within

## SELF CARE: Naming The Vision

Create a self care and spiritual practice plan. Explain it in detail.

## SELF EMPOWERMENT: Living The Vision

Imagine yourself at peak vitality, doing everything you should do for you. What do you look and feel like? What about the clothes, your sense of confidence?

# <u>XV. Completion</u>

### RETIREMENT: Naming The Vision:

Explain your exit strategy if there is one, otherwise, your kick back plans.

### LEGACY: Living The Vision

Invent the vision, where you feel as if your life was very well lived and that good work was done and that you were a part of making a difference and can enjoy some time to just be. Where do you see yourself?

## Dreaming the Future—Create a Vision Timeline

### In 20 Years...In 10 Years...In 5 Years...In 1 Year...In 1 Month...In 1 Week

*Within us*
*springs the very*
*seed and substance*
*of life itself.*

*Within us*
*lives the mighty*
*faith and power*
*to heal ourselves.*

*Within us*
*the heart of true love*
*opens, breathes and nurtures*
*the soul of the world*

*Within us*
*flows the luminous*
*essence and presence*
*of divine Wisdom's spirit.*

*Within us the awakening soul*
*opens and illumines the path.*
*Our courage will light the night*
*with our radiance.*
*~ Shiloh Sophia McCloud*

*Author Confession time*...once I started Cosmic Cowgirls, I thought, I will never have to publish an imperfect book again! For years I have allowed myself the space for imperfection, because making something perfect took twice as long and I needed to get the work to market! With this book I promised myself it would be typo and booboo free. Well, I have had 3 editors, all of which thought it was "done" and I am still finding stuff that I cannot believe all of us missed! I am supposed to finish by 1pm today, it is 8:22 and I am on this page. Reading it for the 25th time! I am delirious and worried I am going to start inventing some new last minute crazy poetry I might have missed! shjdhkshfldz=x! If I don't go to press, we won't meet our liveline. So, the moral is, do what you have to do. Ask for forgiveness along the way and surrender to the fact that life is messy even if you plan for the best. So thank you, dear reader, for continuing to take this journey with me, to supporting me in creating a finer product when I am able, and enjoying what we have now! Consider this your permission slip for imperfection! *Shiloh 8/25/08*

# ABUNDANCE

## The Power of Giving and Receiving

**Shiloh Sophia McCloud and Mary MacDonald**

**Illustrations by Shiloh Sophia McCloud and Sue Hoya Sellars**

Tree of Life Blessing By Reverend Shiloh Sophia McCloud

May you choose outrageous actions that challenge who you are and encourage who you are becoming.

May you take one step, however small, toward that which you have always longed for.
Now is the "right time."

May you recognize the unique and powerful contribution that you bring to the people whose lives you touch.

May you be as wonderful as you really are, and do things because you want to, not just because you should.

May you celebrate your creativity and believe that you are an artist with a unique vision that no one else has.

May you find peace and purpose and possibility amidst the chaos while remaining aware of the unrest in the world.

May you reach towards the Spirit with a longing that keeps you awake to the miracles available all around you.

May your faith move any mountains that stand in your way and bring you great teachers to awaken your understanding.

May you give up shame, guilt and self-neglect and replace them with qualities like freedom, integrity and self-nurturing.

May you offer the gifts and blessings of your soul to beings of the world when the time is ripe for you to release them.

May you passionately and deeply love and be loved by someone who can see who you really are.

May your body speak to you and teach you how to care for the temple that houses your bright spirit.

May you walk gently on the earth and honor your hearth and family with your action and your rest.

May you find and enjoy the fruit of abundance so that your life path can be fortified and furthered.

May you embrace the Tree of Life and be informed by the wisdom she brings to those on her path.

May LOVE be at the center of all your choices and may you, with me, send this blessing to all beings.
Amen.

may love be at the center
of all our choices

# Opening the Door to Your Abundance

**Mary MacDonald**

*Once we recognize what it is we are feeling,*
*once we recognize we can feel deeply, love deeply, can feel joy,*
*then we will demand that all parts of our lives produce that kind of joy.*
*Audre Lorde*

Abundance is all around us. It's the hot water flowing over our bodies after a day planting the garden. It's the laughter we share with friends. It's finding the perfect pair of jeans that make our butt look fabulous. It's in the air and earth and water. Acknowledging the good that is already in our lives is the foundation of abundance. If the only prayer we say is "Thank You" that can be enough.

Gratitude is the first step in creating abundance for ourselves. Gratitude is not just an emotion, it is a way of being in the world – seeing from a place of awe and thankfulness for all that we already have. Gratitude is not about getting, but about looking at what we have already received and giving it back – our thanks, our smiles, our resources, our time, and our appreciation.

We keep seeking instantaneous gratification wanting what we want NOW, and when we have it we'll be happy and live an abundant life. I have lived so much of my life that way – when I lose weight, when I make more money, when "they" validate my worth – then I will be happy. It was when I began my gratitude journal that my life changed in glorious ways. At the beginning I struggled to even come up with five different things that I was grateful for every day, because for so many years I had looked at what was missing in my life instead of all the amazing gifts that were all around me. Yes, I was grateful for so much in my life, but it wasn't until I made a decision to write it all down what I was able to see more clearly how I got in my own way of an abundant life.

Dr. Wayne Dyer tells us, "Change the way you look at things and the things you look at change." The only control we have is over the way we perceive the world and the way we react according to our perceptions. When we put our attention on the things we want as opposed to what we don't want, it changes how we feel and what we bring into our lives. When we are focusing on abundance, love, joy and harmony we behave differently.

Focusing on what we don't want can have as significant of an impact as our thoughts of gratitude and what we do want! How we feel emotionally and physically informs our inner guidance system. When we feel peace and inner calm we know we are on the right track. When we feel worried and anxious we need to examine what these feelings are telling us. When Mother Teresa was asked whether she would come to an antiwar rally she said no, but if they were going to have a peace rally she'd be there. It's all about the focus!

From the beginning of time much has been said and written by wise sages about the laws of attraction. Some of the Wise Ones tell us that our thoughts become our reality and that whatever is coming into your life you have attracted. How does one attract health, wealth, wisdom, love and joy into our lives? How do we NOT attract poverty, illness, and unhealthy relationships? I don't know why abuse exists or why the people in Darfur endure such atrocities. When we talk about abundance and the law of attraction I can only speak of it in the context of the world I live in – one of entitlement. I am often befuddled by how we in the West are riddled with depression, anxiety, addiction and hopelessness but people in countries who are struggling with violence, hunger and oppression can seem so much more hopeful. What I know for sure is that if I look at the privileged and abundant world I inhabit with deep and abiding gratitude, I have the unreasonable belief that I can contribute to the lives of others.

When we look around us we can't help but feel the need for transformational healing, in our own lives and in the world we share. Accepting responsibility for our actions and ourselves allows blaming to fall away and takes us out of the role of victim.

Have you ever noticed the multitude of voices inside you that are continually nattering, judging, criticizing, cajoling, shaming and sometimes even cheering you on. I might be feeling absolutely wonderful and then one of the voices tells me I would feel better if I had some chocolate ice cream, immediately leading me to believe that something is missing which in turn causes me to eat a pint of Ben and Jerry's and sabotage my healthy eating plan. And then my thoughts turn to others – she doesn't like me, he thinks I'm not enough, if they really knew what I was like they'd fire me. Now my thoughts lead me to believe it's someone else's fault that I feel like this. We take the words or actions of others personally and make assumptions about why they did what they did based on how we look at the world. Anais Nin tells us "We don't see things as they are, we see them as we are."

Living the life of a sage isolated high on a mountaintop may allow us to live peacefully but it is in relationship to others that we can learn the most about ourselves. When someone makes a statement about us or we respond defensively to a situation we can look at it as an opportunity to stop and examine why it sparked us and what we can we learn about ourselves.

Which voice is reacting to the comment? Is it the rebellious teenager who was told constantly that she was unreliable? Is it the vulnerable child who never felt loved for who she was? What wisdom are these voices imparting? What needs are underneath those feelings? How can we get to know where it is coming from?

Become friends with all the "voices" that live within you – your inner critic may think she's protecting you from being hurt – so thank her and let her know you need her to take a break!

Opening the door to your abundance is not about “positive thinking” that ignores your feelings of sadness, despair, anger, guilt or shame. Acknowledge those feelings, take them out for a walk and ask them what you can do to help and what can you learn from them to move on in a positive balanced way.

Our words are another way that put up barriers in our search for abundance. We say things like “I have to go to work.” Well actually you don’t. In the worst case scenario you could quit your job, not pay your rent, and become homeless. You choose to work because you want a home, food and to go to the occasional movie. We use catastrophic thinking and language almost by rote without realizing how much it affects the outcome of our actions.

To have abundance in the external world we need to feel abundance internally and not have an inner state of scarcity because that too will be reflected back at us in the big old world. Put out a specific intent that includes clearing the obstacles that obstruct your path. Don’t tell yourself you are uncreative, or not enough because you will believe it and it just isn’t true – you are perfect exactly as you were created. If what you believe or say about yourself is negative – work to change it. Creative action is a very powerful way to become clear about what you want and then work to create it. Use words, pictures, drawing, and visualization to help you become clear. Learn to use the right word for

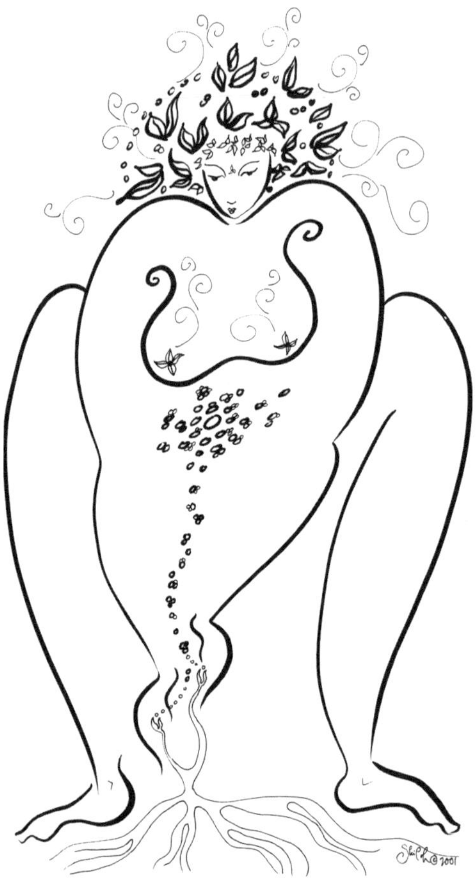

what you’re going through. When you can, sing and shout and pray and laugh your thanks out loud and the world will thank you back. Most of time anyway!

Be clear – what do you want that million dollars for? So you can travel? Not ever have to work again? Put your kids through college? Ask yourself why you want those things. If you had everything you wanted – a loving partner, healthy and happy children, a beautiful home, fabulous friends – would you need that million dollars? Maybe it isn’t about the money but about how it makes you feel. So figure out what you can do at this moment to make you feel that way. Pay attention to how you interpret the world, how you make sense of it and how you give meaning to it.

## abundance for me

*Explore what abundance means for you. What would it look like if you were living in abundance? Include personal, professional, spiritual, physical, financial and creative aspects.*

# Inspired actions

## Mary MacDonald

Get inspired through making choices that support who you are choosing to become! Affirmations are not just passive words we say to ourselves and then sit and wait for our dreams to come true. They are meant to focus our mind and emotions on positive thoughts that can shift our energy. Write affirmations down as often as you are inspired to! Put them up around your home, car and office. Shout them out loud with passion and conviction. At the end of the affirmation you can say, "for the highest good of all concerned!"

***Working with abundance has to do with a total way of being, it is not just money or stuff, it is who you be. How you think. How you work with what you have. How you perceive life. Shiloh***

- When you get in and out of the shower, use it as a time to thank your body, put on yummy cream and tell your body how much you appreciate what it does for you.
- Remind yourself, "I choose to love myself just as I am."
- Tell yourself, "This too shall pass."
- Get rid of the "shoulda, coulda, woulda's."
- Tell yourself, "I can choose to have wonderful relationship with money."
- Start a gratitude journal.

  When you find a quarter on the sidewalk say, "Thank you for this sign of abundance."
- Ask what you can give now and to whom. Ask how you can be of service.
- Keep a list of what excites and interests you and use them as clues.
- Distance yourself from the need to defend yourself or your desires.
- Expect that what you want is on its way.
- Think, feel and act as the kind of person you want to be. "Know Thyself." Pay attention.
- Entertain prosperous thoughts!
- Practice smiling—it is almost impossible to feel bad when smiling.
- Forgive—don't let resentment keep you imprisoned. You can't control the past so stop letting it control you. Forgiveness is not about forgetting since we become more of who we are through out experience. You are not responsible for the pain inflicted upon you—What you are responsible for is what you do with it NOW.
- Ask the right questions—Don't ask, "Why am I so depressed?" because you will then focus on all the reasons why you are. Ask, "What could I be happy about if I chose to be?"
- Release judgments about yourself and others.
- Read and learn from fabulous inspirational authors who are doing what you want to do.
- Visualize what you want—Close your eyes and see what it looks like. Spell the words out so you see them in your mind—What does it smell like, taste like, where is it?
- Unclutter your life of the unnecessary. What is needed in order for you to feel abundant?
- Be in awe of the world around you! Celebrate the beauty!
- Practice Loving Kindness as a way of being.

- Show others you value them by listening to them—Just listen—don't be formulating your answer.
- Practice being generous—do one thing every day for someone else—it can be as simple as offering a smile to a stranger.
- Look for opportunities to be inspired.
- Observe what you don't want so you'll know what you do want.
- Change your thoughts, change your experience.
- Spend time alone in nature.
- Learn to trust your intuition – it takes practice to hear it properly so take the risk that you might fail. Practice on the small things.
- Be on the lookout for synchronicities. If someone suggests you read a particular book and then the next week you see it at a friend's house and then the next week you see a review for it – PICK THE BOOK UP!
- Be clear about what you want. If you want money be as specific as possible.
- When something shows up in your life allow yourself to be aware of it and question why?
- Be willing to be a lifelong learner as well as a teacher. "In the beginner's mind, there are many possibilities. In the expert's, there are few." --Shinryu Suzuki
- Ask for what you want.
- When something challenging happens look at it as a gift and ask what it can teach you.
- Stand in your own truth. Seek truth.
- Pray and ask for help.
- Be aware of the words you use.
- Meditate –there's no big secret to it—start with 5 minutes by concentrating on just paying attention to breathing in and out and when your mind wanders off, gently bring it back.
- Take three deep breaths. When you breathe in let your stomach expand and when you breathe out feel it flatten.
- Before speaking take those deep breaths and resist the urge to tell people what you think they want to hear. Honor them and yourself by speaking the truth.
- Read, watch and listen to works that are inspirational instead of just the news.
- Be infinitely curious about yourself, others and the world.
- Ask, Expect, Take Action and Have Faith that your good is on its way to you right now!

*My great hope is to laugh as much as I cry, to get my work done, and try to love somebody and have the courage to accept their love in return.*

*Maya Angelou*

# Valuing Ourselves

## Mary MacDonald

*Learning to value ourselves is a gift and a challenge for most people. We often underestimate our own value, or do not recognize our innate value. Sometimes, we don't even celebrate our successes and accomplishments. If we are not careful, we can focus too much on how others view us, even over our own sense of self value. Take this time to ponder questions of value and how you create value in your own life and the lives of others. What does self value mean to you?*

1. What have I done that I am really proud of?

2. What did I accomplish that I haven't taken credit for?

3. What value do I bring to others?

4. When have I gone above and beyond the call?

5. What am I really good at?

6. What celebration can I create to honor myself and my accomplishments?

7. What do I like best about myself?

8. What are my most important priorities?

9. What do I do that doesn't serve me?

10. What would I like to say no to?

11. What kind of recognition do I like and want?

12. What do I do that feels thankless to me?

13. How do I over commit myself?

14. How can I learn not to let others take advantage of me?

15. How do I sell myself short?

16. What boundaries would I like to have in my life that would support me?

17. Who gets me and what is it they get about me?

18. What do I do that makes me feel good about myself?

19. What have I learned to do even though it scared me?

20. What do people tell me I'm good at that I don't like to do?

21. What do I say about myself that is judgmental and unloving? What can I do differently?

22. What beliefs do I have about others, the world, and myself, that are positive and nourishing?

23. What courageous acts have I done?

23. In what ways am I living abundantly? Or can I be?

24. Where and with whom do I feel most safe and why?

25. List things that you value yourself for.

26. List or write about your accomplishments. Use additional pages as you need for this one!

# Gratitude for what is coming

*Give thanks in advance, for what is coming, and how it is coming. This gets you into the feeling of receiving, and it helps you to pay attention to the pathways through which abundance is traveling to your door!*

If we only say one thing a day,
let it be Thank You.~Mary MacDonald

# my generosity—giving and tithing

*What changes do you want to see made in the world that your financial and physical present abundance could assist? In other words, how would you like to give and where? Design a giving strategy to go along with your abundance strategy. Are there teachers you want to offer your fruits to? Taking workshops can also be a form of caring for you, and giving to your teachers.*

Even after all this time, the sun never says to the earth
"You owe me." Look what happens with a love like that, It lights the whole sky. ~Hafiz

# Create Your Abundant Legend

*Imagination time! We at Cosmic Cowgirls Rodeo Queen Quarters like to use the cowgirl metaphor to create our personal legend. Use that one, or pick one of your own. This is play space, so write as if it is a children's adventure story. Consider: How do you want to be thought of? What are you wearing and carrying? Who are you riding with? What do you feel about yourself? What songs are on your sound track? What is on the invitation to your success celebration? What will be on your memorial? Write a ballad about yourself. If you have difficulties being effusive about yourself try writing this in the third person. As you work, look for the symbols and totems for your personal vision and legend. Draw a sketch of you! And remember, this is YOUR legend, so journal it your way and then live into it everyday for the rest of your life! You can start by closing your eyes and see yourself walking down a path of beauty...*

You will do foolish things, but do them with enthusiasm.~ Colette

# our actions create abundance

**Shiloh Sophia McCloud**

**Taking action is one of the most essential parts of realizing a Vision**. If we do not take action our project remains an idea. An action can take many forms: an action plan, a drawing, a mission statement, a luncheon with someone who can assist, building a model, a business card, a web-presence, attending a workshop, planning an event, joining a club, opening a bank account, calling a circle, hiring a coach, creating a space in which to work, buying a binder, setting up a desk, creating a recording, making a collage, a vision board, painting it, singing it, praying about it, enrolling others in it, putting it on your computer, starting a blog even if it is just for you, posting affirmations on your mirror, getting friends to remind you of it, calling people who are doing it, volunteering where it is happening, getting in the presence of it somehow. Practice believing in yourself and your project. Walk about it. Dream about it. Make up names for it. If you are a prayer person, pray, if you are a meditation person, meditate, if you are a wish upon a star person, wish and wish and wish. If you are a 'mostly intellect' person, think on! As it is all very much about our thinking. If you are a chef, cook it in your soups, if you exercise, move it! FOCUS on it! To create with good intention, can be an act of personal and collective abundance.

**The structure of this book illuminates some basics on the visioning process**. If you work on it, it will work on you. Each action brings us closer to the vision – is vital and keeps us engaged. We are, ourselves, the receiver, the garden, the space where the vision is both planted and grows. Our visions build momentum and bring people and opportunities into our field. Suddenly possibilities are all around us – we can see them – they make sense – we can see how each thing can serve the unfolding of our vision. To work on a vision, is abundance in action!

**Manifestation begins with a step by step process**. It is a decision and a design.
**There are two questions we must always be in touch with PRIOR to manifesting.**
***How does it serve, bless, and enrich others?   How does it serve, bless, and enrich me?***
In answering the questions, if it is just me, fine. If it is your family, even better. If it is your community, wonderful! And if it is the wider world, fabulous! And if it is any or all of these things, it blesses the whole world, because our evolution is the evolution of all. When we really know that our abundance contributes to the abundance of others, we feel good about doing what needs to be done in our lives. We are encouraged, and feel as if our efforts are being valued.

*We move as women move – circularly and continuously, a wholesome mountain moving samba, an all encompassing and gorgeous swinging of hips and stomping of boots and Yes! We might cause an earthquake or volcanic action in our wake! Footprints of fire smolder behind us as we sashay our way into the unknown but knowable deep soul garden. Our own tree of life waits there, blooming and shedding blooms season after season. Anticipating our arrival, she bursts into early spring shoots of tender white and yellow blossoms. Birds sing our symphony. ~ Shiloh 2003*

# manifestation altar

*What do you want to call into your life at this time? This can be personal or professional or both put together to equal one glorious life! This is not about excess, but what you really want and need. Let your manifestation not just be about getting, but about giving. Let love be at the center of all your choices! ~ Shiloh*

## Materials

**Surface:** Canvas or piece of wood (gessoed) - do not use anything flimsy. Get big if you can, 24 inches at least.
**Components:** Magazines, greeting cards, picture books, YES paste, Modge Podge, paint brushes, pens, paint, glitter, varnish/gloss medium, ribbon, charms, photos of you. I would like you to go shopping and if you are able, be willing to spend $100 for your materials. Purchase magazines that have things in them that you like, at least 5 or six. Get paint and brushes and glitter. Buy yourself some greeting cards with images you want to see on your altar.

## Instructions

- For the text - type ideas/affirmations out in nice font and paper on your computer - make up your own sayings or pick your favorite quotes. Hand-write on separate pieces of paper the phrases you want in there, use decorative lettering. Use letters and words from magazines to create.

- State your intention for the board. Write it out first on the next page as if it has occurred.
  Paint a background color - bright, light or dark so there is contrast with the stuff you are putting on the board.
  Paint a decorative frame or border to put it all in context - flowers, designs, leaves. Put a coat of gloss medium.

- As medium dries, begin to collect and cut out images, don't use too many squares, cut around the image - organize the images and phrases into groups of your choosing: examples: health, wealth, relationship, business, friendship, alliances, travel, personal development, goals, creativity, transformation, success, projects, dreams fulfilled.

- Organize the groups on the canvas to get a basic idea of layout and order, leave some space so it is not so busy that it is overwhelming. Include nature and symbols sprinkled throughout. Begin to glue - use a paint brush and coat the back. You can use some water to thin YES paste but if it is too watery it will warp. Layer the images so they are related to each other - design it - so it holds together as beautiful to your eye.

- Use selective glitter, put varnish in specific places where you want glitter. You can add other things like rhinestones, buttons, milagros, jewelry, other treasures. You can sew through the canvas with a needle and thread.

- Name your altar at the end - but ask yourself all along what the name will be - leave grand space at the top with arches and decor - like a movie theatre marque. I suggest painting it - but practice first and you will need a liner brush. Otherwise, type it out. Use nice thick paper or card stock.

- When you are all finished - you can varnish it to seal it. Use a big not stiff brush and layer it on - you will have to tilt it to make sure it is being covered. Then using white or gold paint, embellish the whole thing - the outline of images, words, borders, add stars, spirals. Hang it in a place where you see it daily. Hang it right on the wall, or staple a ribbon for a French style, or put it on your desk/dresser. Visualize having your life match the canvas. Change and update it as needed! Put a candle in front of it, drape a scarf around it, put a prayer bowl in front of it!

**MANIFEST! ROCK ON OUTRAGEOUS WOMEN! DO YOUR THING! MAKE MIRACLES HAPPEN!**

# I manifest my Life WORK!

*Write a personal declaration about manifesting the abundance to create your work. This is a space to create in language what you are up to in terms of manifesting - and abundance. You can also just make a list or description of what it would look like if it was already in place. Come from HAVING and from JOY! What are your beliefs about manifestation? Notice where you might be blocking yourself with limiting beliefs! Explore the fullness of your ideas!*

# "It Girl"
# Guide to Abundant Manifestation

dream it
want it
decide it
vision it
qualify it
be with it
practice it
articulate it
begin it
plan it
write it
measure it
love it
act on it
create it
give thanks for it
do it again

budget it
brand it
enable it
sell it
fund it
advertise it
keep track of it
research it
nurture it
strategize it
deposit it
rest it
share it
get press for it
improve it
be creative with it
believe in it

give thanks for it.

# Perspective

## The Power of Originality


**Shannon McCloud**

WITH

**Illustrations By Shiloh Sophia McCloud and Sue Hoya Sellars**

**Poetry By Shiloh Sophia McCloud and Song By Kelly Takunda Orphan Martinez**

# A Flock of Phoenix

Shiloh Sophia McCloud

We don't have to know how to do it.
We just have to know we want to do it.
This is the time when women
and work rise together.
A Phoenix adorned
in fire red and diamonds.
Ready to fly to her next destination.
We have worked the whole time.
But we have not always been paid
for that time. Or recognized for that time.
We knew our work was valuable.
Even though we were told it was not.
And some of us got lost in knowing
but not knowing what to do about it.
That is finished now. A new chapter is written.
A new prophesy is being called out.
Women are wise. Women are wealthy.
Women stand for each other. We share light.
Sometimes we stay in the ashes too long.
Mourning for all that has been lost.
And mourn we should. Because of the crimes.
The tragedy happening in our greater family.
We who are able must rise.
And make space for others to rise.
Each of us makes up her own fire rising song.
We sing the words into creation.
And watch the sparks begin to fly.
Just because fire was used against us
does not mean we gave up fire. No.

We have
breathed fire,
taken it into our
being.
Our legend is
not only one of
burning.
Though we have
done that.
Our legend is one
of rising.
Of flying.
Of making the impossible flight. From ashes.
Dusting the gray from our fire red wings,
we extend our shimmering wings.
And the earth in her wisdom
pushes us from beneath.
And the air in her understanding
pulls us from above. Up we go. Free at last.
Leaving gravity to its daily chore
of holding all things in place.
But not us. Not today.
Today we soar and we are whole.
We find the sky full of radiant Phoenixes.
A whole flock of Phoenix Women.
And together we fly
on the wisdom of the shared flock.
Bright and beautiful. Bold and dangerous.
Wild and full of hope. Brave and abundant.
Let us rise oh winged Sisters
and claim our skies!

## *Note From Shannon ~ The Cinnamon Cowgirl*

Since I am still recovering from my corporate past, I was apprehensive about accepting the invitation to write about my business career for *Heart of the Visionary*. I was able to do so by default. I happened to be studying birds at the time. I was surprised at how reflecting upon my experience caused me to identify with and love birds. I decided to start writing by using their journey in migration as a metaphor for my own journey. This provided me with the distance, perspective and courage to not only write my story, but to examine and evaluate my journey in a way I had not been able to before. Embracing this writing opened a path of healing and a long awaited desire came, calling me home to creativity. I have been able to expand my thoughts and enter them in written form far beyond my initial expectation and ability! This can happen for you too! It has been years since I wrote, except in my little sister's journals, but once I got started, I haven't stopped and that is almost a year ago now! So I encourage YOU! And I hope what I have written for you here, sheds some light on your own migration towards who you are!

So, I write this as an invitation to women who, like myself, might be apprehensive about pouring out their souls, to consider entering into their personal journey from another angle. My angle came to me cloaked in birds and how they spend their lives migrating. What is the thing that you love and trust or that holds your interest that might provide the angle or metaphor to enable you to begin the creative journey awaiting you?

The writings in this chapter are about my experience and are from an upcoming volume of my writings called, *The Outlaw Journals*.

# WINGS OF MIGRATION

## The Power of Metaphor—Business Is For the Birds

For nearly two decades I was responsible for supporting my employers in achieving their goals to "Build and Enhance the Company's Corporate Vision, Improve Profitability and Increase Shareholder Value." I had a vital "Corporate Business Vision" which was specific to achieving these goals critical for success, not only for my company but also to help other key business leaders in doing so. I became an expert negotiator, sales woman and consultant and my success was measured in terms of "The Bottom-Line." Clearly, "Vision" and the goals that build "The "Bottom-Line" are of utmost importance to creating our value as businesswomen.

*There are endless species of birds with different migratory cycles and processes, some migrating daily, others seasonally and annually, or not at all. Some migrate over land by day, others are nocturnal travelers who migrate at night and over water. Other birds migrate on foot, never taking flight but still having their own migratory planning and vision with which to deal.*

While I graduated "Summa Cum Laude" with my expertise in "Street Smarts," the prerequisites required in my line of work, specifically my company, were/are that one should be a white male, graduating from an "Ivy League College" with an MBA or PhD. Nevertheless, I became highly successful, respected and rich. To me, not being or having any of these "qualifications" meant that I HAD to succeed. In my mind I had to prove, not only to everyone else that I was competent to get the job done and then some, but most of all, I had to prove it to myself. While my statistics quickly reflected my success and the money was great, I didn't experience feeling truly wealthy or worthy and due to the challenging nature of my work and its complex dynamics, I simply didn't have time to care for myself.

*A bird's survival depends upon the condition of its feathers and they work hard to make sure their feathers and wings are well preened, strong and waterproof.*

I made a big mistake and left me behind. Fortunately, I never left my Cowgirl Boots or Lipstick behind.

*Most species who fly over large bodies of water are not able to land and have rest. There are small birds who have the most difficult journeys to make, flying over thousands of miles to their destination. The migration journey of the ruby-red-throat Hummingbird, for instance, is 2,000 miles and they can fly nonstop for over 500 miles, at speeds up to 60 mph.*

My work hours became out of control as did my personal life and health. I have a big spirit, but I am indeed, a small bird in body frame. My journey, although exciting, was taking some of my vitality out and not putting enough back in.

*Prior to entering into their seasonal and annual migration cycles, birds have to carefully plan and prepare for their journeys. They rebuild their bodies from the inside out, nourishing themselves to provide strength within. They go through a molting period which helps regulate their body temperatures to help them stay warm over cold waters and adjust to climate changes.*

Then came a new challenge—supporting our company and our clientele to incorporate our expertise into their businesses internationally. One of my special clients and I helped launch this new calling in the marketplace. Specific to negotiation and conflict issues, the integration of those topics on a worldwide basis required intricate attention.

*Birds select their flight patterns based on different celestial compasses and adjust them to pervasive environmental changes. Most birds migrate at night because winds tend to be more calm and there are fewer predators. Also, when flying over enormous bodies of water at night they focus on their celestial compass, such as star patterns in the sky. But sometimes when clouds obscure the light, the flock can become scattered and disoriented. However, they still learn to adapt and seek polarized light. They also use the light of the moon as a compass by its reflection on the water. They sing out to their pals to make certain they are on track and not separated from one another along their journey. Many birds even migrate in mixed flocks.*

Our team members were called to incorporate multicultural values, belief systems, politics and multilingual translations both in written and in verbal form. Further, the nuances of the underlying meanings of those translations and what they meant to the multitude of cultures was vital. We not only had to learn and teach our individual cultures these new business disciplines, but to learn and teach other cultures reaching far beyond America how to integrate with each other and us as well. When this was particularly difficult and these cultures often resisted, we at least tried to guide them to inquire into and honor one another's differences and to realize that they must adapt to this dynamic if they were to be successful in the business world.

*The primary danger isn't a lack of sleep because birds take little naps and rest their eyes, sometimes partially closing them to soften their vision and sometimes they might even fly with one eye closed. Though napping, they cannot rest their wings but must keep flapping them and flying in unison.*

I had to adapt my work schedule based on International Time Standards. When I was on conference calls or attending meetings, I had to learn how to reframe my mindset and strategy to consider multicultural differences, manage conflicting goals and internal competition with different leaders in the same company. I somehow became, by default, the one to whom people looked to solve "the problem." Most people tend to be conflict adverse, and this, coupled with a significant variance in belief systems, requires a substantial amount of time when attempting to resolve their issues. As the world and my career became more complex, my goals were increased each year by approximately twenty percent.

*The major danger to survival is weathering storms and strong headwinds. The stronger birds that care for themselves and better plan for their journey greatly increase their chances to survive. While the little birds that are more fragile, or don't know how to care for themselves prior to migrating, become exhausted and fall into the waves.*

In the beginning of my migration into the corporate world my wingspan was mighty and strong. I could fly endlessly for thousands of miles under any conditions. But I failed to take care of myself. After flying furiously and mightily for endless distances through uncharted territories, I was forced to fold in my wings. I went into what is commonly known by the human species as "burn out."

While shedding the familiar feathers of my corporate cloak, the stress and pain reached so far inside of me that I had no strength left within my wings to fly any further. Losing, first my personal source of origin and then my point of destination, broke my heart. I didn't know who I was except a successful business woman without a personal vision of my own or the strength to carry myself either onward or back to the nest full of creative possibilities that I had abandoned for so long. But, in spite of broken wings and a broken heart, I have no regrets, except that I did not take better care of myself. I am grateful for the opportunity and what I accomplished and learned. I am so very grateful to those special people in my flock who helped guide me in my journey to "Destination Business." After having lost my business, personal vision, health, creativity and income, I am grateful that I had been able to generate capital enough to see me through a painful and seemingly endless time of recovery. Napping. Nesting. Nurturing.

*And now, I am so grateful for my new journey, for the strength to rebuild my wings, my heart and my passion. I am finding new flight patterns as I go and I sing in unison with my flock of Cosmic Cowgirls while migrating to my favorite place, "Destination Miracle."*

*I hope you will join our mixed flock and fly with us to new destinations!*

Laurel Thatcher Ulrich said:
Well behaved women rarely make history.

## Tips For Bird Watching

1. *Bird's flying abilities take practice and evolve gradually.* We need to take our life-path steps gradually, making notes of goals we can reasonably achieve over time and taking time to observe and to learn. And to stop when we are tired.

2. *Birds plan and pay careful attention to nourishing themselves both inside and out in order to achieve maximum power prior to their journeys.* What, as women, must we do to nourish ourselves? This is not a luxury, but a necessity.

3. *Birds have a vision and an internal compass for their flight-path, which is celestial. There are many meanings such as "Heavenly Body" or "Celestial Peace" derived from the origin of the word celestial and other definitions signifying a sense of peace and beauty, but they always relate to the Sky.* So, we reach up as far as we can! What business values do we wish to bring to the operation of our company that will guide ourselves and others? What tools and processes need to be considered to ensure we are leading our business in a way that is true to our personal style, integrity and to our team members and customers?

4. *Birds live their life in a hurry with high energy which shortens their life span.* As women in business we must find ways to choose our own speed limit and to determine where our energy is best focused. Remember, although birds live their lives in a hurry to survive, they still learn to fly gradually. We can pay attention to our vision and create options which support us if we are to have a long and abundant life, both professionally and personally. What should we contemplate? What are our priorities? What can we enter into our journal of thoughts and ideas that we can reflect upon when we feel stressed? How can we use this wisdom before we find that we have to give ourselves a ticket for unhealthy, unproductive speeding?

5. *Birds have daily, seasonal and annual migrating cycles.* As women in business, we are also required to achieve goals in daily, weekly, quarterly, monthly, semi-annually and yearly cycles. We can learn to pay attention to these cycles so that we can better plan and be in alignment with both our personal goals and the goals of our business which are all a part of that greater cycle of seasons that naturally occur in our universe. We can also plan for our personal cycles.

6. *Some Birds fly in mixed flocks.* Given the increasing tension among race, religion, culture, etc. how can we best adapt with as much ease as possible? What are the important things to consider? What can we use to guide us to honor our own individuality and that of others? We don't have to agree with or even like each other, but we do have to work together.

7. *The primary cause of death for birds is from exhaustion.* How can we rest and care for ourselves and balance that with the business world which requires so much of our attention and so much of our life? We cannot wait until we have a crisis to stop.

8. *Birds sing.* So should we, even if we can't carry a tune. This is an incredible way to manage stress, fight depression, increase breathing and become inspired. What songs shall we sing? Write them down and learn to sing them! Make up your own little tunes! Hum!

9. *Birds like to take baths.* A lot. Need I say more? I take several actual baths a week!

10. *Birds are miraculous and amazing*. So are we. Each of us must find that part inside of ourselves that we love and write about it. If that is too foreign or scary for some of us, think about oneself as a much loved friend. Ask, "What are the reasons I find her magnificent," and "Why do I love her?" Give her a beautiful name. Write about her.

11. *Birds belong to a different species*. The women contributing to our vision in creating this workbook are a species we call Cosmic Cowgirls. Cosmic Cowgirls are women who "Dance between the worlds, with our bare feet in the grassroots, a song in our hearts and our head in the stars. We create our own legends." Want to join us? Are you a Cosmic Cowgirl?

*Finding Wings*
*Shiloh Sophia McCloud*

*The act of "finding wings" is a life long journey.*
*We cannot wait for inspiration to strike*
*or circumstances to improve.*
*The time to "take wing" is always*
*and ever, right now.*
*Right now and*
*Right Now.*
*We each have to find*
*our own wing cadence.*
*The pattern within*
*that invisible force and flap.*
*We can practice knowing*
*our wings will lift us when we need them.*
*We can pretend that we feel it even when we don't.*
*Especially when we don't.*
*Imagine that the whole gorgeous universe*
*has your back.*
*That you don't have to rely on your strength only.*
*That preening your feathers is vital important work.*
*That expecting miracles is your spiritual practice.*
*In the privacy of your own bird bath*
*lift your wings - flap flap flap*
*hear the sound...?*
*Now, look ahead...*
*What is it you are flying toward?*
*Do you see your dream up ahead?*
*What comes first?*
*The dream or the wing?*

## *An Invitation to Write A Poem To Your Wings or Your Bird Self*

# THE SEVEN PHASES OF A CAREER WARDROBE

## The Power of Dressing and Undressing

*When I started my former career I was very young. I read all the books, took all the seminars and workshops and became fully convinced that power dressing was key to success. It transformed me into Wonder Woman, complete with bullet deflecting bracelets and golden lariat accessories. When my mother asked me where I had gained the confidence to walk into the offices of some of the top executives of the largest corporations in the world and facilitate six hour meetings, I pointed to my Alligator belt. You see this belt Mama? I paid three-hundred and fifty bucks for this belt at Saks! I can talk to anybody in this belt!*

*Eventually, as a proven and trusted servant of corporate America, I was promoted to being able to work out of my own home. Translated, this means that I was no longer welcome in the white boyz lack of head-quarters. It saved them a little overhead expense, but what they really wanted was my office with the view of Mount Tamalpais for the son-in-law. He got the view and I got a progressively transformed wardrobe.*

**Phase #1: Woman Entering Radical Corporate America**
At home, most of my business was handled on the phone seated at the desk in my office. But even on those days when I didn't have to meet anyone in person, I continued to dress as I had for the office. I always showered, shampooed and blew my hair dry and made certain that my toenails and fingernails were freshly painted "Very Red" (the Hummingbird's favorite color) to match my perfectly applied lipstick. I accessorized the power suit with the skirt length appropriate in those days with the mandatory long strand of pearls and stiletto pumps. Being in full tilt boogie corporate drag helped me be more confident and professional over the phone.

**Phase #2: Woman Rapidly Gaining Status and Self-Promotions**
Confidence and independence grew with success and, since they couldn't see how I was dressed anyway, I chose a more casual form of wear: the pant suit. As my career evolved, this was substituted with slacks and sweater. I retained the pearls. By this time, survival in both my professional and personal life required heavy duty multitasking. This attire made it easier to move around in my new house conducting business, while performing domestic chores, tending to my critters, working in my garden and passionately caring for my racing machines, purchased with my hard won commissions in lieu of well deserved, but not forthcoming raises.

**Phase #3: Woman Ascending Corporate Ladder**
When I became so successful that I could negotiate any power shuffle, I turned to the uniform of my true self: Blue denim work shirt (my favorite had pearl snaps and was shredding) and my mama-lama cowgirl boots. Some people can walk in them and some can't. I was born with

my boots on! They provided me with protection while riding the shiny black and silver Harley I bought, customized and worked on between calls. My bike helped me deal with corporate stress during off hours, somewhere between midnight and 2 A.M.

**Phase #4: Woman Becoming Full Fledged Senior Executive**

As my star climbed I became more and more liberated. I graduated to working from my bedroom. Following my morning (or afternoon) shower and applying lipstick, I would simply change one nightgown for another—something soft with lace and ribbon trim. For heavy duty conference calls requiring a bit of armor, I'd add a robe. Time constraints didn't allow for many costume changes or bike rides, so this was also what I was wearing while adding shiny chrome and black leather to my bike and making the repairs that replaced those lost midnight rides and pool games at the 2AM Club.

**Phase #5: Woman as Highest Achiever and Total CEO**

I reached the "highest achiever" level of my career at a time when women were becoming what was called, in corporate speak "less transparent." I quit showering and grooming. I did brush my teeth and apply lip gloss, since by then I was really tired and needed something to help keep my lips moving. I also stopped dressing. I knew I had finally attained my goals when I could be on a critical conference call with twenty or more corporate leaders (mostly male, of course) from all over the world while I reclined on my bed with the zillion thread-count sheets, buck naked.

**Phase #6: Woman Breaking Glass-Ceiling and Finding Diamonds**

At the zenith of my career I was asked to attend a Board of Directors Meeting with a world renowned, much respected business leader, CEO, mentor and dear friend. He requested that I come as myself. He knew that I understood. I attended the meeting and closed the largest most profitable deal in, not only my own personal herstory, but in the history of my line of business. After that meeting, I was last seen leaving the parking lot tricked out with bandanna, denim shirt, black leather jacket, jeans and my silver-toe capped Alligator cowgirl boots. Shifting between second and third gear on my massive Harley set off the executives car alarms and sliding my right silver toe cap across the cement caused a veritable explosion, shattering that glass ceiling that hangs over the heads of women and minorities in corporate America into fiery diamonds jet streaming out behind me. I looked back at those good ole boyz (that I actually love) and returned their smiles as we waved good-bye. It was cold and the wind blew those tears that I didn't let them see me cry into my hair where they froze into hard little pearls as I sped off to my next Great Adventure in Cosmic Cowgirl Land with its Celestial Ceiling.

**Phase #7: Woman As Cosmic Cowgirl:**

Creating my attire to reflect who I really am! Jeans, Cowgirl boots, sunglasses, silky tops and sometimes, pearls.

# THE GLASS CEILING

## The Power of Hanging On and Hanging In

The expression "Glass Ceiling" became commonplace in the business world in the 1980's. It is most often used in referencing corporate levels. But it reaches far beyond the corporate arena in subtle and not so subtle ways. It is applicable to women, minorities and the underprivileged who are caught in jobs where they are barred from promotions. This invisible barrier keeps us from rising up the "Corporate Ladder." We are held back, sometimes shoved back and referred to ladders that have fewer rungs or are broken.

We are paid lower wages for jobs with responsibilities which are the same or greater than those for whom the Glass Ceiling is not an issue, while being required to meet or exceed performance levels of a white male in the exact same position. Offices are actually built and designed so that these men occupy floors which are literally on higher levels than those of women and minorities who are unable to reach executive levels of promotion. Consider Executive Suites and where they are located. I think of having had to walk up to offices on the Executive Level to report on my work.

Meanwhile, Back at The Good Ole Boyz Corporate Lack of Head Quarters: Over two decades ago, I was grateful to be hired by a man who had a very small company with not much in the way of personnel or resources but the huge vision of going Global. My "superior" and I, with the understanding that I would be promoted to Chief Executive Officer or President as we grew, were the two individuals responsible for generating the sales and revenues that would make all this happen. And happen it did.

Besides partnering with him to generate the capital, I was responsible for supporting the development of our Corporate Vision, Values, Product and Quality Improvements, all of our marketing and sales strategies and I played a key role in developing the systems within our company from which to sustain and expand. Part of my job was to hire people (mostly white and a few family member boyz, for whom no glass ceiling ever existed) and train them in every aspect of the business, from how to sell, implement, manage, become an expert and everything else you can imagine. As the company progressed they were given the best and biggest accounts. I would be selling and servicing 200 accounts to their one to three. They were not only promoted, but were making over four times the income that I did. They bought houses, travelled and could retire anytime they wanted. But they didn't want to retire, because, for the most part, they actually liked time away from their families and were also waiting for that extra buck or billion.

I had come on board when the company was small and new and I (YES! ME!) had literally strategized and launched its initial success. I was, unquestionably, the highest performer and per capita revenue generator and the fastest closer, not to mention having the happiest clientele.
I loved my clients, my trainers and consultant team, my coworkers, my assistants, my strategies, using all my skills, the money and, at that time, I loved working in big business! However, as we

grew and realized the company's global vision, instead of climbing that corporate ladder and shattering the glass ceiling, I watched the rungs on my ladder disappearing and my own personal vision shatter.

Nevertheless, I am grateful for what all this has provided. Though I didn't get the promotions, I did finally break through the Glass Ceiling. I made a lot of money! Enough so that, at a relatively young age, I have been able to take a few years off, and I came away with enough experience, competence and confidence to begin work on my next fortune with the Cosmic Cowgirls!

Obviously, we have to get our ladders somewhere else or build them ourselves. We can create new companies that will be owned and operated by women and call them things like Rungs to Rings (Diamonds, that is!) and work with those who want to climb our ladders which don't lead to glass ceilings but to where we can "Break on through to the other side!" Yeah! And we can paint pretty things like roses and put glitter all over our ladders! Yeah! And we'll write directions on how to climb those ladders! Yeah and, and, and Oh! I just realized! That's what we are doing here at Cosmic Cowgirl Queen Quarters with our first project, "Heart of the Visionary!"

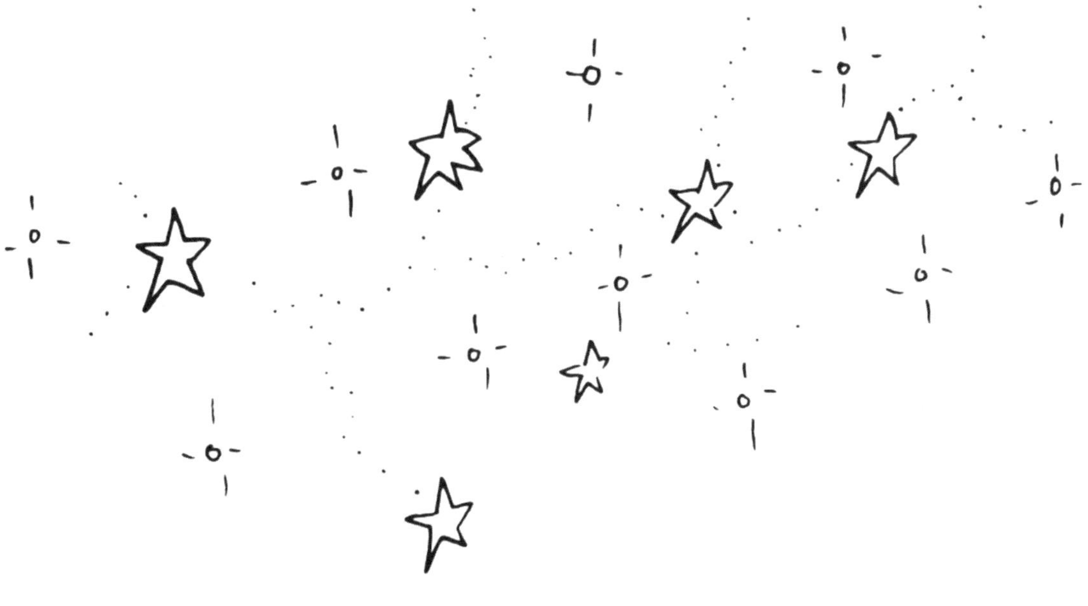

**Dream BIG!**

# MARILYN WAS RIGHT

## The Power of Breaking Through

Hitting the glass-ceiling gave me a first hand experience of the fact that women indeed do not receive equal pay for equal work. Nor are we given the promotions we deserve, or even acknowledged for what we do. We are captives in the work place, barred from rising high enough to even hit the glass-ceiling, let alone break through it.

I use the word *diamonds* to symbolize what I found when, against the odds, I was finally able to rise high enough. I felt like I could see sparks flying from all that broken ceiling glass and they were like diamonds to me. Marilyn was right, symbolically speaking, at least. Diamonds *are* a girl's best friend. Diamonds symbolize clarity, abundance, achievement and a reminder that when we aren't being awarded as we deserve to be, we need to leave that which no longer serves us. We can't expect we will be offered these things as a result of jumping through Good Ole Boyz hoops and serving up the coffee, while also graciously doing the same jobs for which they are being awarded all the perks.

We have to get our own diamonds. We need to find and create our own wealth and though obviously this includes money, I'm not just talking about wealth in terms of money. It goes beyond money. We need to find paths that illuminate our soul and support us in knowing that we deserve to be compensated and acknowledged and respected for our efforts. Then we will no longer allow others or ourselves to hold us back, but behave as though we are worthy of receiving wealth. We can begin to experience rising up and breaking through to abundance. For this, we need new perspectives and the disciplines they provide. We need perspectives that define what it is to be a woman in business in our own paradigm on our own terms. This is what "Heart of the Visionary" is all about. Stars have always reminded me of diamonds. Now, when I look at the stars, I think of Cosmic Cowgirls. I think of us as stars and I wish upon, not just the first star I see, but all the stars. I wish for us to have the greatest success and the courage to tell our stories.

*I'm Pretty But I'm Not Beautiful.*
*I Sin But I'm Not The Devil.*
*I'm Good But I'm Not an Angel.*

*Marilyn Monroe*

# SHARE ONE OF YOUR BREAKTHROUGHS!

# LOLA NEGOTIATES THE TERRAIN

## The Power of Knowledge

### FLASH! CINNAMON COWGIRL RESCUES COWGIRL FROM DOING TIME IN TEXAS PRISON!

*Note: The woman's specific crime is not mentioned here, but let's just say that many of us have been guilty of it at one time or another. The point of this story is not the crime itself, but how one woman helps another using the powers of compassion and negotiation.*

My job was to help – lets call her Lola – to grasp, as best she could, the language and politics of the legal system and how that would play a role in her serving or not serving a 6 year prison term. Although I did the work, my goal was to support her in realizing the impact that not knowing this information and the potential consequences could have on her life. And to help her understand the dialect of the "system" and be able to speak to it in her own personal style within her own level of sophistication and comfort zone.

My focus included interpreting the roles of her Attorney, the District Attorney, the Judge and their individual histories and perceptions. Most important were things such as records any of them might have had for the same thing she was facing, the key dynamics of the relationships between them, favors owed and so on. If her existing attorney wasn't on good terms with the D.A. or the judge, we needed to find an attorney who was. Immediately, as her sentence was three days away!

Lola lives in a small town in Texas. I learned the Texas laws for the crime and researched Lola's potential probation terms. Since we had to handle all this over the phone, I then researched down to the last detail, things like the town's population and geography, the distance between schools, the nearest prison and its environment, community service options and what the courthouse looks like. It gave me a better idea about the overall level of sophistication and the culture I was dealing with. I wanted to create the experience for myself of being able to virtually see and smell the place and mentally adapt my thoughts and plans as if I were there. Not surprisingly, based on the research, it was clear that "making a deal like a good ole boy" was the right approach.
I adapted my own language and strategy accordingly.

Lola was totally unaware of any of her rights to have access or any interaction whatsoever with her attorney, unless initiated by him. Once I was able to get across to her that, although she was the one with the legal issues, the shame, the guilt and the bad records, the attorney was working for HER, she was shocked.

Essentially, I became Lola's power-base, serving as counsel, not only for her, but also as the invisible counsel for her attorney. I proceeded to coach Lola in a plan to negotiate a concession strategy as part of the plea bargain for the many fines, court costs and any and all monetary expenditures that she was unknowingly facing, taking into consideration her hourly wage of $6.50 per hour.

After a few sessions Lola called the attorneys office, made the appointment, walked in, sat down and said, "Now here's the deal…!" Afterwards, she called me. "Shannon!" she said with such fire, gratitude and confidence, "I did it Shannon! And I used those words you told me about!" She yelled out loud, "Hallelujah!" and "Yahoo!" More than anything else, she was excited about having a sense of her own power and arriving at what for her was an unfamiliar and glorious place – self liberation!

Lola and her attorney went before the Judge and were able to negotiate the optimal plea bargain, instead of serving 6 years in prison, being sentenced to 5 weekends. "Hallelujah!" and "Yahoo!" indeed.

And so goes another chapter in the Cosmic Cowgirl's rodeo of the soul. Ride on Lola!

**Three Key Learnings:**

1. **Knowledge is Power.** Knowledge applies, as it does to everything in life, to negotiation. It is endless in its inquiry and limitless in its impact.

2. **Know the Other Person.** As women in business we must learn everything about those with whom we are dealing. We must equip ourselves to be able to interpret and adapt to their perceptions, values, cultures, etc. They then will be better able to adjust to what is shared in common and will be much more comfortable with us and whatever services and/or products we want to provide. Revenues are generated from a greater source of mutual exchange. This applies not only to our customers but to our suppliers. This is far reaching and, besides establishing good business relations, transforms the transaction of business into an experience of one another's human souls.

3. **Know Our Own Power.** Particularly in this day and age, it is essential that we be our own authority and manage those "Systems" traditionally viewed as the final authority. This applies to all systems, including legal, medical, educational and all finance related systems, including the IRS and Big Brother. That they have power doesn't mean that we don't. We need to know how to take care of ourselves. We need to be our own authority.

Katherine Hepburn Said:
If you obey all the rules, you miss all the fun.

# Identify and Name Your Sources of Power

# HOW I GOT MY FIRST HARMONICA AND MADE A BUNCH OF MONEY

## The Power of Inquiry

It is no secret that success in both our professional and personal lives depends on our ability to relate to others. An important skill in relating along the lines that we are addressing in *Heart of the Visionary* is the power of inquiry. We need to be able to invite others to answer questions in a way that they feel both safe and inspired. This is the environment in which we can contemplate possibilities and are empowered to come up with exciting answers and innovative ideas.

There are two factors which make up this dynamic of inquiry. The first is to inquire within ourselves. This could include meditation, contemplation, the use of creative tools such as journaling on our own as well as group work and guidance or counsel from others. The second is for us to open inquiry for others, encouraging them to express what's meaningful in their lives.

In the absence of this dynamic of inquiry, and some form of creativity through which to express ourselves, we can find ourselves lonely, caged in and held hostage from our own lives, often without even understanding why we feel that way. Learning the skills for the power of inquiry supports both our personal and business endeavors and opens us up to the discovery of endless forms of creativity and opportunities to interact with remarkable people.

**The Power of Inquiry: My personal example—How I Got My First Harmonica**

I was in Santa Fe with a friend one holiday and we met a young man who had, within the past year, endured a heart transplant and also the recent loss of his heroin addicted father who jumped off the Golden Gate Bridge. Specific to his heart transplant one of the questions I asked him was if he had made love to anyone since his transplant and if it was different and new? He cried and answered, "No one has asked me that because of their fear. I am aware that so many people have wanted to know about that. Thank you for asking me as I have been thinking about it myself and have been waiting to reply to that question for so long now....."

He gave me his favorite (and first) Harmonica along with his bandana. He asked me to play it with him. I still think of him as I blow my tunes into his harmonica. In fact, I have played that Harmonica so much that I have blown out most of the reeds but I still find one or two willing to take in my inhale and exhale as I bend the notes to the blues with Bonnie Raitt, Eric Clapton and Norton Buffalo. These kinds of exchanges with people are what makes life meaningful and abundantly filled with magic. And most of them happen when we dare to ask one another uncomfortable questions, in comforting and welcome ways.

**The Power of Inquiry: My professional example—How I Made A Bunch Of Money**

For quite a long time, in the pursuit of a contract, I had been trying to develop a business relationship with a very important leader in the corporate arena. The woman in charge at this company was impenetrable. Even getting through her door was close to impossible. Once I did get through her door I was promptly informed that she was tired of being "sold to" regarding a "tangible product" not based on solutions to the challenges in her business. Sales people were zealously doing all the things we all hate about sales! The familiar way of selling is by pointing to the features and benefits over and over again. I used to call it "licking the vinyl" selling.
I realized that salespeople often totally miss the opportunity to identify and address the problems their prospects were trying to solve. Solutions are what is needed. Potential customers are longing for questions and inquiry in order to get to the bottom of their real needs which they often aren't entirely clear about themselves. This worked for me because I hated making presentations in the selling tradition in which most of us are trained. I began to inquire about what things in life were important to her both personally and professionally and what her goals for herself and her company were. I asked her to explain to me what kind of problems she was encountering and started responding with how what I had to offer might just be an important part of the solution. She signed on the dotted line.

From then on, as opposed to just selling a product, I developed my skills of inquiry and focused on customer service, becoming an inquisitive sales and negotiation expert. Essentially persistence does pay off. But usually a bigger pay off happens if we are prepared and internally present with people. We need to ask the questions, "peel the onion," and get down to what is needed and be sensitive and ready to be part of the solution in possibly more ways than you had initially supposed. I learned that it wasn't just a case of asking the right questions but of knowing when and how to ask them. There is no way that you can learn this unless you sincerely care about your customer and want to know her and help her solve her problems. The power in this method of inquiry lies in authentic compassion and caring.

Years later, my company wanted to conduct a customer survey and she and her company were selected because of the size of the company and how much business we (me) were writing with them. When they interviewed her she literally replied: "Sure I love your company and your products, they are excellent. But I now have developed a template I use that I call my 'Shannon Template.' Shannon has provided me with what I need to know, how I need to know it and exactly what questions to ask anyone of my current and future suppliers. She is what I use as a reference in selecting companies such as yours to do business with. No matter how great the products seem, I will not be sold in a way or by anyone that doesn't first support me in learning what I NEED in order to make the right decisions."

If you are in inquiry with your customers, you will create lasting relationships, they will remember you when you call on them, they will choose you above the others and they will refer you and endorse your business journey.

I HAVE NO SELF IMPOSED LIMITATIONS TO LIVING MY LIFE

AS AN OUTRAGEOUS ADVENTURE. ♛ SHANNON

# AFFIRMATIONS

## The Power of Declaration

*Note from Shiloh: Shannon is my Wild Woman sister. The affirmations she has created are how she lives her life each day. Hers are unlike those where nothing bad is mentioned. Challenges are acknowledged. Most people find it difficult and scary to acknowledge their challenges and suffering, but my sister and I have chosen to see it for what it is—the truth that no matter how good the thoughts we are thinking, bad stuff still happens. These affirmations do not "call" in the bad, nor does identifying the challenges override the empowering energy of the declaration. Rather, in the power of spoken truth, they call in the protection which provides a safe place for the release necessary for renewal to occur, give us permission to reach for the good even in situations where things seem impossible and generate the faith and ability to surrender ourselves towards "Destination Miracle."*

I LIVE MY LIFE TODAY, BASED ON
HOW I WANT TO FEEL AND BE REMEMBERED TOMORROW.

IN BOTH GOOD TIMES AND CHALLENGING TIMES,
MY INSTINCTS AND INTUITION ARE ACCESSIBLE.

NOT DOING WHAT IS IMPORTANT TO LIVING MY LIFE, IS NOT AN OPTION,
NO MATTER HOW GOOD OR BAD I MIGHT FEEL.

I SEEK TO HAVE GRATITUDE IN ALL THINGS. IF I DON'T FIND IT EVERY TIME,
I AM GRATEFUL THAT I AM AWARE ENOUGH TO ALWAYS BE SEEKING IT ANYWAY.

GRATITUDE IS FAITHFUL IN KEEPING HER PROMISES.
IF I LOSE SIGHT OF HER, SHE ALWAYS COMES BACK HOME TO ME.

WHEN I HONOR MY OWN AUTHORITY,
I DON'T FEEL THE NEED TO QUESTION THAT OF OTHERS SO MUCH.

I WON'T SELL MY SOUL TO SOMEONE ELSE'S ROCK AND ROLL.
IF WE DON'T MAKE THE MUSIC TOGETHER, I MOVE ON.

I HAVE NO SELF IMPOSED LIMITATIONS TO LIVING MY LIFE
AS AN OUTRAGEOUS ADVENTURE.

I OWN MY POWER TO CREATE.
CIRCUMSTANCES DO NOT PREVENT ME FROM BEING CREATIVE.
I FIND INSPIRATION IN CHALLENGING CIRCUMSTANCES.

I AM MY OWN SHEROE.
TODAY, I AM TRANSFORMING MY LIFE INTO LEGEND.

WHEN I FEEL BURIED UNDER THE CLOAK OF DARKNESS,
STRONG DISCIPLINE AND CLEAR INTENTION ENABLE ME TO FIND
REMARKABLE BEAUTY AND GENTLE LIGHT.

I WILL LIVE DEEP IN MY HEART AND LIGHT ON MY FEET.

I AM INVITING THE HIGHEST GOOD FOR ALL
EVEN WHEN I DON'T KNOW WHAT THAT IS.

I CHOOSE TO WALK FORWARD IN WHOLENESS,
NO MATTER HOW BROKEN I HAVE BEEN IN THE PAST.

THROUGH COMPASSION FOR OTHERS,
I FIND THE COURAGE AND THE ABILITY TO LOVE MYSELF.
LOVING MYSELF IS NOT CONTINGENT ON THE SHIELD OF BEING GOOD.

I WILL PURSUE WHAT MAKES ME HAPPY, WITHOUT GUILT.

I WILL NOT LIVE A LIFE DEFINED BY POVERTY AND LACK.
ALTHOUGH MONEY IS IMPORTANT, I WILL NOT BE STRIPPED OF
OTHER WEALTH AND ABUNDANCE AVAILABLE TO ME.

PROSPERITY AND GOOD RELATIONS COME TO ME BECAUSE OF WHO I AM.
I ASK PEOPLE ABOUT THEIR LIVES, WHAT'S IMPORTANT TO THEM AND WHY.
THEN WE EACH ARE FILLED WITH THE ABUNDANCE OF SHARED WISDOM.

THE BEAUTY THAT SERVES ME BEST,
IS THE BEAUTY IN HELPING OTHERS SEE THEIRS.

EVERYDAY IS AN ADVENTURE IN BEAUTY.
EVEN IF I AM LIVING WITH PAIN, I WILL PRACTICE MY DISCIPLINES
AND MAKE BEAUTY HAPPEN TODAY.

TODAY WILL BECOME TOMORROW
AND TOMORROW WILL BECOME MY FUTURE.
MY FUTURE, AT RADIANT LIGHT SPEED, BECOMES MY HERSTORY.

*I AM STRONG AND BRAVE, NOT WEAK AND AFRAID.*
*Molly Lewis*

# AFFIRMATIONS

*Write your own Affirmations that will guide you along your path.*

## Eagle Woman Must Fly

Kelly Takunda Orphan Martinez

Feeling the weight on her shoulders isn't a new burden to bear,
But like wings of a dove she's gonna fly, fly right through the air,
She walks outside her little cocoon,
Takes a deep breath and looks up to the moon,
She's ready to fly.
Eagle Woman must fly. eagle woman.
No more compromise, eagle woman.
No more hiding, step out to the light. Eagle Woman must fly!
She's not particularly beautiful; her spirit isn't plain to see
But if you look in those eyes, you'll see the bird that she's trying to set free,
She walks outside her little cocoon,
Takes a deep breath and looks up to the moon,
She's ready to fly,
She walks and most of the time people passin' her by,
Not seeing the eagle, the eagle that's in her eye,
Just let them go, one day they will know,
They cannot miss that woman in the sky,
Flying high as she passes them by,
She looks deep into their eyes.
But she won't fly to the sea, she'll fly to the people,
Show them the spirit of the eagle and set them free.
No, no, she won't fly to the sea; she'll fly to the people
And set them free...
Just like, just like she was, just like she was free...
Eagle woman, open your arms, Eagle woman ready to soar....
See the Eagle in her eye, always knew she could fly... Eagle Woman...

# She's Ready To Fly

# WISDOM

## The Power of Experience


**Caron McCloud**

**Illustrations by Shiloh Sophia McCloud and Sue Hoya Sellars**

# How These Spells Begin

**Caron McCloud**

Eden is in her sun room. She is
surrounded by a jungle of house plants—her
Garden of Eden. It is morning—her
time of day. In the corner of the window screen
a spider annexes silver and magenta veined leaves
from the Wandering Jew into her doilied domain.
A tiny lizard suns herself on the toe of Eden's slipper.

Eden is standing at her ironing board.
She is sewing, of course, a Wonder Woman uniform
for my doll. She is frowning her famous frown
of intense concentration—that frown
that I diligently practice throughout my childhood
because my mother is beautiful and I want
to look as much like her as I can, as soon as possible.

# Heritage and Spells

## How Paths and Light Inform our Careers

*Each and every one of us can recall some moment when the light fell in a certain way or on a certain thing and cast a spell calling us to a creative path.*

How I came to be involved in my various business endeavors goes back to my earliest memories of being caught in the spell of some creative process—reading and writing, singing and dancing, drawing, coloring, painting, sewing, crocheting, knitting, carpentry—making things, the feel of a tool in my hand. Even when I was a little kid, I knew there was not going to be time enough.

My love of poetry and drawing came from spells cast by my father, Gene Grant—poet, musician, carpenter, fisherman, saw filer, who used to sign his gifts and letters to me: "Love, Trust, Dare." I added "Create" and "Pray" and made it my slogan. I remember my father's hands in the amber lamplight, peeling the wood with exquisite precision from a yellow #2 pencil with his pocket knife, the smell of tiny shavings and lead scrapings drifting from the emerging, long, shining point; my ecstatic anticipation while waiting to feel the pencil between my fingers and the excitement of the exact moment when that point would make contact with my clean, white, 8 1/2x11 sheet of paper, then—getting to watch where that little trail it laid down would lead me. It led to writing over a dozen chapbooks of poetry and some efficiency in drawing and painting.

Sitting in the light of the fireplace with my step-mother Lillian Grant—also a poet—I fell in love with the Bible. Her romantic approach to everything in life cast a spell over the scriptures that brought the people and their message alive. I continue to want to know all about them. What tribes were they from? Who did they love, hate, go to war with? Who were their children, their children's children? How did the Creator use them? Where did they go? I feel like a detective, my excitement growing as, following clues and making notes, I relentlessly track them through scripture and history and into the world—into my own heritage. I just published a book about women of the Bible, *Rachel's Bag, In Search of the Qabalah of our Mothers.*

My love of fabric started with the delightfully printed cotton sacks in which feed companies used to package grain for farm animals. As a child, I watched my mother, Eden McCloud—also an artist, poet and story teller—empty these sacks to feed our chickens and then transform them into beautiful little dresses for me. This cast a spell informed by the feel of warm powdered dust between bare toes on a path leading to a chicken yard, the sound of soft cluck-clucking, the smell of scattering barley, sunlight in Mama's hair. Little did I know where that dusty little path would continue to lead. Thinking of her, I see that gesture with which she became identified—rubbing a piece of fabric between her fingers, "testing the goods" like an old Jew. And finally that magic Mama made, whirring away on her Singer sewing machine. Whatever I could draw, she could cut and sew, from doll clothes to prom dresses to wedding gowns. This led to a career in thc fashion industry for both of us, from which we are now retired. In 2002 Mom, with her Landscapes in Thread was on the Art Port Townsend Studio Tour and in 2007 I was on the tour with my McCloud Cover Tapestries. In 2006, at age 95, Mama won a Northwind Art Center award in the Earth, Air, Fire and Water exhibit.

As for business, besides my involvement in my daughter Shiloh's many projects, my main focus is writing, and I am still involved in the visual arts; painting, stained glass, working with fabric, the one thing crossing over and informing the other, as all skills do. Materials from former businesses have provided me with a vast collection of fabrics, remnants, trims, buttons, beads, lace. Because Mom raised us—as evidenced by my little feed sack dresses—on axioms such as, "Necessity is the mother of invention," and "Waste not, want not," I take great satisfaction and pleasure in putting together the pieces to create what I call McCloud Covers: Coverings for Body, Bed and Wall. I even think of my poems as coverings: "Thought covers" to warm—or sometimes to warn—the soul. I also design using themes and color schemes customized for my clients, trying to include their totems and spells. Like Mama, I love the feel of "the goods" of my palette of textiles, my tools. Working with my hands provides me with a much needed balance and reprieve from the intense concentration and involuted process of writing.

My parents continue to inspire me, as my children claim that I inspire them—but it is my children who light the path and cast the spells. I pray to bring some form of expression to the light pouring from and the spells cast by all those I love—including lovers past, but still casting; and precious friends, my brother Bob and sister Janet, their amazing offspring, the Cosmic Cowgirls, all those I think of as McCloud Clan, especially my partner, Papa Jimmie, who is also an artist. And then, yesterday, there was the sun shining on this red-headed girl on a bicycle and..and..and there is this way that the light loves the cheekbones of my beautiful children….

**LOVE . TRUST . DARE . CREATE . PRAY . DANCE**

# YARN SPELL

*for Eden*

The old woman's
experienced eyes
easily measured
the child's size.
The child's eyes
were firmly fixed and
fastened by
the stream of string
which flipped
betwixt her fingers
and slipped
beneath her chin,
as it ran from her hand to the hand
of the old woman who wound
the yellow yarn 'round
the yellow wool 'round
the ball.
"Thumbs up!"
the old woman cried,
then laughed
when the little girl blinked,
surprised,
and frowned
a little girl's frown
with her little girl's face.
"The movement tries
to capture your eyes.
If you follow
you'll fall
and we'll lose our place.
No need now to frown
or your thumbs'll fall down,
your yarn'll fall down
in a spell."

In the loose
end of the yarn
the old woman looped
a small noose,
then picked up her hook
and with fingers crooked
she began.
She struck through the loop
again and again.
I will never forget how it felt
as my grandmother
leaned over me
where I knelt
and on my neck laid
the soft crocheted braid,
the soft golden braid,
like a necklace.
As I saw her then,
I see her now.
The firelight glows
on her hook as she goes,
back and forth
cross the chain
again and again.
My little coat grows
in neat little rows,
from right to left,
as though written
in some old
language she knows.
From the dish on the bricks
the yellow cat licks,
the yellow fire licks
the log.

# It *Is* About The Coffee

## How Assumptions Create a Headset

I was early for an appointment with my Los Angeles rep and was having a conversation with the woman who shared the office with him and one other man, neither of whom was present. When Ralph came in, after greeting me, he turned to her and said, "Did you make the coffee?"

She said, "No, I didn't." He said, "I'm going to go out and get some," and he left.

She looked at me and said, "It doesn't matter which of the three of us gets here first. They always want to know if I've made coffee, but they never ask each other that. If I haven't they almost always go out to get it rather than make it themselves. Mostly to make me wrong, I think. Hey, I'm not the receptionist here. We share the office and split the rent equally. Yet there is this expectation that I should make the coffee and answer the phone. Sometimes I do, but recently I made the decision that I do not want to cater to their expectations and behave as though my position here is somehow subservient to theirs."

I told her that I understood that it wasn't about the coffee, but about the principle which, if not addressed, did carry over into other areas.

"But it is about the coffee!" she said. "It's all about the coffee. In fact, my life would be so much easier if I just made the coffee. I actually expend more energy on *not* making the coffee than I do on making it. Worse yet, my not making it sets up this uncomfortable dynamic that wouldn't be there if I just made the damn coffee."

While the reasons for presenting *Heart of the Visionary* as a "Feminine Business Paradigm" have been explained, I want to address the headset that makes this choice necessary. There have been certain ways of thinking, certain assumptions that are so set in our culture and language that they create a default. Some are so insidious that we don't even notice them, in spite of the fact that they serve to define the reality of our existence. The default is so automatic that men don't notice either, so this is not about making them wrong.

Sometimes it's easier to get the necessary distance for perspective when someone other than ourselves provides the example. Here is one that I got from a black man. He explained that reality is not just defined by men, but specifically by white men. "Say there's a little group of some white guys standing on the street corner and a black guy is coming their way. They might say, or at least think, 'Here comes a black guy.' Now, let's say there's a little group of black guys on the corner and a white guy comes up. They will say or think, 'Here comes a white guy'."

I'm wondering what he is getting at. "Yeah. So?"

"Well," he says, "If the guys on the corner are black and a black guy comes over they will also say something like 'Here comes a black dude or here comes a brother,' but if the guys standing on the corner are white and a white guy shows up, it would never occur to them to say, 'Here comes a white guy,' because reality is defined within their white guy paradigm. If it is not other than themselves, there is no need to call it. Whereas, the black guy does call it because he also defines himself as 'other'."

It is practically impossible to get enough distance to see that our perceptions are based on a headset of assumptions. It's like the cartoon of the two little fish looking down as they are jumping out of the water and one is saying to the other, "Look! Quick! That's the stuff I've been trying to tell you about!" The white male defined paradigm is like the water that we live in and it is very difficult to extract ourselves from it enough to know that we are operating in the default.

Once upon a time, when Shiloh was about three, we moved into a new apartment. Then we let a nice white man I had been dating move in with us. The apartment was small but had a big entry way. I built a dividing wall and made a little room on the other side of it so that Shiloh could have her own space. I built in a little bed with a play house space under it. Out of red and white floral coordinated fabrics I made a quilt and pillows and curtains that pulled in front of the bed and playhouse space. I covered one wall in paper with brightly colored dolls.

Well, when friends came over to visit they invariably said, "Wow! Nice work!" to *him*. These were *my* friends, mind you. My friends who knew I could do carpentry and some of them were even feminists. But there it was. The assumption.

We have attempted to make that leap to dispel assumption and distinguish women's work by presenting our writing within the context of a "Feminine Business Paradigm." Look! Quick! This is the stuff we are trying to tell each other about!

**Original cartoonist unknown - this version by Caron**

## The Feminine Business Paradigm

*Women have strong reactions to this concept. What is your reaction? Idea? Write it down here.*

# The Essential and The Paradoxical

## What Will I Be When I Grow Up?

In all things, I seek that which I experience to be "essential." What is essential to an entrepreneur is to identify what we are going to create and bring to the marketplace. What one can offer in the marketplace falls into three categories: Product, Service, Information. While these categories overlap and some businesses provide two, or all three, an entrepreneur will be primarily identified with one of them. What that is to be comes out of our own personal identity.

For one of the businesses I created, I chose product and the product I chose was a dress. This identified me with the world of fashion. This might lead one to believe that I'm just crazy about clothes and some of my politically active and/or spiritually questing friends frowned upon my "superficial" focus. The thing is, even if one's focus is on saving the world, the first decision we have to make upon arising—unless we sleep in our clothes—is, "What am I going to wear?" Everyone has got to get dressed. Also, it's a simple fact that the first impression that we make on someone, unless it's over the phone, is visual. Like it or not, this includes what we wear.

Paradoxically, it was my seeking the essential and my love of minimalism that informed my entrepreneurial choice. It was my desire to expend as little energy as possible on figuring out what I will wear. My personal choice is simple—cowboy boots, Levi's and a black jacket. The problem was that back in the days that I started my business, there was still a protocol in quite a few circles that required a woman to wear a dress. Hence, my slogan: "If she really did have only one dress to her name, it would be a Karen Johnson."

I went to market with that one dress. Six months later I had eighteen employees, soon followed by two contractors, two reps, two permanent show rooms and was doing five shows a year at the Hyatt Regency in San Francisco and shows in Los Angeles, Seattle, Dallas and New York. That dress, along with others, was sold from Guam to Alaska in stores from the "Mom and Pop" venues to Macy's and Magnin's.

Choosing what we want to take to market can be best informed by something we personally need or desire for ourselves, even though friends may find it strange or it seems contra indicated at first glance.

*Success looks like getting to plant your seeds instead of having to eat them.*
*Caron McCloud*

# The Fine Art of Business

## An Italian Master and A Woman Banker

When I became a clothing designer I went into business for myself because I wanted to be able to make a living by using my creative gifts. As anyone who has done this can tell you, the time it takes to run a business leaves little time for what one originally considered one's creativity.

I wasn't designing my line on a drawing table in a well lit studio like I had imagined, but while driving to and from appointments. I was so obsessive that every personal experience was translated into some aspect of business. The colors in a sunset were immediately adapted to the Fall line. Shiloh, who was just a little girl at the time, had asked me what was in a certain bottle on my desk. I explained that it was whiteout and used to erase unwanted marks or lines. After days of no quality time with Mommie, because Mommie had deadlines to meet, she came to me with that little bottle in her hands and wanted to know if I would please erase my deadlines so I could play with her.

I became more and more frustrated with the demands of running a business and how divided my focus and energy had become. I especially hated and resisted the part that was about "running" a business, like all that paperwork. But as I came to understand business, I was amazed and delighted to discover that it is yet another form of art—most especially the art of design.

Computers were not yet part of our everyday lives and bookkeeping was all hand entered. I used to say that happiness was finding the right form to fit the shape of the information that needed to be recorded. I very often designed my own and experience soon taught me the importance of that right form and of being able to fill in the blanks.

While I was still in the stages of resisting the business part of running a business and leaving most of that to others, I applied to a bank for a very small loan to produce all the orders I was so excited about getting. At the time, there was a television commercial showing a young designer walking into a bank with her samples thrown over her arm and they can't wait to roll out the red carpet for this budding entrepreneur. I actually believed it was going to work this way.

Not only was there no red carpet, I was unceremoniously turned down flat. The bookkeeper I then hired to help me put a more professional look on things informed me that I was bankrupt. To make matters worse, I was scheduled as a guest speaker at a How To Succeed in Business seminar in two weeks. As I picked up the phone to call to cancel while they still might have time to get someone else, I decided to call an accountant—an Italian accountant I had planned on going to as soon as I was successful enough to afford him. I came away from our meeting with an understanding of what I needed, such as bank statements, balance sheets, spread sheets, projection sheets, etc. to create a loan package that as he put it, "would wash." Unfortunately after mocking up some of these for practice and filling in the blanks until the wee small hours of several mornings it appeared that I was indeed, bankrupt.

After many tears and much agonizing, I decided to figure out how to close my failed business with the most integrity. I had to start by canceling my speaking engagement. As I picked up the brochure to call the number, I looked sadly at the title for the event, "The Game of Business." Surrounded by the evidence of my losses, I thought, "Well if business is a game, I sure know what losing looks like." Then I distractedly wondered, "Hmm, I wonder what winning would look like?" Then I really thought, "Hmmmm, I wonder what winning really would look like?"

I thought about how when teaching my kids to play a game I would explain the objective and show them what a victorious end game would look like— like a king in checkmate. I figured, what the heck and spent the day filling in the blanks the way the numbers would look if I was winning. When I was done, it was like having the picture on the cover of the puzzle box in front of me. I worked backwards putting together the pieces to get back to the numbers as they currently stood. I came up with an illustrated procedure of how a loan for a specific amount of money would allow projecting these numbers over a specific period of time to agree with what winning looked like. I took this down to my new Italian accountant the next morning.

He congratulated me on having done, with a little tweaking from him, just what was needed. He explained that most bankers can't read a profit and loss statement if their lives depended on it. They just recognize the right forms when they see them. "It's gotta wash," he said, "and Baby, this we can wash and hang on the line." He picked up the phone and called the bank manager and said he was sending someone over with a loan package he wanted them to approve. By the time I got there, it was closing time. They locked up after I was inside and rolled out the red carpet. In less than an hour and with no collateral and no credit, I came out with a bank balance which exceeded the amount for which I had originally applied times seven. It made a great story for my speech.

I came to really love the whole creative process of running a business and being able to take an idea out of my head and convert it into cash, whether by designing a product or a system that would wash. But the first rule is: Learn to keep impeccable books that YOU understand. And, of course, it doesn't hurt to have an Italian accountant. Oh! and by the way that bank manager was a woman.

# The Catbird Seat and Other Vantage Points

**Some things that make the difference between winning and losing fall into the "Water is wet and rocks are hard" category.**

**Impeccable Bookkeeping:** This is necessary for the IRS—you know, those are the guys with the guns who can legally either break down your doors or close and lock them and not give you a key. Oh yeah, and they can put you in jail.

Also, impeccable bookkeeping is necessary to be able to tell how to run a business from inception to fruition. I repeat—even after you can afford that Italian accountant (maybe especially after you can afford the Italian) you need to pay attention to and be able to analyze your own books.

A man who supervised big construction jobs, like dams and highways, once gave me some very valuable information. He said that when he was on a new job, the first thing he did was find a spot that would best position him to be able to tell what was going on. He called it the "Catbird Seat." (I've since been told that the expression originated and circulated in prisons in the early forties. I haven't researched it, but it makes life and death sense, doesn't it?) He took me out to one of his highway work sites to the Catbird Seat he was using at that time. He pointed out that not only was it the high ground from where he could *see* what was going on, but could also *hear* what was going on. I stood there with him listening to what he called his symphony. If any of the heavy equipment operators was not up to par or any of the machinery not running well, he could locate it in seconds. For me, it was a "peak moment" that continues to inform how I operate, not just in business but life in general.

When I went into manufacturing I looked for my Catbird Seat. In my operation it turned out to be standing at the ironing board and I periodically worked that spot throughout my career. It was central to the flow of production and not only could I tell how much was being produced, but how fast and what the quality of workmanship was. However, "at the end of the day," to use a catch phrase I hate, but without which no politician or media spokesperson can seem to articulate, the Catbird Seat is "clearly," to use another, the accountant's chair.

**Impeccable Taxes:** Make your tax deposits and pay your taxes in a timely manner. Don't file late or file extensions. People that work for the IRS are like people that work for the bank. They don't start out looking for the devil in the details. They migrate toward those details when something catches their eye, like the form that doesn't wash. Extensions are a red flag and the system is designed so that if they do have to begin looking at the details they WILL be able to find something to make it worth their while.

**Integrity:** Integrity is a word with so much attached to it one does not want to use it lightly and I don't. Let's say, I come to your place of business which has it's operating hours posted in your ad in the phone book and/or newspaper and/or on your business card and/or it is stated on your telephone answering service and there is a sign on the door also stating your business hours and no one is there. Simply put, I won't be back. Also, being late for an appointment will automatically limit your options for doing business with me. My rule for integrity in business relations is the same rule I have for integrity in personal relationships, especially in raising children. Of course one can't dump the kids or friends for not complying, but one can dump flakey business associates. There's plenty of businesses out there ready to jump in when we don't honor the rule and the rule is: **Be where you say you are going to be when you say you are going to be there.**

**Convenience:** I do not want to have to look for prices and I do not want to have to ask what the price of something is. This is especially true in retail. I hate shopping and I am very calculating and focused on those rare occasions when I deign to do so. I want all the figures right where I can see them so that I can be about my calculations with as little small talk as possible. I do have a story about asking someone for a price, however.

Before I went into manufacturing, I was in retail and I was at a San Francisco show shopping my favorite line with my favorite rep, David King. As all buyers know, trade shows are grueling for both the wholesaler and the retailer. Bless those reps who by the time you get to their booth can make it easy for you and even better if they can make you laugh or teach you something. I learned all kinds of things from David. Things like, there is a degree of mastery in the art of manufacturing. This company had a person who knew their materials and product so well that once they had a sample made up and hanging on a hanger, she could put her hands on the shoulders and by the time she had run them down the sides of the garment to the hemline once, she could tell you what it was going to cost to within pennies. But that's not the story.

The story is that I asked David how much one of the dresses in his line cost. I expected to hear something like twenty-nine ninety-five, but instead he said seven-hundred and fifty. "What?" I couldn't hide my dismay. Then he laughed and said, "I will wholesale these dresses to you at twenty-nine fifty, but you asked the cost of this dress. Counting everything it took to get this particular sample from the designers mind to the hanger cost us seven hundred and fifty dollars." Aha! Another peak moment! David gave me an insight into the world of manufacturing that was connecting with the other insights leading to the Gestalt that led to my career.

So, what's the moral of my story? If we're going to inconvenience someone by making them ask questions about something that could have been made obvious, we better be ready to make it worth their while by educating them or at least, make them laugh.

**Business cards:** Water is wet and rocks are hard and there is no acceptable explanation for not having a current business card. And these days, a web-site too! Get the word out about you!

# Zola's Counsel

## How Much Should I Charge?

When going into business, after identifying a product, a service, information, or a combination thereof, the question of how to arrive at a price must be answered. For this, a formula is needed. While formulas differ depending upon what kind of a business you have there are some guidelines that adapt quite well across the board.

While leading seminars on how to start your own business and how to turn your hobby into a business, I discovered that what people found to be the best and most basic advice—not surprisingly—was exactly what had been the most powerful for me at the time I heard it. The best advise on pricing did not come from reading all the books and periodicals, taking the business seminars, talking to others in the business, or hiring consultants. It came from an experience I had long before I ever went into business for myself.

Back in the early 60's I was young and hanging out on the Jazz Scene, not that I'm that crazy about Jazz—I'll take the Grateful Dead and Willie Nelson over Miles and Monk any day—but I was dating a guy with a jazz combo. His drummer was dating a young woman engaged in what is commonly referred to as the "world's oldest profession." We'll call her Zola, although she wouldn't care if I used her real name because she was not ashamed of her profession. In fact, you could say the first thing I learned from her, though I didn't realize it at the time, is that if you are uncomfortable about any aspect of your profession, whether it be its impact on the environment, how much you pay your employees, where your stuff is being manufactured, or the quality of your product, you need to make some changes or find a new business.

Zola worked under the auspices of the classiest Las Vegas casinos and among the clientele that graced the pages of her date book were the most prominent stars, celebrities, sports figures and politicians of those times. Those were the times when one-hundred dollars was a lot of money. Which is what Zola charged for her services. After her telling me this over a few drinks, while listening to our guys in the combo, I sputtered, "One-hundred dollars a night!?"

"Are you crazy!?" She fired back. "Time is money! I order a drink in the casino and expect to be back at my table before the ice melts." There was no question that Zola was beautiful, sexy, smart and funny, but this was the dawn of the age of Aquarius and "free love." Logically, one would be expecting an end to the world's oldest profession. Why would anyone be paying for sex, let alone that kind of money? Well, I couldn't pass up such a rare opportunity to find out just what special thing she did for this kind of money. Could you? No. I had to ask. "What's the difference between a hundred dollar trick and a ten dollar trick?" Without a moment's hesitation Zola said, "Ninety bucks, dummy! Can't you subtract?"

While regaining my composure, there was considerable hesitation on my part, before blurting, "Well just what is it that makes you worth a hundred bucks?" Her answer was simple. "Because I say so."

While this doesn't supply one with the formula itself, years later when trying to determine prices for my clothing line, I realized that the privilege of Zola's counsel supplied the perfect context out of which to begin the process. The value of what she had said only becomes more amazing as contemplated and applied. As for the formula, well, that's another story.

# Fixing The Formula

## Not for Babies

The following is not intended to be a comprehensive detailed plan, but merely a way to begin thinking about what is involved in arriving at a formula for pricing a product. The numbers used are arbitrary and do not represent reality in time nor geography, but are provided to give an idea of how we must think about our financial structure in the necessary percentages and ratio's.

While my experience is in pricing products rather than services or information, the same basics apply and can be modified to suit the business. Wholesale and retail formulas vary with product, so this example would have to be modified accordingly. My referenced product will be a dress because the design and manufacture of clothing is basically a general standard. Also, it's the business that I was in and best understand.

The biggest mistake in pricing is to charge too little. We do this for two reasons: 1. Starting out, we are unaware of all of the costs involved and 2. Out of eagerness to have our product well received we make deals that are not in our interest over the long run. Many enterprising entrepreneurs have been dazzled, then chewed up and spit out after making price and advertising concessions and then being replaced by the next newcomer inexperienced enough to give their product away for the prestige of being in a high-end department store.

The first thing we need to consider regarding the viability of a product is that price-wise it has to fall into one of two categories: It has to be of a nature that selling just one over the period of time it takes to produce will meet our financial needs, or it has to be reproducible.

By the time we know how to price what we have to offer we have a basic understanding of what it takes to run a business, period. A good pricing formula basically consists of the same five categories that a good bookkeeping system does: 1. Goods, 2. Labor, 3. Marketing, 4. Overhead and 5. Profit. The first two have to do with the cost of producing the actual item or service, the third has to do with the cost of getting it into the hands of the consumer and the fourth has to do with the cost of doing business, like rent, utilities, phone, etc. Once these are established and we determine how many units we have to produce in order to cover these costs, we must add the amount needed to meet our own financial needs, which is also labor but rather than determined on an hourly basis is usually categorized as salary. The fifth has to do with whether or not we are going to be successful. If we are not able to generate profit we need a new or revised product or way of doing business, or we will not be able to sustain and grow our enterprise.

In order to arrive at the numbers for our formula, we must answer the following questions: How many units or dresses do we have to producc to pay for: Materials, Labor, Marketing, Overhead? How many do we have to make to pay ourselves and other employees enough to make all this worthwhile? How many do we have to produce to make a profit?

The easiest formula to arrive at price is to double the cost of Labor and Materials. After we are in business for awhile and have some actual figures to work with we can be more accurate by totaling the dollars needed for Material+Labor+Marketing+Overhead+Profit and divide by units.

Let's say it takes 4 yards of fabric at $5.25 per yard to make a dress. It'll take time to determine the price of thread but it must be factored in. Let's make it $1.25. Our cost of materials is $22.25. Now, let's say it takes 2 1/2 hours to cut and assemble the garment for which we pay $12.50 an hour. This is $31.25.

We add the two together and get $53.50. The formula for this particular industry, as well as many others, says you must be able to double this price in order to cover your overhead and make and market a viable product. This puts your wholesale price at $107.00. The retailer is going to double it again, which means it has to hang on the rack at $214.00. One quickly sees why companies go "all the way to China" to manufacture their products, but this is the hard reality.

Marketing is basically figured as percentage of the wholesale price. We can either pay for our own show room and have a sales rep and their expenses on our payroll or pay an independent rep with her own show room a commission. Either way, we need to figure we're going to be out at least 10% of our wholesale price in order to market our product. We're now down to $48.15 out of the $53.50 created by doubling the cost of labor and fabric to cover our overhead. Advertising is a whole other part of the story, the cost of which may be shared by our sales reps, but this is too complicated to include in this short example. Let's just use 5% of wholesale as a very low token marker leaving us with $45.47 to cover overhead, create salaries and profit.

Out of the $45.47 we must pay for equipment, whether leased or purchased. The equipment is considered an asset and subject to depreciation but the calculations are too complicated to go into here and it isn't that important to our example because if you take the alternative route and have the production done by a contractor it replaces the cost of labor, but is still going to cost about the same since they have to pay labor and overhead and make a living and a profit same as us.

Some forms of bookkeeping look at the cost of doing business over and beyond the cost of the actual product as overhead. It is basically divided into three categories: 1. Fixed, 2. Variable and 3. Miscellaneous. Different bookkeepers use different systems since Fixed and Variable tend to overlap. If the Miscellaneous category runs high you need a new bookkeeper. Payroll is a category of its own. Along with those involved in the assembly process, payroll must include regular employees such as a designer, pattern maker, shipper and office help.

Once we have grown enough to have to move out of the spare bedroom and garage, let's pretend we can get the space we need, including utilities, for $1200.00 per month. If we divide that by the $107.00 wholesale price we see that we need to sell about 12 dresses just to pay the rent.

Now, let's say that I am going to do the designing and fabric purchasing myself since liking to do that is part of why I created the business in the first place. If my personal rent or mortgage payment is $1500 and I have a $500 car payment, after food and gas and utilities, maybe I could live on $3000 per month while scrimping to build my business. Say we could get by with another employee and some part time help and now payroll looks something like $6,000 per month. Divide this by $107.00 and we see that we need 57 dresses to meet payroll. So rent and payroll comes to 69 dresses, let's call it 70. But wait. The Materials and Labor and Marketing to make 70 dresses will cost us $61.63. $61.63 x 70 is $4,314.10 divided by $107.00 is 40 more dresses, plus the ones to cover the cost of those 40 will mean (where's that Italian when we need him?) that we need to make—if I've got my math right—and sell about 133 dresses per month to cover these costs.

Obviously this does not include all expenses like loans, interest, licenses, taxes, etc. Nor does it include profit. If you don't make a profit you can't grow and would have been better off to have left your money safely in the savings account. Like most things in life you don't get to stand still for long. You either move forward or back. In order to minimally include these we would need to add at least 20 percent and the dresses it would take to generate that. What becomes evident very quickly when you crunch the numbers is that in manufacturing, volume is key and finding and fixing the right pricing formula is indispensably the first order of business.

Once we put together these figures we can determine not only how much to ask for our product, but what our volume needs to be. We can then create the 5 and 10 year projection sheets that will help our Italian accountant get us on that red carpet in the bank, with our samples slung over our shoulder.

# Product and Pricing Ideas

*Write about the ideas these writings have inspired regarding your pricing.*
*Make a menu of services and put some numbers down.*
*Imagine receiving income for one of the items your are selling.*
*How does it feel? How does it add up?*

# Money Matters

## It's All About Style

Since it is impossible to say how this or that would have turned out if one had done this or that instead, attempting to do so is unprofitable speculation. All I can say, at this point in my life, is how I feel about the decisions I have made as to whether or not they worked and to what degree.

My greatest weakness as a business person is that I am not a consumer. I hate shopping and I am physically and emotionally appalled by aisles and aisles of products that are so unnecessary. I do not understand the things people buy nor why they want to buy so much of them. How many pairs of tennis shoes can one person wear, for heaven sake?! I definitely belong to the less is best, one to wash and one to wear, side of the equation. However! I want both the one to wash and the one to wear to be of the very best quality!

My daughter Shiloh still thanks me for teaching her to invest in a couple of really classy good quality outfits as opposed to spending the same amount of money on a lot of trendy little items like her girlfriends were wearing, that were going be out of style even before they were worn out. Her appreciation grew as she found herself being able to go directly from school into the work place with the wardrobe she had acquired while in school and that once that foundation wardrobe had been established it was easy to keep it going and growing with a few items and accessories and be well dressed and in style. And it *is* all about style, Baby! Invest in it!

As for bigger investments, I cannot say that I regret not having invested in property. While building equity is really nice, unless it is equity in income property it means that a lot of money is tied up that could be invested in a business that is generating goods and employment and circulating cash. But these are just different modes of operating, and again, it's a question of style. The thing, however, that makes me reluctant about owning property is that from what I've seen, the saying that property owns you, is true. I can't believe the lousy miserable relationships I've seen people stay in for years and years because of what they considered the disastrous results of having to give up or split up the property. And that's just one of the ways property owns us. There are lots, like paying protection money in the form of insurance, the constant upkeep and repairs and all the anxiety that goes with the above. I know people that can't even leave home for any length of time because they are afraid that something is going to happen to their house or their stuff while they are gone. When making decisions one of the first questions I ask myself is, "Is this going to tend toward freedom or toward bondage?" In my experience, which has included property, I have to say, property ownership tends toward bondage. Not my style.

As for walking away from a few marriages with no settlement and no alimony, this I do not regret. The idea of some guy being severely pissed off once a month as he writes out a check to me is energy I just don't want coming my direction. On whether or not it was a good decision not to pursue child support, the jury is still out. It seemed like a good idea at the time since it was based upon not wanting to give the fathers of my children any more control over their lives (and consequently mine) than I had to. It worked well for me because we pretty much did as I pleased and moved when I chose, which was often. Like my mother, this rolling stone had no interest in moss gathering. Looking back, I see that the freedom this gave us deprived my children of the financial support that might have given them another pair of tennis shoes, or made their lives better. Maybe. They never complained.

As for all that moving around, Mom, my kids and myself on our Great Adventure, although traveling light (except for books, record albums and a sewing machine or two), it was our style to move into each place as though we did own it and were going to live there forever. Really move in and make the investment. Paint it, hang a little token moss, make curtains, make friends, make it home and make everywhere better than it was before we came. It made for good references and good karma. And don't forget—style!

As for planning, I'm surprised that the hip philosophical "Be here now" concept that started emerging in various forms out of the East in the sixties and seventies is still around or being revived, considering that those of us who went for it at that time and lived long enough to have seen the consequences of operating in the great eternal NOW, know better. I mean, it's okay for Oprah: she's rich. And even okay now and then for the average girl, like a little trip or vacation, or having a piece of cake, but the further one gets past that age that Bob Dylan told us not to trust any one older than, the more one realizes the need for a past to examine and a future to consider. Nowhere, other than in health matters, is this more important than in money matters and it has been shown that these two are connected.

So, as I continue to make decisions that I hope will create freedom and independence, and as I somehow become a little older than Bob Dylan himself, I recognize that a certain transformation guru was right when he said: "Money is not important—it's just to human beings what water is to fish." And I realize that if I had lived a little less in the NOW and planned a little more for the FUTURE, I would be enjoying a greater sense of freedom at this point in my life. It's a good thing that the one to wash and one to wear that I did invest in will never go out of style and will not be worn out by the time I am, which (probably due to the fact that there's not too much hatred coming my direction from those ex-husbands I wouldn't stay with for love nor money, or even for the children's sake) should be quite a long time yet. Long. Like my sentences. And that's style, Baby!

# The Magic of The Market

## It's Called Hard Work and Sacrifice

There is something absolutely magic about Market!—the word, the place, the people (whether a buyer or a seller) and what it takes to get there. The word "magic" implies such things as the use of tricks, illusions, slight of hand, smoke and mirrors, in order to create something that appears to occur miraculously, as though out of thin air. And this *is* market. Anyone who has set up for Market, whether on a street corner or in a convention center, knows—Yes! Market is Magic!

Picture the vast empty stage of a convention center a few days in advance of a trade show before the coming of administrative staff, union labor, all the invisible and unsung "stage hands," the venders and finally the customers. Now listen to the cacophony created by cosmic levels of chaotic commotion as the smoke and mirrors are conjured and wrestled into place, forklifts negotiating the maze, containers delivered and broken open, booths raised, lighting wired. That this arena will be transformed into all the court and spark and glamour of a Hollywood production would be beyond comprehension if we hadn't seen and done it so many times before. On opening day when our customers begin to make their entrance it's all we can do to keep from breaking into tears and applause. For us! For them! We've all come through another season!

Newcomers see the glamour and—oh my yes! know that there *is* glamour! But let us not overlook the commitment and years of rigid discipline needed for the mastery to pull this rabbit out of this hat. Someone must catch the rabbit. Someone must make the hat. Someone must put the act together. Someone must perform the act. Someone must sell the act. And someone must buy the act. Are you one of these someone's who must?

When addressing seminars on how to go into business for oneself, I used to start with the question, "Why work eight hours a day for someone else, when you can go into business for yourself and work sixteen?" We know that magic has a dark side, and she who is unaware of, or will not consider, the dark side of her venture is without Wisdom. Have you noticed by now that our little Positive Thinking Warriors, while they may wave or even visit, don't hang out for long in venues not graced by Wisdom's presence?

As for the slight of hand and tricks of the trade, know that some of us crossed desserts and oceans to come to Market. Some of us slept with our children on the floor between our sewing machines in order to make it all the way to Market. Some of us slept in our cars in order to be able to attend Market throughout the show. Know that you *will* make sacrifices. Know that even if you have lots of venture capital—you *will* make sacrifices.

There are three movies from which much can be gleaned from the main characters. The first, while brilliant, is so depressing I can't recommend it, but all address, so much better than I can, what it takes to get us to Market and finally there, make it look so magically easy.

In "The Pawnbroker," Rod Steiger's character Sol Nazerman responds to a young man's question as to why "you people" are so successful. At one point in Sol's brilliant, wrenchingly bitter and intense bring-you-to-your-knees speech he says, "You go out and buy a little piece of cloth and you cut it in two and sell it for a penny more that you paid for it. Then you run right back out and buy another piece of cloth and cut it into three pieces and sell them for three pennies profit. And in that time, you *never* succumb to buying an extra piece of bread for the table or a toy for the child. No! You run right back out and get another piece of cloth and...."

Then there is Jack Lemmon's academy award winning performance as the tragic Harry Stoner in "Save the Tiger." When asked what he wants most, the desperate clothing manufacturer whose business is on the skids replies, "Just one more season."

Finally, in the "The Devil Wears Prada," when Meryl Streep as Miranda Priestly explains in impeccably understated, soft and sardonic tones, the history of the "lumpy blue sweater" that Andrea wears with such self-righteous, politically correct snobbery, I wanted to jump up in the theatre and shout Bravo!

So, for those of you who truly can't help being entrepreneurs, who truly have been seduced by the magic of the market place, who make the sacrifices you never imagined you'd make, who work until three o'clock in the morning putting the last touches on your sample line, then with only a few hours sleep, or none, even if you have to dress in a "Last Chance Texaco" gas station on the way there, you put on that lipstick and those high heeled shoes, then Baby, then you walk into that convention center like you own the joint—yeah YOU!—I applaud you! I jump up and shout Bravo! And my prayer is that the Good Spirit of Market Magic continue to grant you one more season.

## SACRIFICE

The show is almost over. Buyers and sellers alike
are exhausted, but relaxed and lingering with old accounts.
Tonya has kicked off her shoes and conjured a silver flask.
The guys are all standing around Mel's booth across the aisle
listening to the ball game.
We discuss a few items that make a "strong statement"
and there's some review of "price points"
along with a little gossip, a little politics.
Some of us are gathering energy to pack it up,
some to dash off so they don't miss their commute.
"Is it possible to 'miss' your commute," Brenda jokes,
"when you live in California?"
"What I want to know" Tonya says, "is—is it deductible
like my shrink, or does it go on my expense account
with the price of the show and the martinis?"
We're all hoping our kids haven't gotten too old
to play with the empires we've been out building.

# The Gesheft

## Tithing—What a Deal!

I took a series of "transformational" seminars back in the seventies that attempted to address everything in life for which one could invent a seminar. About halfway into the seminar on "Money" the nice looking gentleman in a business suit who was sitting next to me, leaned over, put his head between his knees and threw up on the floor. He raised up, dabbed his mouth with his handkerchief, turned and looked at me and, in the vernacular of the day, said, "I guess I've got quite a charge on money." He wasn't the only one. There was more vomiting, dropping out, acting out and other reactive behavior in this seminar than in all of the rest of them put together, including the one on sex. When the seminar leader said, "Money is not important—it is just to human beings what water is to fish," the "charge" on money seemed justified.

Some people equate money with work and say they have to work because they have to make money. We do have to make money, but even if we didn't, I would still have to work, because I am one of those that love to work and feel it is necessary to develop our character and define who we are. However, I do really like to "make" money, especially through my own invention. I am delighted with the concept that I can take an idea out of my imagination and convert it into cash. It is that same amazement and excitement one has over putting a seed in the ground and the next thing you know, food is sticking out of the dirt. What a deal!

Speaking of deals, it was a deal that grounded me in my first financial principle. I discovered it in my pre-teen years about the time I started baby sitting to make money to buy a Greyhound bus ticket to get me out of the small town we had moved to and back to San Francisco. I happened to be reading about this guy in the Bible who was my number one hero because he wrestled with God. As it turns out he also established the cornerstone upon which I would build all my financial thinking, probably for the rest of my life.

As the story goes, Jacob—that's my guy—was leaving town (probably another reason he appealed to me—if I had run into him I would have hitched a ride on his camel) under somewhat disreputable circumstances and along the way he got into this wrestling match with God. Afterwards Jacob vowed a vow, saying, "If God will be with me, in this way that I go and will give me bread to eat and raiment to put on, so that I come again to my father's house in peace; then shall the Lord be my God...and of all that thou shalt give me I will surely give the tenth onto thee." In other words Jacob was saying to God, "Let's do a gesheft!" Let's make a deal! Wow! The idea of making a deal with God blows my mind to this day. At that time the idea that I might even have something God wanted—besides for me to open that little wooden door to my heart the pictures always showed Jesus knocking on –shook my universe.

And such a deal! To say to the Almighty, "Okay, so just take total care of me and cover my butt and you can be my God and I will give you a ten percent kick back on whatever comes my way."

Well, anyone who's followed Jacob's career knows that Jacob's little ten percent, which I have come to think of as an investment, really paid off! It's still paying off, but that's another story.

The most important thing about tithing is what it taught me and continues to teach me. Although this is another one of those things like ice cream or sex that you can't learn by being told or reading about, but have to experience first hand for yourself, I'll tell you a few things I learned anyway. Tithing taught me to think in percentages, starting with tenths, which happens to be the base of our mathematical system. Hmmm. I also—since I didn't belong to a church—had to give a lot of consideration to what or whom I was going to do with that two and a half cents on the twenty-five cents an hour I was making baby sitting. I decided to give it to the March of Dimes which was the organization raising funds for the cure of polio. My folks wouldn't let us kids swim in the local pool because they were so afraid that we would catch infantile paralysis, as it was called at that time. As one who loves to swim I already had a vested interest in curing polio. It seemed like every grocery counter in town (all two of them) had a jar with a picture on it of a little kid on crutches. Depositing those pennies, dimes and dollars into those jars was a big thrill for me. So was the bus ticket stash that was growing in my piggy bank as
I learned what it feels like to work and save money that you can exchange for something you really want. I was blessed in so many ways that I can't even explain, perhaps the greatest being that when they did develop the vaccine for polio I got to feel like I had some small part in it and—even though I hadn't made it back to San Francisco yet—it made me feel really good.

A lot of years have passed since then and I have continued to tithe. I could write an entire book of tithing stories, what I have learned through the process and how it has blessed me. Things like being able to figure out the financial basis for running a business by thinking in tenths. Things about human nature wanting to hang onto everything it can, when I find myself wrestling with questions like, "Now is that ten percent before taxes or after taxes?" Things like how easy it is to give a dime on a dollar but the more money one makes the more inclined one is to renege on the deal. Since I don't tend to participate in organized religion there is always the question of what to do with the tithes and what governs that for me continues to change. I do tend toward the principle that one should tithe to one's teacher, but confess that I stretch that a bit by saying that all of God's children are my teachers, so if instead of dropping it in a collection plate, if I want to leave wet twenty dollar bills stuck on the inside of a dryer at a laundromat in a poor neighborhood or throw them off of a roof top and watch them float to the street below, that's okay too. Because the greatest thing I have learned from tithing is that it is so much fun! Especially when people don't know where it is coming from. They start being nicer to everyone because maybe it was them who stuck the rent money under their door.

Has this practice made me rich like Jacob got rich? No, but I do believe it has given me the fullness of riches for which I am intended and equipped to handle at any given period in my life. Also I am always amazed at how far money goes for me. Sometimes I am shocked to discover how much more income some people I know have than I do, yet how much higher my standard of living is. One thing is sure. No matter how tight it gets, I never really worry. As long as the "charge" that I have on money is ten percent, the gesheft I've made works really well.

# Experiencing Our Wins

## Remembering to Dance

I cannot stress enough the importance of having an awareness of what we are accomplishing, of being able to experience a sense of completion with each step on our path as we create and grow our projects and businesses. It comes with the territory that we plunge headlong into relentlessly pursuing our goals, and then the next goal, and the next, without having much experience—other than meeting a deadline—of what we are achieving as we go. This not only sets us up for burn out, but we become driven and cease finding pleasure in our work.

I had been designing and manufacturing a line of women's wear apparel for years, putting in the long hours required to start and grow a business, running hard and running fast—definitely not taking time to smell the roses. Then, at one of my five annual trade shows at the San Francisco Hyatt Regency, I broke away from setting up merchandise in the room to go down to the main floor where the fashion show was in progress.

Evening wear had just been introduced on the runway. As I watched, my eyes were drawn past the oncoming models back to the very beginning of the platform, to where a very regal model was making her entrance. Her sleek black hair was pulled back in a tight bun at the nape of her elegant neck and her shoulders shown broad and bare above an expanse of gown cut on the bias from a black and white tweed knit that closely skimmed her long body to flare from her knees to the floor. Amidst all the frills and froth worn by the other models, the contrast of this business-like tailored fabric used for evening wear was stunning. I was so mesmerized that she was practically on top of me before I realized it was a "Karen Johnson." People were wildly applauding as she approached the end of the ramp and her Dior turn exposed her back—bare to the waist—its sprinkling of freckles complementing the speckle of the tweed fabric, the bias cut panels swinging into a wide ark in the footlights. "Oh my God!" I cried, "That's my dress!"

For the first time in my years in the industry, I actually had an experience of myself as a designer. Suddenly, everything was different, like a black and white movie changing into technicolor and gaining a great sound track.

That afternoon, I walked from the Embarcadero Center over to the Golden Gate Apparel Mart on Market Street and instead of going in through the back alley, the way I used to deliver my samples to the showroom, I went in through the front entrance. I found the name of my company on the directory in the lobby. Yes! There it was against the black background in little white letters, "Karen Johnson Inc." I stood there and really looked at it. I took the elevator to the 4th floor. I walked over and really looked in the showcase window beautifully displaying samples from my line. Yes! My people made those dresses!

I was shocked to realize how long it had been since I had attended my first hotel trade show, not as a designer, but as a retailer, and asked myself, "Why am I buying other people's lines? I want to design my own line and come to these shows to sell instead of to buy." I had achieved this years ago without stopping long enough to catch my breath and really have an experience of my accomplishment.

That evening, instead of staying in the hotel room and continuing to work, I went out on the mezzanine and gazed down on the floor below where the runway, now dismantled, had been. People were dancing, the world was still in Technicolor with a great sound track and I was ecstatic. As I punched the button on the elevator to go down and join them, I promised myself that from then on, I would include in my rigid work discipline that discipline I most needed: Stop and take a little time to experience and celebrate the wins. And dance.

**ALTAR**

*For Eden, New Years Morning 2005*

The Gypsies can't move on just now. We are
too tired to dispose of one thing more, too
weighted down with the thefts of all those shrines.
See Mother, I have made one for you. An altar:

From the five-spool thread-rack on the overlock, I hung
your last high-heeled dancing shoes by their T-straps,
along with the blue velvet which, like an old Jew,
you used to test between your thumb and fingers.

That sewing machine hasn't sung a stitch
Since you got up and walked away from it.
No one else knows how to thread it, tune it, time it,
sharpen its needles and knives, make it hum.

**Caron McCloud**

# Experiencing My Wins

*Write about the moments you have experienced a sense of accomplishment.*

# Work Aesthetic

My business was born out of the inspiration to create,
the need to provide full tummies and warm beds,
the desire to do it my way, doing what I love to do.

I imagined myself sitting at my drawing board
in a well lighted studio, sketching designs for my next line,
but instead, I find myself making them up on the road,

While running from one appointment to the next,
or at my desk, between invoices and data entries
succumbing to the throes of entropy.

I feel resentment about how this is turning out,
how my desire to express myself is spent
in the rush to market and business as usual.

But then, as though entering or waking
from a dream, I notice the simplicity and elegance
of the paper clip, its capacity for efficiency.

I hear the sound of my stapler's declaration
that something has come together in completion.
I am present to my pencil point

Pressed to paper grid and spread sheet,
forming number shapes. I begin to understand
how to arrange them to spell profit.

I have awakened to this truly creative process,
recording how something comes into existence
where nothing ever was before.

I am conscious of this beautiful design, whereby
the work of the hand transports an idea
from the mind and deposits it into the bank.

**Caron McCloud**

# Money

## The Power of Enough

**Shiloh Sophia McCloud, Mary MacDonald,**
**elizaBeth Benson-Udom and Jenett Miller**

**Illustrations by Shiloh Sophia McCloud and Sue Hoya Sellars**

# Mama Goes to Market

Shiloh Sophia McCloud

Mama gets ready for market
by putting on her best shawl—
the one with gold threads woven through turquoise.
She carries her baby on her back
and in each hand is a woven basket—empty.

She moves through each stall
with the skill of a gymnast taking the beam.
Quick and steady, she sashays,
sizing up the goods with her experienced eye.
The sellers will not even notice this buyer
if mama doesn't want them to.

On her hip underneath her shawl
her gold coins rest heavy in their leather sack.
She takes pleasure in the thump of the coins
as she turns each corner
and winds her way back to the beginning.
She has already made her choices.

She purchases an apricot and almond scone,
nibbles off a corner chunk and hands it to her baby.
He coos with delight, extending a dimpled hand.
She purchases a cup of black coffee
and pauses to chat with the bean man.
She doesn't rush now.
She feels, tests, tastes the goods.

She fills her baskets,
emptying most of her market purse.
She thinks with the mind of her customers.
What will they need this week?
What will they want?
She repeats to herself the items they always get.
She makes selections for her weekly specials.
She loves to measure, assess, calculate and choose.
With the baby now sleeping
she pauses at the last stall
Medicine Woman has some turquoise beads,
and rose petal ointment for love, for healing.
Mama buys both for herself.
Medicine Woman and Market Mama
laugh easily together.
They have bought and sold
and laughed this way for years.

She is done making all her purchases
in one hour and it is still early.
She makes her way back,
opens the door to her shop,
sweeps the walk, waters the bougainvillea.
She turns the sign to OPEN!
and lays out her goods.
The baby is still sleeping,
So she picks up the quilt she is stitching.

"Good Morning!" calls her first guest of the day
coming through the doorway.
Her customer's basket is empty.
and she has a purse
filled with gold coins on her hip.

# A Personal Test-i-Money

## Shiloh Sophia McCloud

Let's talk money! Let us begin the money conversation in terms of some of the beliefs that we have about it. I just lit a candle in a green glass with pale and emerald green rhinestones. Green light is shining on my computer. They say that green is the color associated with prosperity and abundance. I am praying about receiving money right now, so the timing could not be better!

**Beliefs - Mama's Law:**
**If something good can happen, it will.**

I am someone who has always believed that my good is on its way to me now and that money will flow towards me as long as I live in love and act powerfully on behalf of my family and my world. And continue to create value in the world for others. In many ways, this has proven to be true for me. With plenty of challenges along the way.

I like expressions like "Follow your bliss," and "Do what you love and the money will follow." They have helped make a lot of folks rich—specifically those who use them as marketing tools to peddle their products about the same subjects they are selling. But those of us who have spent years doing what we love, besides following all these positive thinking maxims and laws of attraction, know that there are a few sentences missing. Many times I have been in a group of powerful women and mentioned the missing sentences after the "Do what you love..." part and the laughter lets me know their shared sentiment.

We can and should do what we love and do it with all of our might. But we must be really smart about it. We need to plan carefully and count the costs. If you are a singer and want to sing and sing, making it into a business might cost you the joy of just singing. If what you love is people and art then an art gallery could work for you, but if what you want to do is paint, the hard reality is that opening a gallery will leave you with little time to paint. For each project we must consider things like what the day to day fulfillment of that work might look like. And what is the market likelihood of being paid for that?

As I mentioned before, I have sold almost two million dollars of artwork over the past eight years. By some standards that seems like a lot. And indeed it is. I have consistently, powerfully, without ceasing, continued in my purpose and vision for over thirteen years and have been able to support myself. My husband, Isaiah, who has worked with me has also realized sufficient income. Our business has provided jobs and income in a great environment for many women. I have lived powerfully and joyfully doing work that is vital and needed in the world, work that makes my spirit sing and leap to get up in the morning, work that actually brings me bliss. To me, this is success. However, I must still work smart and with great diligence to cross the threshold of my financial limitations. So, I am not writing this book from a place of saying, "Here — if you do these ten steps you will become a millionaire", or "By thinking like a millionaire you will become one."

What I am saying, based on my own experience is: GO FOR IT! Isaiah and I have sometimes started projects and opened galleries with only five bucks in our pocket and sometimes with five-thousand. But we just keep on keeping on, no matter what. We keep reinventing and creating new income streams.

The information in "The Heart of the Visionary" is what has gotten me to where I am today — Writing a book for you, with some friends, family, powerful allies and fellow Cosmic Cowgirls. And we will demonstrate bringing this project to market with no outside funding. Never let money be the reason why you don't take action on behalf of your vision. I'm not recommending that you drop everything, quit your job and "Follow your bliss," though some of you might, I would be there to cheer you on. I am saying that no matter what you are doing for a living — you should also be doing YOUR WORK. Even if only a little bit. I am saying: YES! Begin a small enterprise, project or business!

**Cash Flowing**

Some say money is just energy. I think that is trite. Everything — people, buildings, cars, can be said at some cosmic level to be just energy, but what does that thinking get us? If we are somehow running "right" energy, money will just come to us?

Money is an agreement. Money is an agreement of value that we make. Most of what we think of as money is expressed by computer entries and some paper which is no longer backed up by the gold it is supposed to represent. It is all "perceived" value. When we agree to work for money, we agree that we will do this for that. And that is how this money game is played. We agree to abide by a value applied to "money" by people who we personally probably wouldn't even trust or really want to hang out with. While we have all heard about this before, I believe if we can change our understanding around the agreements we have with ourselves about money it can, yes, change how money comes to us. Each of us must seek what our own understanding of money is. We can read book after book, hear story after story and still it seems the cash doesn't flow in the way the books say it will. Regardless, we must do the work, as our money understanding affects all other areas of our life!

I believe and have witnessed a momentum building around cash flowing. Seeds sewn with an income intention and plenty of good systems usually equals money if you have what folks want. I do feel there is enough to go around and that all of our abundance is available now, in one form or another.

**Privilege**

The act of writing this book and the act of you reading it means we are living in relative privilege. I want it to be known that I do not think this book, or any others dealing with this subject, can work for everyone. There are severe economic disparities. There are people who don't have access to clean water and food, let alone the education it takes to read and write. They can't wake up tomorrow morning and say, "Wow! Cool, I think I'll write a business plan today." How can someone focus on a vision when they must figure out how to just get safe?! Nor do I think, with any wisp of my being, that those folks, with a few exceptions, have called their misery upon themselves. There is vast variety in how the 'universe' responds.

As long as there are oppressors intently focused on destroying the already oppressed, how can the already oppressed lift their heads enough to even consider their possibilities? Are there even possibilities? At a core level this book is dedicated to those women who will not ever be able to use it, who cannot lift their heads and see any possibility, those women who aren't even able to work for their bread, let alone follow their bliss. For those whose very existence is striving, thriving is not even an option.

We can cite a wonderful handful of folks who have gotten out, who have "risen from their low estate," and we use them to remind those who can't do it that they should be able to do it too, since some such five or less percent did it. Can't we see how abusive it is to use our success heroes this way? Should we hold them up as inspiration? YES! To look to, work towards? YES! But never to imply to the person who cannot pay their rent for the third month, or who is going blind and can't get health care, or to the pregnant woman who can't get access to the hospital because she doesn't have insurance or the $45 fee, that they are somehow at fault. In some places, women are dying on hospital steps right now. How can we say, "You chose this?" How dare we imply that some child with cancer is somehow responsible for their condition? What does that serve? It serves to give people the impression that if you buy a certain product and get your head right, you will have ultimate power over these circumstances. Obviously this is my opinion; I am not seeking agreement.

**Belief Systems**

And how do these systems of belief make us feel, about ourselves and about "them" the afflicted ones? Do we lose our compassion through thinking it is their story and I have my own to work out? How do our decisions make us behave? Within the context of what we choose to do to help relieve suffering, does it even matter how it got there? What beliefs do we adopt that make us feel guilty about what we have not achieved so far? So not only are we losers, but it is indeed all our fault that we are losers. Never mind that we are at war, being poisoned by mattresses and water, or that we are heavily taxed. I just ask that we pay close attention to how the hawkers of these concepts and programs make us feel. If you are sick, do you now get to feel guilty about being sick? When we have bad things happen to us and the so called "support" we are receiving is guilt inducing, then how can it be good for us, right and divine?

A lot of folks bristle when I talk about this in groups. But mostly, before it's over, people are sharing, or they come to me afterwards, saying how grateful and relieved they are to hear someone saying this. Many of us unconsciously pick up popular thought like radio signals, and before we know it, we believe something that we have not even thoroughly researched or analyzed for ourselves. We find ourselves thinking, "Oh, she has cancer; I wonder what is wrong in her thinking that attracted that?" Or, "They don't have money because they are not thinking right about abundance." Really?!

In no way do I intend to diminish the power of the mind. I wholeheartedly believe its power to influence good. But systems of thought, in order to work, have to be studied and practiced. Let us be aware of the judgment seat "enlightened thinking" can cause us to sit in. We can find ourselves looking down on, or dismissing the struggles of others in a second of positive thinking juju.

**Compassion**

It is from years of working with thousands of women that the opinions stated in this writing have been formed. Instead of attacking the victim, we must ask: What held them or bound them? And what liberated them? Only the thoughts that liberate us are thoughts that we should live by. Who has ever healed from battering oneself? Who has ever added self value by saying how terrible she is? Here is where the power of our mind and our words, can really work. We raise ourselves up by creating as much good as possible towards ourselves and others. This very process will illuminate what needs to change in us by throwing a light on it and we say "Ah ha!" not, "What a jerk I have been." Compassion for ourselves and others will illuminate our hearts. If we have been at fault, then we can make amends in a graceful manner with ourselves and others through an empowered position instead of a victim position, which inherently reeks of blame. Even how we say we are sorry can imply the other person is somehow responsible. But, when we can actually feel good and relieved about the exposure of our harmful and limiting ways of being, then we can act in power that is informed by intelligence. Making amends is a matter of emotional intelligence.

Let the new systems we adopt be tried. And let us make every effort to manifest them in ourselves before we apply them to others. Those who can change for the good, hopefully will. And those who cannot will remain in our prayers and thoughts. In what ways have we misled ourselves, or beaten ourselves up about money and our relationship to it? We CAN change our relationship to it and it WILL change how it comes to us. But it is not a magic formula, or a secret where suddenly the stream is opened and all flow comes to us. It took a lifetime of living into our money thoughts and it will take some time to live out of them once we have made a choice of HOW we will relate to it. For starters, let's get clear, money is good!

I realized that I had been saying to myself for years, there is never quite enough to go around, in my life, or in the lives of my loved ones, or in the world. Through doing this work I discovered that for me, this was a lie. I actually have always had quite enough — just not everything I wanted. I would take the world's problems and make them my own to the point of limiting myself. So I have a new story now. And I live it daily. I have to remind myself of it over and over, so I make new declarations. You can make up your own statement like: "I have all I need and more is always coming to me, through the grace and wisdom of Divine Providence."

# Getting Unstuck

*If you have felt stuck around money this is the time and the place to work it out. The money section in this workbook is not as much about teaching you about money as it is about getting you to look at your relationship to it and patterns around it. Once you have worked out some of what you believe, you will be able to make more solid commitments around how you are going to perceive money from now on. This is a decision. You make it and then you stick to it. Okay, now articulate what YOU believe.*

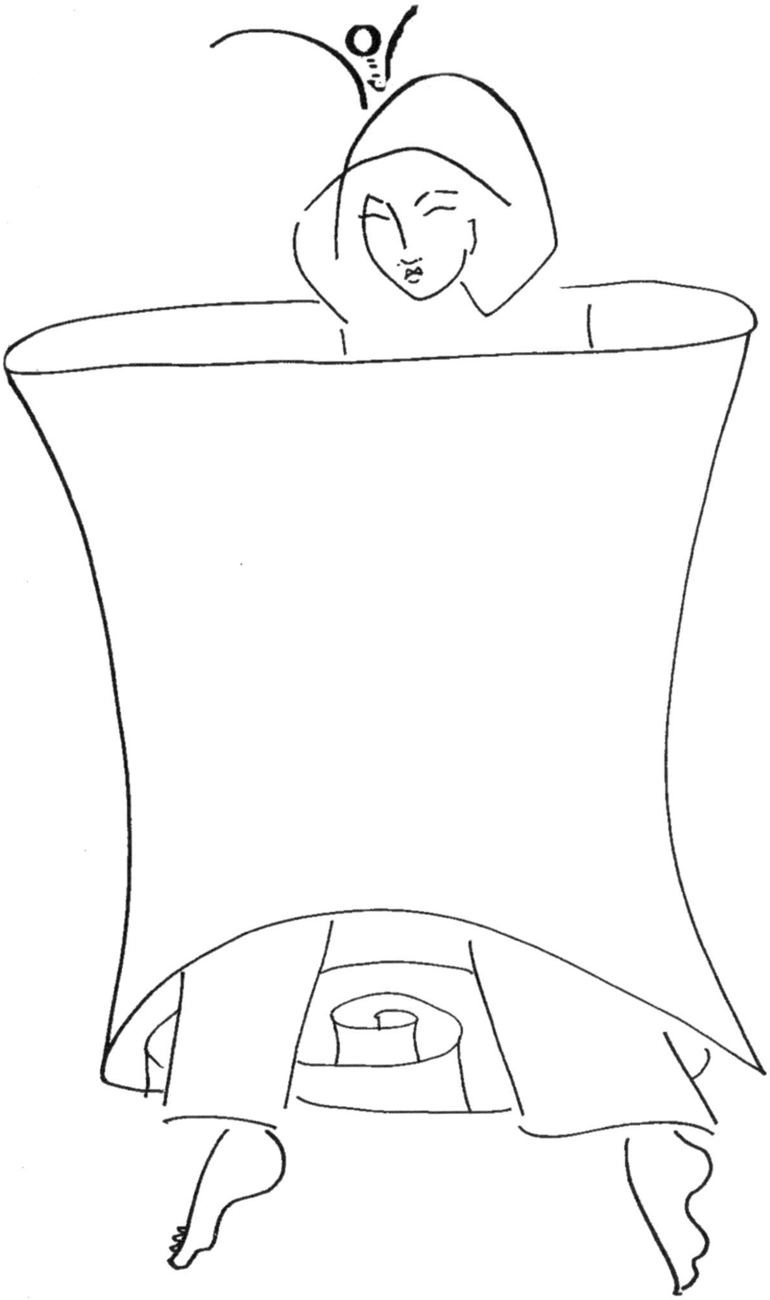

# Challenging our Money Beliefs

**Mary MacDonald and Shiloh Sophia McCloud**

- What are my beliefs around money?

- Are the belief systems I hold now about money true for me?

- Has someone else's opinion/ideas/dominance informed my beliefs about money?

- Why am I holding on to this belief – how does it benefit me?

- How is this playing out in my financial life?

- How have my parents beliefs about money informed my own?

- List words or phrases that you feel about money now:

- List words or phrases that you would LIKE to feel about money now:

# Perception Shapes Reality

**Shiloh Sophia McCloud**

Each of us must determine what success is for ourselves. It is not a number or a destination - although that is a part of it. Success, like abundance is a way that you BE about what you are doing. In my life I have often felt that since I am not more financially wealthy than I am - that I am not successful. So I have had to redefine what success is so that I do not get discouraged. I have achieved profound success - beyond my wildest dreams. AND it has not, as of yet, equaled secure, consistent financial wealth. HOWEVER I have been able to LIVE from the fruit of my hands for eleven years and continue to paint, have an art studio, make books, buy art supplies and get cowgirl boots as needed. That for me, is success. And I am ready for more, all the while recognizing and celebrating what has already been achieved on so many levels!

You know how there are moments when your entire perception shifts? I look for those moments. Well recently I was listening to an interview with the amazing entrepreneur Moses Asch who co-founded Folkways Records with Marian Distler. They founded it in 1948 to bring folk music to the main stream. He is famous for recording what HE wanted to - from the sticks to the streets he chose music based on what interested him about people - his financial bottom line was secondary. He defined success as being able to make a living doing what is important to you. Not having a lot but enough. He continuously invested in projects that he knew may not be lucrative but he was creating a part of our musical history. This was one of those "AHA!" moments of perception where my reality was informed by another person's story. His story was not coming from the starving artist mentality - it was coming from a position of investing in what is important to you - and understanding success by your own definition.

This track of thinking causes us to wonder: What is enough? Do we need a lot? Just enough? By getting as clear as possible on what you actually need you can be liberated to choose how much you are going to work. If you know 20 clients equals what is needed or 100 jars of jam, or two sales of $2,000 each - ask yourself - do I always need to make more or can I spend the rest of my time growing the rest of my life?

"I got myself a start by giving myself a start," said Madame CJ Walker. Have you ever heard of Madame CJ Walker? When I read her story it was another perception shift for me because she became a legendary business woman, starting with nothing. I think of her so often and what she accomplished against the odds. Her story brings courage to my soul when I think of what she overcame. She was a black woman entrepreneur who developed and sold hair products for black women clients in 1906. She toured the country with her products, employed her family, ran a beauty school for women, trained sales reps, was a public speaker, philanthropist and political and social activist and mother. She was known as the first self made African American woman millionaire. At her death she passed her wealth and her business onto her daughter Lelia.

*I am a woman who came from the cotton fields of the South. From there I was promoted to the washtub. From there I was promoted to the cook kitchen. And from there I promoted myself into the business of manufacturing hair goods and preparations....I have built my own factory on my own ground.*

*Madam Walker, National Negro Business League Convention, July 1912*

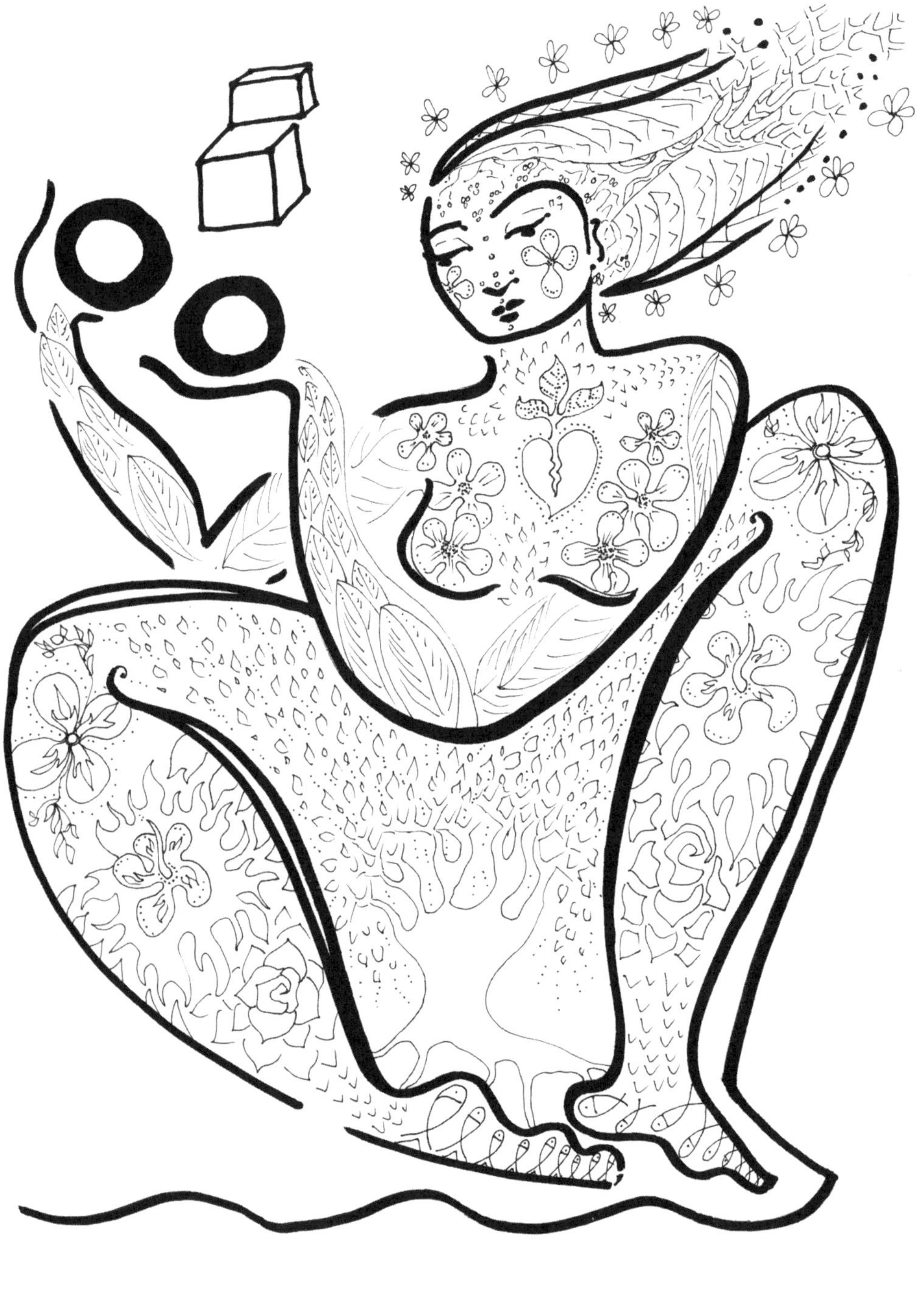

***I am educated and empowered to create and sustain income! I have a healthy relationship with money and every day I am learning to manage and grow my resources.***

# Declaration of Enough

*Create a declaration of what your new money beliefs are going to be and decide to stick to it. Our words are powerful creators, so be clear and concise. Within reason start with something you can believe, almost believe, or think you can believe soon. Be honest with yourself about how much is "enough" to align the personal with the business.*

# SIMPLE MATH AND GETTING PAID

**elizaBeth Benson-Udom**

When starting any new thing, you want to generate some money from doing it. You have to pick what you want to pay yourself, then do some simple math to determine how you can generate what you want to pay yourself. For example: you want to make $50K(thousand) - if you generate $200/day (five days a week for fifty weeks/year) you are making $50K/year.

Now that the "what I want to get" math is over, you need to figure out what you give, ex: sell (the simpler the better) and then how to give/sell it. You need to give/sell it for $200 every day for five days, fifty weeks a year. Then figure out what you need to spend to earn $50K/year.

You must consider what it costs to produce and provide your service, what costs you need covered for the who, what, where, when, why and how questions to ask when determining your invitation. These cost figures are the basis for your budget (or bud get--I like to think about it in terms of how to get my business to bud, in order to get bud, you have to bud get).

You determine how much you are willing to spend in regards to time, money, energy, effort for the return you are willing to pay yourself. ex: I will spend 5 hours/week, 5 days a week to earn $50K. I will spend $10K to earn $50K.

Now, you make the best decisions you can within the perimeters you've set for giving your gift. You make the best decisions you can about how to spend your time. You make the best decisions you can about how to spend your money. Now, you adjust your pricing to recover your costs: you now need to make $60K, to pay yourself the $50K you want.

Now, you must generate $240/day (five days a week for fifty weeks/year) to pay yourself and cover the budget. When you make a change in the budget, you make a change in the calculations, to figure the generation/day numbers.

You use these numbers to determine your prices. This is a profoundly simple brush stroke—but one that illuminates lots of complicated calculations. Like everything else in life, keeping it simple makes it that much...simpler. As with every thing else recommended in this book, continuing to do the simple math at every intersection with your business will keep you on track. Living inside your budget will keep you honest about your intentions regarding spending your time and money--and honoring the equation that keeps you giving. In and out. Breathing in and out. Budget in and out. And if you do it long enough, smart enough, true enough, with just enough faith, you win. You keep it simple. You do simple math. You simply win.

*For what is done or learned by one class of women becomes, by virtue of their common womanhood, the property of all women.*
*Elizabeth Blackwell (1st woman in the U.S. to become a physician).*

# Angels, Guardians and Good Hearted Investors

*Who are they? Make a list and write them a sample letter telling them about what you do. And what you need!*

# How much do you want to make?

*Be very specific. Dream big and small. Now and Future. Talk about it here.*
*The more familiar we become with money talk, and*
*being in a space of receiving, the better our relationship with money becomes.*
*When we explore it, it takes the negative charge off and puts the positive charge on.*
*The one with your name on it!*
*Write yourself an imaginary check! Draw the fruits of your abundance!*

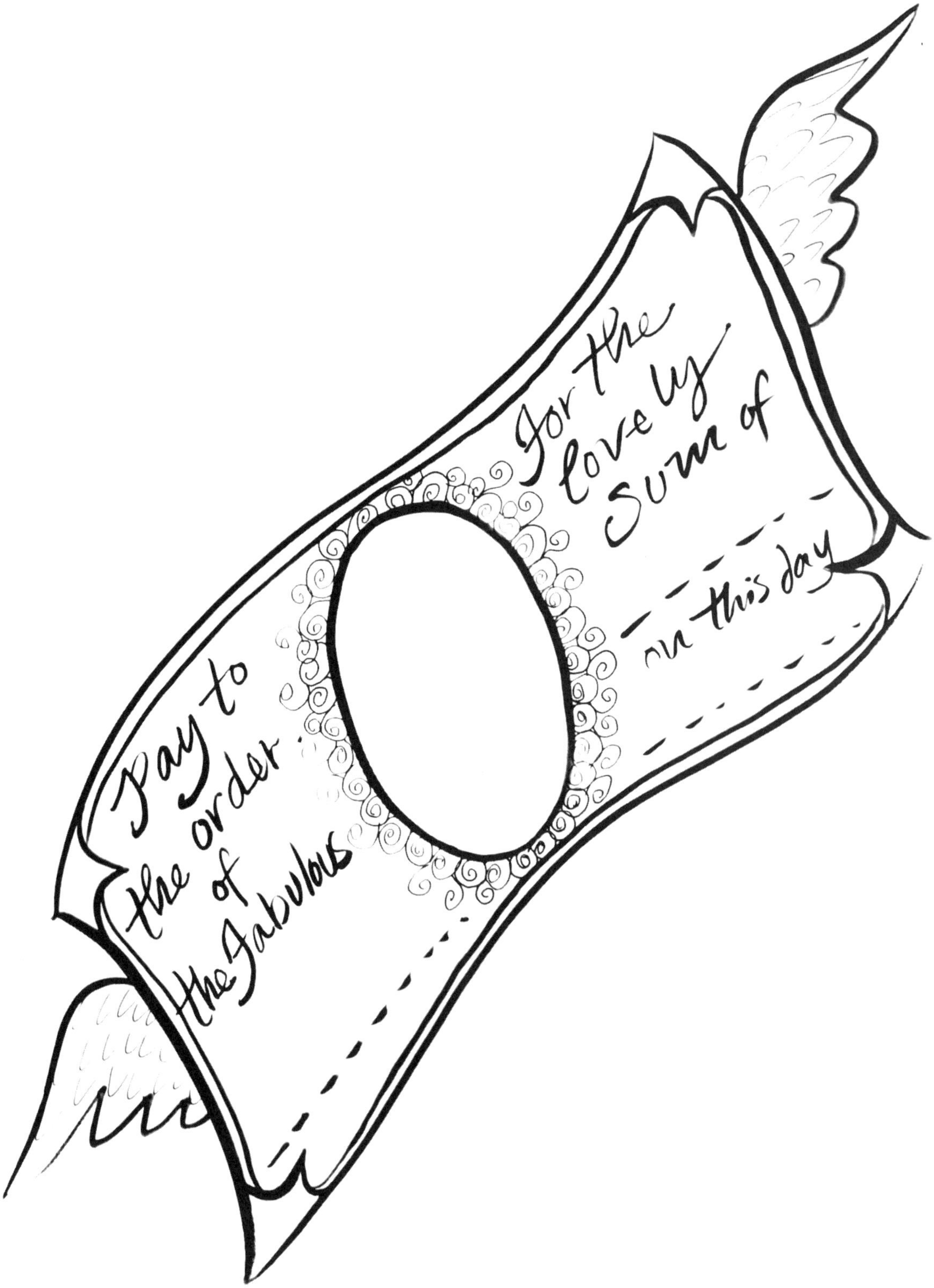

Pay to the order of the Fabulous
For the lovely sum of
on this day

# Women's Business Statistics and Strategic Partnerships

Did you know that nearly half of all privately held firms are at least 50% owned by a woman or women! Women own 26% of the nation's 20.8 million non-farm businesses which is about 5.4 million firms! Yahoo!

These firms employ more than 13 million people and generate upwards of $2 trillion in sales!

Good news includes:

- For over twenty years firms owned by women have continued to grow at two times the rate of other firms!
- 3% of all women owned firms are earning revenues upwards of $1 million dollars - and yes, that is still half of the men's statistic of 6%, but we are gaining!
- Women business owners are twice as likely as men to pass on their business to a female relative or daughter.
- From 1990-1998 the number of women's sole proprietorships grew from 5.6 million to 7.1 million, with over 70% of those in service industries.

While reviewing this good news, some startling revenue statistics came up as well. Women owned business' gross revenues are still low - 87% create less than $50K annually and only 2.7% of women-owned sole proprietorships produced at least $200K annually. There is speculation that some of these businesses may be part-time, or home-based, as two-thirds of those women are married. We are making great strides and let's keep up the good work! And, work this workbook to make the most of your Visionary Business!

***Research Project: Spend the evening on the Internet researching additional statistics and women's organizations. Take notes in the space below. Look for strategic partnerships that might need what you have. How can you align yourself with other women's organizations? There are opportunities everywhere to collaborate with others who are established in a different arena. Design yourself and your business to be an asset to others.***

# Women Who Run With Money

*My Abundance and Manifestation Journal - Who would you be, look like, think like, feel like as a woman who runs with money? Imagine yourself as RICH or as having enough. Tell us that legend....*

# PERSONAL EXPENSE TEMPLATE

**Monthly EXPENSES:**

**SAVINGS:**

General

Retirement

**HOME:**

Mortgage or Rent

Homeowners/Renters Insurance

Property Taxes

Home Repairs/Improvements/Maintenance/HOA Dues

**UTILITIES:**

Electricity/Gas/Oil

Water/Sewer/Trash Removal

Telephone (Land Line, Cell)

**FOOD:**

Groceries

Eating Out, Lunches, Snacks

**FAMILY OBLIGATIONS:**

Child Support, Alimony, Allowances

Day Care, Babysitting

**HEALTH AND MEDICAL:**

Insurance (medical,dental,vision)

Fitness (Yoga,Massage,Gym)

**TRANSPORTATION:**

Car Payments

Gasoline/Oil/Auto Repairs/Maintenance/Fees

Auto Insurance

Other Transportation (tolls, bus, subway, taxis)

**DEBT PAYMENTS:**

Credit Cards

Student Loans, Other Loans

**ENTERTAINMENT/RECREATION:**

Cable TV/Videos/Movies/Internet connection

Hobbies, Subscriptions, Dues, Vacations

**PETS:**

Food, Grooming, Boarding, Vet

**MISCELLANEOUS:**

Clothing, Toiletries, Household Products

Gifts/Donations

Grooming (Hair, Make-up, Other)

Miscellaneous Expense TOTAL

# MULTIPLE INCOME STREAMS

*Most entrepreneurs and millionaire books talk about multiple streams to gain wealth. List Possible and Fantastic Income Streams for Your New Business Venture that make it possible for you to meet your expenses from the previous page. Get Creative. Nothing is too small. Some folks build their world around the sale of a postcard. Include things you are going to get income from, like real estate, investments or web-site sales.*

# BOOKKEEPING FOR BEGINNING BUSINESS

**Jenett Miller**

The need for impeccable bookkeeping records cannot be stressed enough. Not only is it imperative for the IRS, but it is the only way we can evaluate whether or not our strategies and practices are working and whether we are making or losing money. No matter how big our company becomes or how much we trust our staff's integrity and efficiency a wise business woman will *always* be cognizant of what is going on with her books. If you ever find yourself saying, "I don't know, I leave all that to my bookkeeper," an alarm needs to go off in your head.

As entrepreneurs, we think big and understand that as we grow our business we will eventually need to go with a computerized bookkeeping system. However, with all the expenses involved with starting a business, we may not be ready to invest in a software program, so records must be kept manually. Starting with a manual system will also familiarize us with the process and the items which make up bookkeeping and help us identify exactly what kind of a program will be needed.

There are many manual bookkeeping systems which can be found at any office supply store, or even your local drug store! I recommend the "Dome Simplified Monthly Bookkeeping Record" which can be acquired on-line at domeproducts.com or by calling (800) 432-4352. It is simple and easy to use and gives step by step instructions. It includes a list of legal deductions and (for those who have employees) a section to record payroll information.

A divider filing system for records and receipts is also needed. These are the main items to be collected, organized, filed and entered into the system:

1) Bank statements for the entire year. You need a separate bank account for your business. If you haven't opened one yet, highlight all business related debits and charges on your bank statements or in your check register.
2) When making a bank deposit, attach deposit slip to the related checks/cash payments.
3) Check Register for reference as necessary.

4) Sales receipts with required information on them. It is a good idea to make copies of checks you receive as payment.
5) Paid Invoices and Bills with proper notations of how they were paid (cash, check, charge) as well as the date, amount paid and check number. For entrepreneurs who work out of their homes, phone calls, utilities, rent, Internet access and other recurring bills may be shared with your business, so be sure to make copies of these bills and highlight all charges made on behalf of the business. On the copy of the bill, total the charges, write the date you reimbursed your home and the check number or credit card transaction number.
6) Business expense receipts need to be identified as to type, such as Postage, Shipping, Office Supplies, Materials, Labor, etc. Be sure to separate your "Merchandise for resale" receipts from all other receipts, as they will be entered in their own column and applied to their own account.
7) Fee/Commission statements.
8) Expenses requiring separate tax forms such as independent contractors or cottage industries.

- Use a pencil for making entries so that changes and corrections can be easily made and follow the simple instructions supplied in the chosen system or book.
- Keep all information up to date.
- At the end of the month total all expenses and income.
- At the end of the year add up all totals and record "Statement of Net Worth" and fill out the "Tax Advisor Detachable Summary Sheet" and the section for payroll (included in the book) if you have employees.
- Take this book into your tax preparer.

**Congratulations and good luck on your business!**

***Below, write down your bookkeeping plans and a list of what needs to be done or purchased.***

# Joy Description

*Write about what you do and how much you get paid for those activities. Make a list of all the ways you get paid in your position. List increases and bonuses and benefits. Dream into the future. Then on the next page, write your MONEY AFFIRMATION!*

Everyone has been made for some particular work,
and the desire for that work has been put in every heart. - Rumi

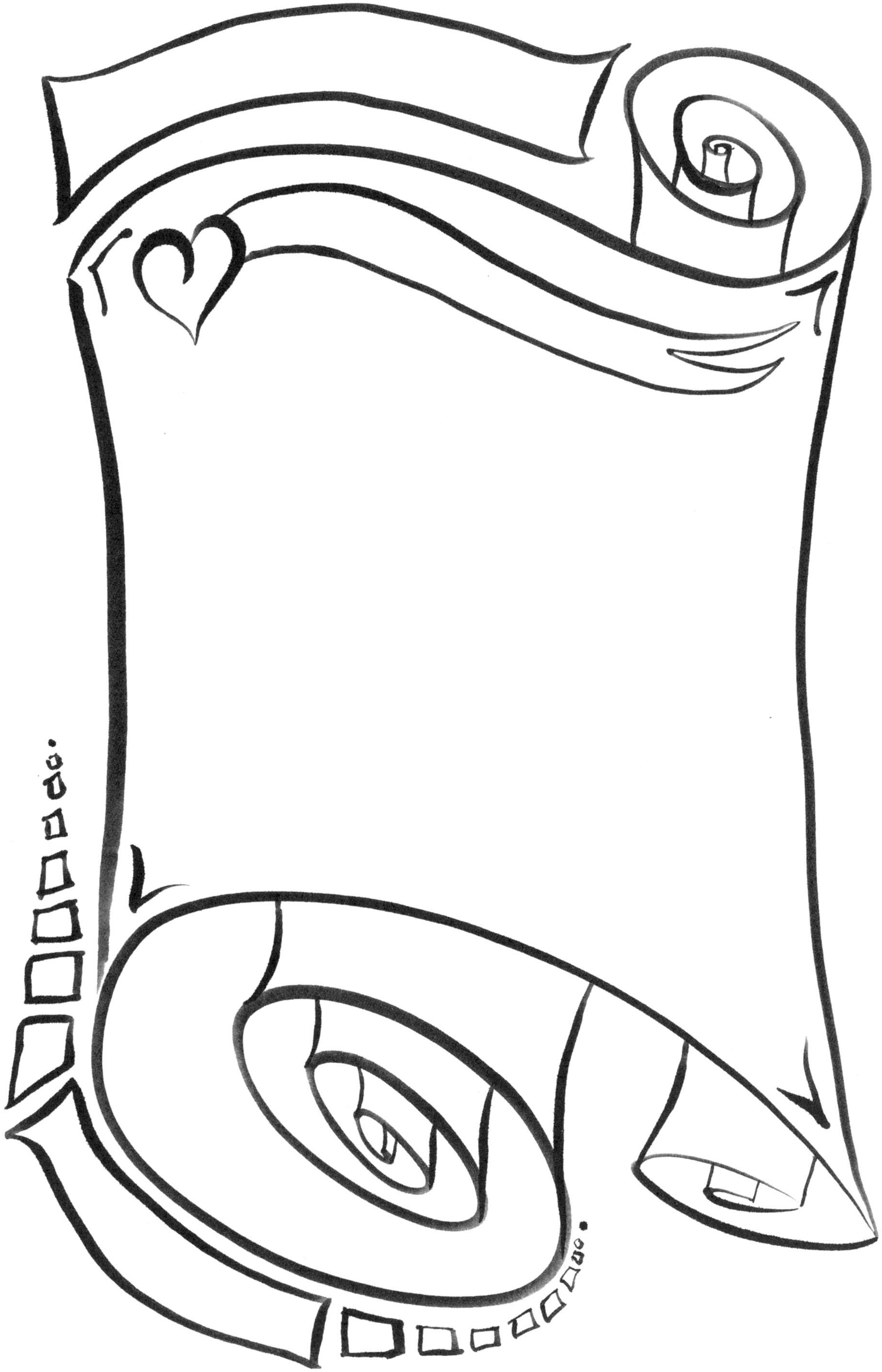

# What will money buy me?

# WHAT DOES SUCCESS & FINANCIAL ABUNDANCE LOOKS LIKE TO ME

# NOTE FROM SHILOH

## *Here's the thing...*

We are each going to have to do our own work around money. I definitely suggest reading the classic money masters. But no matter what anyone tells you - the reality is that you are going to do what you are going to do until you stop doing it that way. Many of our patterns are so deep that we don't know that they are even operating. We think we have dealt with something, only to realize - we are still operating from a previous headset.

As we were researching the best way to do this money section I realized that the primary authors had chosen their own interests in life, their own dreams first and money was secondary. Each of us wants to create income for ourselves and our families - and indeed we are! And still, we each chose our dream over being 100% realistic financially. To learn about a topic, they say to study someone who has done it and so that is why I am recommending the research date. Even though I have sold upwards of two million in my work, I am not a millionaire yet!
They say it is a formula and that anyone can do it - but I have yet to break that code. I just keep reinvesting in my projects and when folks ask about my exit strategy, I say, what exit strategy? I am in this for life.

Tons of the women I work with truly do want to make money and when I ask them why, it is usually so that they can finance their projects, send their kids to school, open up a shop, be able to do what they love. Most of the women I speak with would rather not compromise their dream even for a regular income. I haven't. And so, I invite you to study other money material. I am the one who will tell you to start your new venture even if you don't have ANY money - so I am not the most reasonable counsel where money is concerned. Do what you do no matter what!

**This workbook is for visionary entrepreneurs who are making plans for their lifework. And the thing is, if you have what is wanted and needed and you share it consistently, money will follow. That is the formula.**

I LOVE to make money. To sell paintings. To create books. To give women and men work. I actually truly value the process of how income works and I am continually learning more and more about the way to relate to it in my life. Folks often comment, wow, an artist who is interested in business and money, how unusual. I am way over that comment. Most of the serious artists I know are very much into their 'business.' Does that mean they do all the bookkeeping and marketing? Maybe not. Does that mean money is their bottom line? No.
But it does mean they are creating VALUE in the universe and KNOW that they deserve to be paid for it.

I feel the first and most essential step to making money as a visionary entrepreneur is learning one's own value. To learn and honor one's own value will guide the rest of the money process in a natural flow towards financial abundance. Know your worth and ask for it. We can still give away things for free, but first, get what you need. And know what you need!

**Making Money Research Date: 2 HOURS**

Go to the big bookstore and pick out 5 books on making money. Bring your journal and take notes. Look for essential wisdom, something you have not heard before, or something that strikes you as powerful. If you find one you really love, buy it. But if not, then take good notes.

# Market

# The Power of Presence

**Mary MacDonald**

WITH

**Shiloh Sophia McCloud, Nancy Ballard,**
**Julie Lampros, Dori Etter and Ama Zenya**
**Illustrations by Shiloh Sophia McCloud and Sue Hoya Sellars**

# Marketing and Public Relations - The 4 Ps

**Mary MacDonald**

Marketing and Public Relations are business terms that provide a framework for the understanding of concepts. The present business paradigm coins terms such as the 4Ps: Product, Pricing, Place and Promotion, which are simply "business speak" for concepts that speak to the unique you, like being passionate about what you're doing or selling so that it nourishes your soul, knowing your value and building lasting relationships throughout the world.

It just so happens that women are innately aware of these concepts and have been using them in all aspects of our lives for as long as we've been roaming the planet. Product – You know what you want to get out into the world that will brighten the lives of others. Pricing – Well, we've been shopping all of our lives, so we definitely know how much things cost, so pricing, with some research, will come easily. Promotion – Well my friends, building relationships is our birthright. And we were born to network! Place (Sales and Distribution) – With a little networking, you'll know the best placement for "your stuff" in order to make it available for Purchase (the 5th P) so that it can begin to bless and enrich the lives of others.

## The Culture of Labels

We can get so wrapped up in the roles that society has created that often it is difficult to find ourselves underneath the rubble of our culture's expectations. Labels define our clothing, our cars, the products we use and whether we are considered pretty, normal, or talented. I was the Director of Marketing and Fundraising at an organization that supported individuals with an intellectual disability. They taught me invaluable lessons about the tyranny of labels. They wanted to be called Don or Susan or Violet — they didn't want to be labeled intellectually disabled, developmentally disabled, or retarded. They wanted, with a little help from their friends, support to go to school, be in a play, play sports and go to a dance. I assured them that that was the long-range goal but in the meantime we needed to tell the public who they were so we could get the funding we needed. As the billboards were going up around the city they asked me why they just couldn't be seen as people like everyone else. Their question humbled me, but didn't they know I, as the marketing guru, knew better? In my sincere desire to alleviate their suffering and give them equal opportunities I allowed the ends to justify the means. In all of my endeavors I have struggled with this concept. I was, after all, fighting the good fight. When I was working with others to eradicate misogyny or racism I didn't want it to be through "fighting" or marginalizing others yet didn't our ultimate goal supersede the "means?" I now know for me the answer is no. You too need to honor the values that reflect your truth.

Thank you to all the individuals at Community Living Toronto for being my teachers and mentors. With your unerring logic you taught me the inappropriateness of labels in a just and kind society and that the end never justifies the way we get there unless it is through love and kindness. Yes, we need to market our products and services so the world knows how to reach us, but not at the expense of ourselves or others. The human experience is about relating to others —in all our imperfections.

Being yourself and being passionate about your life's work will be what makes the difference to your success so use these traditional tools as only that — a tool to develop your own style. Do the "analysis" of whether your wares will be successful based on industry standards, but if they say you don't have a hope in hell of making a success and you are still passionately excited about it — do it anyway and leave the Nay Sayers behind. Take from this model what works for you and forge your own path — create what makes your heart sing and the notes from your song will find an answering song from others.

It is not the answers that are necessarily meaningful but the questions we ask ourselves in order to know our own truth and connecting with those whose truth align with ours. So go forth and prosper in your own wild and succulent way!

## Off To Market We Go

Marketing is now a way of life to the nth degree. Everywhere we look we are being marketed to and told we need to have something in order to be happy, be beautiful, be popular, get the job. So often we are lied to, misled and misinformed just so a sale can be made. Don't misunderstand me — having been in marketing for most of my professional life, I appreciate the value and need to engage in the process. But let's be the change that makes marketing fun, value based, ethical and honest.

The business tools presented here are very basic just to get you thinking in these terms. There are wonderful resources available to you just a google away. Depending on your resources you can hire some wonderful women who are very skilled at developing marketing and business plans. If you don't have a lot of resources you can do research and put together your own plan and then have a professional give you feedback on how to improve it.

So, off to market we go, carrying our wares and excited about what we have to offer, knowing we can help people solve their biggest problems for a reasonable cost. But wait! How will they know who we are and where they can find us?

There is a vital bottom line for successful business—Ya gotta sell something! And ya can't sell something if nobody knows about it, or you. The question is: How can we build awareness about ourselves and what we have to offer? The answer is: By loving your offering, finding the people who love it and want it and then communicating that you are ready, willing and able to fulfill it.

*If you ask me what I came to do in this world, I an artist, will answer you:*
*I am here to live out loud.*
*Emile Zola*

# Product/Service—What Is My Stuff?

This focuses on the uniqueness of your product/service and how your customer will benefit from your offerings. In the beginning you don't have to spend money on focus groups. You already have built in focus groups—friends, family, coworkers, flea markets, farmer's markets. Take your stuff to people and get their opinions. Check out other businesses similar to yours: Who are they and how many of them are there? What is it that people love or don't like about them? Check out your potential customer. Who is your perfect, ideal customer? What gender, age, belief systems? Where do they live? How can they contact you?

• Describe the attributes/features of your offerings.

• How will it benefit your customer? How will it make them feel better about themselves? Will it save them something – money, time, headaches? Benefits can be both tangible and intangible.

• What's unique about your product compared to similar products/services in the marketplace?

• Write down who you think wants what you have.

• How will it solve a problem for them?

• What offerings or services will bring in the largest percentage of your revenues?

# Pricing—How Much Does My Stuff Cost?

Make notes in the following sections, but you will need additional pages to process this. Spend as much time as is needed to set up and explore pricing.

- What will the market bear?

- Write down how much time it takes you to do what you love and how much it costs from production (materials and labor) all the way to getting it to market and into the hands of your customer.

- Research similar businesses and write down product costs of 5 competitors, write down your own and compare.

- Write down ideas about how you can increase your sales and decrease your costs, such as selling more to existing customers, finding new ones, working from home.

- How can you price in a way that allows you to periodically offer discounts and specials—or not?

# Place—Where Do I Sell My Stuff?

Remember, the primary goal of the marketing plan is to get people to buy your products or services. The Sales and Distribution part of the marketing plan details how this is going to happen. How is your product or service going to get to the customer? Will you distribute your product or service through wholesale or retail? What distribution channel is going to be used—Web site, mail, sales representatives, gift shows, catalog? What are the costs associated with distribution? What are the delivery terms? How will the distribution methods affect production and delivery time frames? How long will it take to get your product or service to your customer? If your business involves selling a product, you should also include information about inventory levels and packaging in this part of your marketing plan. For instance: How are your products to be packaged for shipping and for display? Does the packaging meet all regulatory requirements (such as labeling)? Is the packaging appropriately coded, priced and complementary to the product? What minimum inventory levels must be maintained to ensure that there is no loss of sales due to problems such as late shipments and back orders?

- Are there natural partners that you can leverage? Who are they? Dream big and small.

- What trade shows and conferences are appropriate for your stuff?

- Do you want to license (You can get sample licensing agreements off the Internet)?

- What retail stores can sell your product? Visit the stores, research on the Internet, make a list.

- How can you make it easy for your customer to purchase?

- Create, carry and always be ready to present a sample kit. What is in your sample kit?

- When you visualize your work in the most perfect environment, where is it?

- What does your website look like and how will it get done?

# Promotion—How Do I Tell People About My Stuff?

You don't have to spend lots of money. You're not McDonald's and even if you were, once you had those Golden Arches, you wouldn't have to spend a lot more to advertise. But you are going to have to invest some time and energy. It is vitally important that you understand who your customer is, what they feel and how they think, in order to communicate effectively with them.

- Now that you know what you love to do, you have to be able to tell people about it. You can start by developing your "90 second elevator speech." Write, paint, collage what it is that you love about your product and edit it down to something you can say to everyone you meet within 90 seconds.

- Write down 5 things you can do to get the word out about how special what you are doing is and then do them.

- Tell everyone you know about what you are doing. Who do you have to talk to, email, telephone, send cards to?

- You know how to make friends and influence others—make them feel good about themselves. What are some of your winning techniques?

- What is your elevator speech? or martini speech, or trying on shoes speech? Practice it with your support group to get their opinions.

**She knew if she kept her mind focused on her goals she would reach them. Giving up was not an option.**

## It's Market Day!

*Invent and explain in detail what the day will look like, feel like, taste like! Write down your victories!*

# Ideas for Marketing and Promotion

**Do some kind of marketing and promotion every day—put it in your daytimer!!!! Word of mouth can be your least expensive and most valuable marketing tool. It can also be your worst if people are saying not so great things— always know what they're saying and if it's negative approach them to find out what you can do to change their experience.**

• Research what each of your customers like and don't like. Understanding what they want and need allows you to solve their problem. Have a contact sheet listing their preferences so you can call them when you get something in that you know they will like and for reference when you are talking to them.
• Send personal hand written thank you notes, small thank you gifts, samples of your product.
• Find out what your customers need help with, offer help and send information that you think might help with a little note attached.
• Volunteer at something that brings you joy and that could create business leads.
• Make donations of your product to local charities, radio shows.
• Go talk to people whom you admire for what they are doing and get advice—everyone likes to be thought of as an expert in their field.
• Become an expert in your own field and represent yourself to your customers and to the media as the person to go to when they need information in your field of expertise. There are outlets on the net where journalists list what their needs are and you can contact them if you are a match.
• Mentor someone—giving back not only feels great, it also teaches you how to teach.
• Join networking opportunities like the Chamber of Commerce, women's organizations and shared interest groups.
• Talk to your local everybody—radio stations, newspapers, stores, groups, schools, clubs.
• Develop a contact media list—you can buy a media directory, order mailing labels or have a company send a press release out for you.
• Use press release and press kits—I worked for a not-for-profit in a huge city. We did press releases, addressed to the right person, to all the different media outlets in our area. We explained that we were going to have a person with a developmental disability deliver them lunch on a specific day. We followed up with a phone call, got the lunches donated, enlisted volunteers to go with the person and delivered a press kit telling all about our organization. It was a great success and we got on radio, television and in newspapers.
• Write a press release about something you are doing, get it into your local newspaper, put it on the Internet and your website, and send it to your customers and email list.
• Enter articles in e-zines—check out www.ezinearticles.com.
• Look for public speaking opportunities—check out conferences in your area of expertise or develop your own workshops.
• Offer customers exclusive rights in their area for your product/service.
• Be accessible.
• Get a website (you can do one yourself cheaply and easily). Don't get scared – trust me you're talking to a technophobe. Design a "sticky" website which basically means a site that people

want to hang around in. You need to have an e-commerce site where people can buy your stuff. What's most important in a website is that it have great content which generates a sense of community. You need to update regularly and print the address on EVERYTHING including your email signature. Look for other websites that you can link to. Make it EASY for them to find what they're looking for.

- Develop your own blog (again lots of great info out there about how to build or browse blogs) or go onto other people's blogs and contribute—you can't promote your product but you can put your contact information at the bottom of your contribution. Find on-line discussion groups to join. Make sure search engines can find your website. Encourage visitors to register with you so you can build your email database.
- Become an expert in your field. I know someone who was an expert in one particular classic car and he had invented a part for that car. He frequented a particular blog where people talked about that car. He was able to answer questions and because he was honest and helpful people went to his website by the droves. He is now one happy millionaire. The part sold for $9.99!
- Make a checklist of any objections or concerns a customer may have and be sure you can answer them.
- Keep a file of marketing and promotional ideas you love that other people have done.
- Brainstorm with other people and keep the ideas in a file.
- Conduct a survey for your customers, friends, media, vendors to get their feedback and ideas.
- Learn about viral marketing, which is done usually through email.
- Host an open house and have a speaker that is of interest to your community.
- Have raffles on special occasions.
- Co-promotions—Collaborate with other businesses to put on events.
- Hand out flyers, put up posters, send out newsletters to prospects (past and present), vendors, colleagues and trade publications, quarterly. MAKE IT INTERESTING AND NEWSWORTHY using tips, how to articles, customer stories, photos, milestones, new products, interviews, regular columns. Put these on your website and keep them archived for people to read.
- Ask customers for referrals.
- Get testimonials from happy customers.
- Always follow-up when you say you will.
- Be fair and honest and generous.
- Be kind to the people who work for and with you and ask them for suggestions.
- Create an advisory board who can give you great advice and leads.
- Make a list of everyone you know and ask for their support in specific ways.
- Collect, file and make use of the business cards of others.
- ALWAYS carry business cards with you and be ready to hand them out—place them everywhere allowed that they would be effective. There is nothing that makes one doubt your professionalism more than your having to make an excuse for not having a business card.
- Network, network and oh yeah, NETWORK!

*The future depends entirely on what each of us does every day.*
*Gloria Steinhem*

# Creating Sales Tools—Ideas

**Shiloh Sophia McCloud**

- create a sales binder for in-house and one for sharing
- design your look for business cards/brochures/catalogs/web
- set up phone system and voice mail, a toll free number is recommended
- price sheet/order form/receipts - make them yourself
- design order packages, 1, 2 and 3 options with bestsellers etc...
- photos with products or services provided - professional is best
- testimonials page - develop this as you go, add to web page
- develop sales statistics for products - track as you go
- photo and bio of artist/entrepreneur- create your legend
- create sales pitches 1-5 options depending on who you talk to
- how to place an order - how to make a sale - how to fulfill
- benefits page - what are they buying it for - make a list

- company procedure - how will you operate when sales happen
- basic contracts - who and what do you need to protect?
- delivery of goods/product or services - how does it happen
- customer service procedures/client follow up
- what will you pay yourself?
- when and how?
- set goals weekly, monthly, yearly and for five years or more
- know what it takes to meet those goals in real numbers
- work with your customer to agree upon a next action step called "close."

# Sales: Be Bold. Be Brave. Be Beautiful.

**Shiloh Sophia McCloud**

Here's the thing. We have to get in front of people. Whether it is on the Internet or in person. If you are selling a product or service it is about the folks. For some of us it will be about quantity, for some quality and for some it may be a single transaction that takes them to success. The most important thing in sales, in my opinion, is being present and interested in your customer. To create a space for their need or want to be expressed comfortably. We want to give then space, and let them choose what they want on their own, while providing everything they need to make their decision and feel comfortable about it. Enthusiasm and care are the other components to making a sale that feels like a win-win-win. Notice the third win. It means they will be coming back.

**Integrity**

One of the essential keys in the sales world is to get them to purchase more at the time of the visit and to buy again more often. But since we are in the women's paradigm, it is a fine line between convincing and making an authentic sale based on the actual need and want of the customer. Folks are open to suggestion, so integrity is called for here. It may be challenging, because you really want the sale. My approach is to pray for what is best to occur. And if I believe in what I am selling, then that should not be a conflict of interest. People buy for a need or a want and it is great if your offering can address both of those things at the same time.

There are all these fancy statistics about the number of brochures and calls one needs to make before a YES happens. This has always kind of scared me—I have to do *that* much in order to get a result? No thank you! I think a lot of folks feel the same way! Which is one of the reasons a niche market is so important because it decreases the space between sales. For example, if I go to sell paintings at an art show with hundreds of artists and tens of thousands of customers, I might make less than if I went to a women's conferences with 300 women—because they are my audience. So how can you get in front of YOUR audience? Ask this question all the time. Think about what is really needed based on the times we are in.

**Specializing**

When I work with women in the Heart of the Visionary workshops we talk a lot about specializing services. Artists and healers don't like this conversation very much, because they think it means a compromise. I, on the other hand, don't mind if a customer wants my painting to match her leopard bedspread! If someone is an unknown folk musician and they want to make a living with music, I might suggest that they make a CD to be used during massage therapy or healing modalities. That would be a specific customer: the massage therapist and their client. Then those people will actually care about your folk songs. And do both. Do the folk concert that is your heart's desire and do the other work. Living our passion is often mixed with doing what needs to be done to keep the flame burning. When I work with massage therapists, I ask them to market through specializing—that does not mean they have to do ALL special. But what if their service was to work with women after surgery? or after loss? It would address these pockets of need and want. And you can have a lot of pockets and you just market to them a little differently. What will catch the eye of that particular person?

We need to get over our procrastination and make those follow up calls. Just do it. So you will offend some folks. But you will win some too. Now, I rarely make a cold call, most of my calls are above cold but not up to luke warm. I challenge myself to make at least three, then I get the hang of it and realize it is not so bad after all. I will even share my concern with the other person, "I wasn't sure if I should call you, but then I thought..." ALWAYS ask if they have a few minutes to talk and if they say no, then you can ask when to call back and then the call won't be so cool. But if they say yes, they have the time, then they are making a subtle commitment to hear you out. Be generative with your voice, not bubbly like Calistoga, but round and full like a cup of tea with honey. Keep your voice steady and non-hurried while being efficient. Be interested in them, get them to talk about themselves—and don't just give lip service—really care. Interest and caring can be authentically generated. Be present with them in the moment and you will find that you actually *do* care about them. Just because you want something from them - a sale - does not mean you are taking from them. Often you are in the position of the giver. This attitude of abundance and having something to give will create an environment of ease whether it is on the phone or in person.

**Customizing**

Why not make it custom? Why not give the customer what they want? Why not design your product or offering for them? I feel I make every painting for someone specific and I am caring for it until they come for it. This is really how it is for me and for them. The customer is there and they want what you have. Believe that they are always on their way to you! And when they come, be ready with your elevator speech. I was thinking we could call it, at-the-shoe-rack speech or something girlie. But the point is you have 90 seconds to say something about you - making it as simple as possible. My latest approach is a 45 second elevator speech and the other 45 are for me to ask them about themselves. I feel I am always ready for the next customer. I am not waiting but actually anticipating. When we open the gallery and sweep the walk and get the place ready, we are making a space for an exchange to happen.

**E-Marketing**

Be rigorous about getting e-mails addresses. Keep a little book on you at all times for business cards and to get e-mail addresses. Follow up within a week. Create e-mails offering your work, but GIVE value. Don't just expect folks to clamor for your thing; give them something to grab onto, something for free right now. I always have a new poem and image at the top of my e-mails which is TRULY designed to bless my community. And if they take the time to read it and care about it, they might look at something I am offering like a workshop or painting. Because now there is some degree of connection, they have a sense of who I am from my offering and so it is easier to say yes to what I am providing.

**Be Bold** about sharing your work. **Be Brav**e about asking for the sale. **Be Beautiful** so that your inner and outer light radiates that you are who you say you are. If you BE the person they want to be around, they are more likely to consider your offering.

Let's face it. Sales is hard. Folks say all the time how much they hate salespeople. Ouch! Who, might I ask, is not selling something? Everyone who works is selling, in one way or another. I am working to create a culture within Cosmic Cowgirls where there is truly a culture of networking. Of offering our services to one another. That this is not something bad or wrong or pushy. You might need a coach and that coach might need a web-site. Let's find out about each other and share services, for cash and barter. The thing that makes sales so hard is the combination of our resistance meeting the resistance of the other person. If I stop being in resistance I've conquered half the difficulty. What would it be like if we really wanted to sell? Really liked offering our stuff? And it was not a compromise? Do the personal work that is going to make you WANT to make your work available. And then, ask for the sale! What have you got to lose? A lot. If you don't ask, you will never know. Folks can say no. You don't have to babysit their yes; if they say yes, Celebrate! Check in and be excited immediately. Congratulate them. Tell them you are grateful. Get INTO it!

Now it is time for your sales challenge. Are you ready? I want you to make five calls a day for five days. Are you open? This could mean calling friends, cold calling, or handing out brochures. Just force yourself to get out there! Even if you don't have it solid yet, doing this will show you right away what to do and what not to do. Sales is one of those things I encourage you to do a research date on. There are SO many sales books out there and tons of Internet sites. Do your homework. Sometimes just one tip is the right one for you. Lately the tips I have been working with are about creating added value in each exchange and matching my offerings to meet folks where they are financially. So I am increasing what they get, while adjusting my pricing/services to meet a current reality. Imagine LOVING calling folks. LOVING getting sales.

*Imagination is the highest kite one can fly. Lauren Bacall*

A Challenge

**DO THIS:**

**MAKE FIVE SALES CALLS A DAY for FIVE DAYS**

# Know Your Business

## Nancy Ballard

I succeeded in my business because I really, really, really believed in my business. I knew I was offering a service that would help my clients and change their lives. This made selling easy. Learn everything there is to know about your product or service and go on line to check out your competition. Call to hear their sales pitch, pricing, etc. That said, minimize your competition by personalizing your services and products. Provide a product like no other. Make what you have to offer unique.

With regard to pricing, charge for what you do and charge what you are worth. Never apologize for your price or try to explain it. Feel confident about your fees - if you are not, your customers will know it, and not have confidence in you. In my business, I was known as the dollar lady. Every service had its price and my clients knew it. They were grateful and happy to pay for the services I provided.

Advertise. Word of mouth is best, but you need to get the attention of a mouth or two to get started. Make it easy for clients to sign up. If possible, let them 'taste it' - whether a product or a service - for free. When I had my business I invited potential clients to try my service for a day - free of charge - and, they were hooked!

Since you may not get a second chance to make a first impression, ensure your presentation is exactly as it should be - neat and pretty. I always think things look best 'tied with a bow,' meaning, do something that represents the uniqueness of you. That first impression includes being prepared - be able to answer questions. and, if you don't know the answer, don't make one up. Let your client know you will get back to them, then follow up! Have your paper work ready, contracts prepared, billing in place, business cards, etc.

To look professional you must be professional and, be yourself. Know that whether you provide a service, a product, or both, often what you are selling is yourself, so let your clients see who you really are. Get personal. Write thank you notes. Follow up and follow through. Respond. Make, answer and return phone calls and email. Let your clients know that you care. Let them know that you appreciate them as much as they appreciate you. Consider hosting a party for your clients once a year - they all meet and share wonderful stories - about you! The saying that the "customer is always right" is true - even when they are wrong. Listen for what they think went wrong and make it right. Compensate. Common courtesy and sincere interest apply. Listen more than you speak. Never assume - ask questions. Be respectful - not just of your clients, but of yourself.

Have fun. Live in gratitude. And remember: There's no such thing as "I can't." That simply means "I won't."
Go with "I will" and you can do it!

# Passionate Sales and Customer Service

## Julie Lampros Trad

I remember my very first job (although I would like to add for the record I started babysitting at the ripe, pubescent age of 12 years old, parents LOVED me because I LOVED their kids and I would unload their dishwasher.) But back to my very first "real" job. I worked at a neighborhood drugstore where once after a certain pay period I ended up owing the drugstore money because of all of the L'Oreal make-up and chocolate I bought with my employee discount. Ever since then, in every sales job I have had, there have been three main factors that have helped me to be successful.

Make sure you believe in and are passionate about what you are selling. Passion is contagious. When you are passionate about your product, this comes through to your customers. One of the major things which differentiates you from your competitor is how you come across. If you don't have passion, excitement and belief in your product then why should they buy it? If you don't feel these things then it's time to move on. Better things lie ahead. Just have faith and move on.

Be an active listener. Have you ever noticed that most people love to talk about themselves or their business? Of course, some are more this way than others, but even I have to admit, I love it when someone shows an active interest in *moi*! Have a strategy. Ask lots of questions. Get clear about their needs. Then show them how your products are perfect for them based on what they have been telling you is important. If you don't have anything you honestly think can help them, it's not a failure to be truthful about this and then walk away with grace. The Divine Feminine works in such mysterious ways. Who knows, maybe you will do business with them in the future or they know someone you can help now. Even if you get a "no thank you" you are still networking which always is a very good thing in sales.

Be impeccable with your word. Follow through for your customers or prospects shows a lot of integrity. When you say you will do something, then do it! At my last job, it took me a year of soul searching and praying to realize that it was time for me to move on. However, I have several impressive letters of recommendation written by surgeons and administrators from this time of my career. I remember how surprised I was by the huge disappointment several of them expressed when I told them I was leaving. I know that my customer service and follow through was appreciated and this played a huge role in how highly I was regarded. Follow through is one of the easiest things you can do in sales and look like a rock star for doing it! (Okay, maybe not a rock star but a very juicy sales professional with lots of moxie! No wait, really, I think it's better to say a rock star. Maybe along the lines of Stevie Nicks or Sheryl Crow? Okay, enough, but you get my point.) There is no secret formula for being successful in sales and good at customer service. It's about believing in yourself and believing in your product while having fun doing it. When that stops, it's time to move on and make room for something even better to fill the space.

*I am a woman above everything else.*

*Jacqueline Kennedy Onassis*

# Marketing and Promotion Action Plan

*List dates, names, phone numbers and goals!*

All the things I love is what my business is all about.
Martha Stewart

# Branding

## Mary MacDonald

Branding expresses who you are and how others perceive you and is the foundation for all of your communications. By using consistent messages you build trust and credibility with your customers. You do not want to confuse people about who you are or what you do. You must identify yourself in the marketplace consistently and clearly, building an emotional connection between your product and the people who buy it. Make it relevant and then use consistent logos, pictures, tag lines, colors and themes. Be creative and original. Be yourself - branding tells people what you stand for. Think about a well known brand and what you like about them.

• How do you want people to think of you, the qualities and skills of your company?

• What experience do you want your customer to have with you - describe in detail.

• List 5 adjectives you want your customers to say to describe your product/service/you.

• Develop a style that is all your own whether in the way you dress, the colors you choose, the way you decorate your spaces, the way you communicate. What's your style?

• What feeling do you want to convey to your customers on your website, business cards, letterhead - warm and fuzzy, crisp and clean, irreverent and fun?

• Ask yourself what you would be if you were: type of music; movie star; type of food; color; historical era?

# Premium Brands

### Is It Right for Your Business?

### Dori Etter

One of the keys to long-term business success is diversifying and creating multiple streams of income. There are lots of ways to accomplish this and I'm going to talk about one that is simple and effective—Premium Branding.

Look at the Toyota Highlander and a Lexus RX. They look strikingly similar! That's because Lexus is Toyota's "premium brand." So what, huh? Well, Toyota spent millions of dollars on the design, production setup and training for their Highlander...and they sell for a base price of around $27,000.

The beauty of the Lexus RX is that the design and manufacturing setup costs are a fraction of the costs Toyota incurred to bring the Highlander into production. But, with a few tweaks and additions, they sell this model for a base price of $39,000. That is almost one and a half times what they charge for the Highlander, but the Highlander "carries" most of the costs!

This is a classic example of Premium Branding and there are thousands of others, in areas from beer and vodka to chocolate, clothing and household cleaning products. Why would Toyota and others do this? By designating a "premium brand" you gain access to different market segments without going to the expense of creating an entirely different business or product. The point is to stay in your identified business, but look for markets you haven't reached yet.

As you are defining your product or service offering, think about how you might be able to modify it just a bit to broaden your ideal market, or even appeal to a completely different market segment. Then, look for the "economies of scale" like Toyota did, by utilizing the already existing production line for the Lexus brand. This is how you keep costs down...particularly those costs relevant only to the premium brand.

To begin to think about your premium brand, start by thinking about your primary niche market. Who are they? What do they do for a living? For fun? What is their income bracket? How important is your product to their life and lifestyle? Describe their personal life, professional life, the things they do, the places they go. Now, look at that list and think of the people that you know or know of, who don't fit into that description. Is there some feature, addition, or shift to your offering that would appeal to these other people as well? Now, you are thinking about other branding opportunities! Take some time to think about your brand and create some premium ideas. Add them to your menu.

**Niche Market: Who are your clients?**

**Here are a few examples to get things started:**

| **If you:** | **Consider a premium for:** |
|---|---|
| Deliver workshops | Workshops offered at resort destinations |
| Make jewelry | Precious stones in place of crystal or semi-precious |
| Make food | Premium presentation in packaging, portion size, or quality (i.e. all organic ingredients) |
| Operate a retail store | Private shopping hours or personalized buying |

As you go about establishing this new line of business, don't forget to measure its performance separately from your other offerings. By properly identifying the unique costs and measuring your revenues against them, you ensure you are actually accomplishing what you are intending… higher margins. And, higher margins mean more money for your bottom line!

However you look at it, premium branding allows you to reach more customers and provide diversification to your income stream. Who knows, with time and planning, you may find that your premium offering is in far more demand than your initial offering and turn your business accordingly. Or, the opposite may occur, but, either way, you have started to think about your business from a long-term viewpoint.

So while you are visioning and dreaming and growing, it is never too soon to really look at things like improving your brand. Let it be a part of the game of business, instead of something to resist. It really can be fun! And it is very important! And so are you!

# Marketing Specifics

## Mary MacDonald

Although this might look a lot like the Visionary Business Plan, it is important that you have detailed strategies to market your offerings and yourself, and you need a clear picture of the direction you will take. Also, you want to see that accountability is built into your plan so that it isn't just so much fluff, but actually catalyzes action and creates measurable results.

The best way to achieve this is: Define the key strategies needed to arrive at your Goals and Objectives. What end result do you want? If it's to sell more paintings, then identify what you need to do. Identify your ideal market as to age, gender, location, lifestyle, interests, etc. and create the Key Messages and Benefits you want to communicate to your audience. Determine where and how you are going to Tell Your Story—advertise, press, web. Assign specific tasks to those responsible for executing your Strategies using your Tactics within established Timelines. Budget how much money you are willing to spend. Evaluate the results.

**1. Measurable Goals and Objectives:**
Measurable Goals and Objectives define the ultimate outcomes you want for your business and what impact it will have. An example would be to increase traffic to your website by 10% over the next year with the impact being that you would have increased revenue. When you are very honest in measuring your successes and failures, you can make better decisions. List top five goals:

**2. The Ideal Market:** (commonly called, **Target)**
Make a list of those specific to your Ideal Market, which is the audience you want to reach. You can't be all things to all people, so in order to make the most of your budget, your energies and your time, you must be specific about who your audience is. An example would be to select single women, between the ages of 25 and 40, living in the city, who are interested in spiritual growth. Design your strategies to meet their needs.

**3. Your Message:**

Your Message tells your current and potential customers that you have what they are looking for in a way that is consistent with your identity and Brand. An example would be the slogan, "We provide great food at great prices," accompanied by theme tone and logo showing the dish or specialty for which you are famous. What are your possible messages and slogans?

**4. Tell Your Story:**

Define where and how and with what tools you will Tell Your Story. This would include through other people and/or physical locations, such as media, trade shows, and conferences, using tools like product samples, press releases and websites. An example would be to co-create with your retail outlets advertised promotional events like what the fashion industry calls "Trunk Shows" where you make special appearances, bringing lots of merchandise and meeting their customers to enroll them in your vision. What are the components of your story?

**5. Strategies:**

Strategies are the methods with which you are going to accomplish your goals and objectives. Strategies generally fall into one or more of the following categories: market growth, deeper market penetration, getting current customers to buy more or buy more frequently, finding new markets, developing new products for new customers. An example of a strategy in response to any of these categories could be to create a high impact web site. List your strategies.

**6. Tactics:**

Tactics are specific things you need to do to accomplish the strategies you've set out. Examples would be to utilize any and all tactics, such as: hire a website designer, network by joining organizations, advertising in a local magazine, emailing customers quarterly, publishing a yearly newsletter, creating a catalog, asking for feedback from customers.

**7. Timelines:**

Prioritize your tactics and delegate responsibilities by establishing Timelines. An example would be to have Mary hire a website designer by November 5, 2008. Without timelines, the chances of getting things done are very slim.

**8. Evaluation:**

How do you know whether or not you have been successful? To make an evaluation, you must be capable of looking at the big picture and see whether or not you have accomplished your goals and/or feel good about where you are on your journey. For this you need to have defined and established a criteria for what success looks like. What does success look like for you?

Having established this context, an example of how to make use of the tools of evaluation would be to analyze traffic to your website and determine by what percentage sales have or have not increased. Make the decisions needed to implement corrections and continued growth. All of the above information will help you achieve this.

# Got Wheels?

## Reverend Ama Zenya

Time to put wheels on your vision. Put yourself in the center of a circle and draw four spokes of the wheel. Name the four quadrants: Mentors, Allies, Partners and Guides.

**Mentors:** Who's done something similar to what you are doing? How can you learn from them?
**Allies:** Who loves you and will be a cheerleader once they understand what you are doing?
**Partners:** Who will work with you on this? Note: Businesses that are shared have a greater success rate.
**Guides:** Who do you trust to give you wise, honest and discerning input when you need it?

In each quadrant write names of people you know. Then make a specific plan to share your vision and plan with each of the people you've listed. Tell them what you want from them, share your vision plan with them at the level that relates to their role. For example, with an ally, you can share the big-picture, then the places where you'll need cheerleading support, or a shoulder to cry on with someone who won't let you give up. With a partner, you'll want to go fully into your whole business plan and create shared goals and timelines. With a mentor, create a time to hear their story – what worked and what didn't? How did they overcome their challenges? And with a guide, share your heart – both what has led you to your vision and where you're afraid of getting off track. Ask for their sense of how this vision fits for you and what you need to pay special attention to. On your "Got Wheels?" diagram, create a way to note when you've enrolled one of your people and they've said, 'Yes!"

*To love what you do and feel that it matters—how could anything be more fun?*

*Katherine Graham*

# Calling All Team-mates!

**Reverend Ama Zenya**

Once you've unleashed your passion by clarifying WHAT you want to communicate, to inspire, to create with others and WHY - what are the stakes? what will happen if people don't receive what you are offering? - your next step is to build the network to make it happen. Building a business in a way that supports full access to our creativity and abundance involves redefining concepts that have been alienating. So if the word NETWORKING brings images of self-centered shmoozing, let's reclaim the core concept with our own image. What metaphor inspires you in creating connections with the people who will partner with you in this endeavor? WEAVING a tapestry, CULTIVATING a garden, GROWING an organic body. Choose your metaphor and draw it below.Put in the names and types of people that will be part of your network/tapestry/garden.

# Envisioning Your Ideal Market Community

**Reverend Ama Zenya**

Make a drawing that expresses the lives and dreams of the people you want to reach. Your business is the avenue for connecting with hundreds and thousands of people. Who are they? Envision your clientele very specifically. Where do they live and work? How do they spend their time? their money? What matters to them? How will what you offer make a difference to them? Where will you reach them?

As you create the tapestry, meditate on these questions: What is the gift at the heart of my visionary business/project? What real need does the gift at the heart of my business serve? Then see your business as a vibrant life-giving connection between you and them. Draw a heart representing you and your project in the middle of this page. Then draw rays of light coming from your visionary heart. To Who, What and Where are the rays connected? Put words on the rays to express and represent who you are reaching.

*What I know is that if you do work that you love,*

*and the work fulfills you, the rest will come.*

*Oprah Winfrey*

# Mapping Connectivity

**Reverend Ama Zenya**

Put yourself at the center of the page and then make circles around you for all the different spheres of your life: neighborhood, high school, hobbies, places you've lived and worked, spiritual community, etc. Around each circle write the names of people you know in that sphere of your life. If you know that a certain person is linked to another sphere of people, draw a line that connects her or him to another circle. For example, you may know Denise from college, and you also know that she's an avid bicyclist, so put 'Bicyclists' in a circle next to her name. As you draw your map, don't worry if you're writing names of people you don't know well, or haven't spoken to in ages or folks you already wrote about on the previous exercises. Who knows, your business may be a catalyst to connect or reconnect. And don't limit yourself to people who you can see being involved in your vision. For now, include everyone. This free brainstorming will get your creative imagination flowing. All of these practices are designed to get you to connect with who you know and how you can help them - and they can help you!

*Remember, no one can make you feel inferior without your consent.*

*Eleanor Roosevelt*

# Problems Are Possibilities

## Reverend Ama Zenya

OK, Visionary Woman, here we go! You're stepping forward and then something comes up. I don't know if you've seen the saying, "I try to take one day at a time, but sometimes a whole bunch of days attack me at once." And sometimes it feels like the problems are overwhelming.

So, check this out: Someone once said, "In Life, There are Problems." The key is not to make a problem out of the fact that there are problems. Of course there are! Life is a process of relating to things that can be called 'problems.' Your life takes the shape of the problems that you choose. Dr. Martin Luther King Jr. began with a focus on the problem of racial and economic injustice in the US and he galvanized a national movement to end segregation. Mahatma Ghandi focused on the problem of colonial disenfranchisement of the people of India by inspiring thousands of people to make their own fabric and gather their own sea salt. Oprah has focused on the problem of alienation in the US by creating ways to encourage communication and connection. 2004 Nobel Laureate Wangari Mathai took on the problem of soil erosion in Africa and inspired thousands of people to plant trees.

When you decide to start your own business, you'll have the problems that come with starting a business, as compared to the problems that come with working a job. Be ready by having a clear, ready answer for this. What are you doing? What is your real problem? I'm asking you that with a smile. In the face of the problem that you're taking on, what possibilities are you creating for yourself and other people? Embrace the problems that really fire you up and let your business be a way to transform them into new possibilities.

## Medicine Woman by Shiloh Sophia McCloud

Medicine Woman holds tools for healing in her magic basket.
She dances in the moonlight and sings her prayers.
Medicine Woman knows herbs and signs, stars and sums.
She is between maiden and mother, mother and crone.
She is a the part in each of us that knows deeply.
That sees clearly. That listens between worlds.
Medicine woman cannot be domesticated, at all, ever.
Even when we don't recognize her, she is always here.
She has butterflies in her hair and gold cowgirl boots.
She can be seen at the movies with teenage girls on Friday night.
She may get a tattoo, in the Mission, of the Guadalupe on her
bicep or the sacred heart of Jesus on her right shoulder.
You may catch a glimpse of her as she roller skates
through Central Park.
She may teach a workshop on tantra or the geometry of accounting or raw food or revolution.
She makes potions, jams, sopa and lotions. She definitely runs with wolves and wolfey women.
She is fierce about many things. She is compassionate about almost everything.
She plays hard. She takes action. She tree sits. She pays for everything with cash.
She may paint glitter on her toe nails. Just don't think you have her figured out.
She may let her armpit hair grow and her mustache too.
She is the place within us that wants it all. And wants to give it all up.
She swims naked in the ocean. She rides motorcycles up the coast.
She paints, writes, dances, dreams and has multiple income streams.
She is medicine woman. She heals the unexpressed in us.
She asks the question - Who are you not being?
If you want to find her - she is always at Market Place
in the early morning with her baskets of goods.
Hawking her wares. Like Wisdom she calls out into the streets.
Her life is her own. She is on her own. She likes it that way.

# BUSINESS

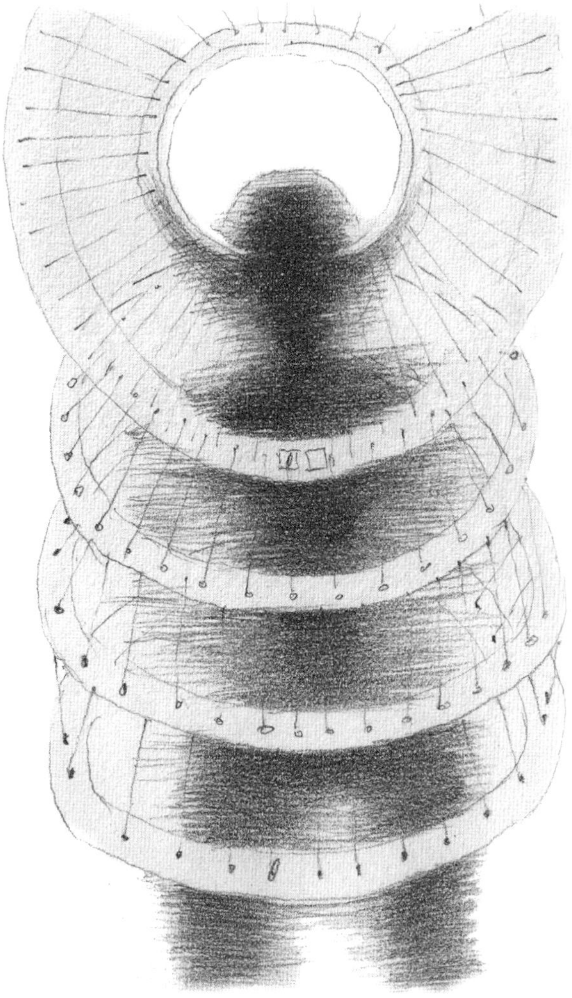

## The Power of Strategy

**Mary MacDonald**
**WITH**
**Dori Etter**
**Illustrations By Shiloh Sophia McCloud and Sue Hoya Sellars**

# Why A Visionary Business Plan

Now you begin the journey of entwining your dreams and visions with the excitement of action. As you dance these steps remember to imbue the choreography with your values, your heart and your own rhythm. We want to enjoy our days, surround ourselves with people who "get us," learn how to be at peace with who we are and with great glee enjoy the energy of the gobs of money we are receiving for what we love to do. So remember to be as honest with yourself as possible about the resources, the skills and the benefits of your offering - the value you bring and who you want to be involved with in your next evolution. And with that knowledge you can now begin to make it a reality. Let any "imperfections" inform you and guide you, embrace them, don't shun them or let them shut you down. A visionary business plan is an important and exciting tool when you are passionate about an idea you want to bring to fruition. Even if you are unsure about the direction you want to take it helps you flesh out what it is you want to create. If you want corporate America to give you money you will need at least a 15 page Business Plan. Otherwise you can use a great one-page template such as www.onepagebusinessplan.com.

After having an "AHA!" moment of what you want to do with your life, it is important to take the creative vision to see if it is a viable idea, and a Business Plan will help you get there. Doing the work of creating a Business Plan will enable you to have clarity about what you want to do, how to go about achieving it, how long it will take and what it will cost. A Visionary Business Plan is like a road map that shows you where you are and how to get to where you want to be. If you don't care where you're going, it doesn't matter how you get there, but that's not for a visionary woman!

By developing a business plan you will demonstrate that you have a thorough understanding of your offerings and the people you plan to serve, that your strategic and financial goals are SMART (specific, measurable, achievable, realistic, targeted) and you have the right people and experience to make your vision a reality. The Business Plan answers the questions: Who, What, Why, Where and When. Your business plan is your guide to planning, launching and growing your business. When developing it, be clear and concise, be compelling, use simple, active language and avoid jargon.

There are many wonderful resources that teach how to build the best plan for your purpose but don't just copy someone else's - be creative. Once you are finished drafting the Vision Plan it is helpful to have others give you input on what you've written. Just working with a friend or family member can be enlightening. If you can afford it, get professional help to build the plan or have a professional look at it when you're finished. A Visionary Business Plan is a great tool if you use it, measure your success against it and revitalize it as you go along.

*Our visions begin with our desires.*
*Audre Lorde*

# I have the power To Create A Visionary Business Plan Reflecting Who I Am!

*This is a big girl section. To get into the mood, feeling and mindset write a Declaration Affirmation*

# A Passionate Mission Statement

### *Put the Sparkle in Your Sizzle*

### Mary MacDonald

A Mission Statement declares to the world your reason for being. A passionate Mission Statement sings and dances and paints a vivid picture to your customers, your staff, and your potential investors of why your offering exists. It defines the essence of your business and focuses you on your essential purpose - your reason for being.

A mission statement can be short and succinct or it can be a few paragraphs long. Let it state what you will do to ensure your vision is reached based on your values, beliefs and your audience. A good Mission Statement guides your decisions, actions and how you communicate who you are and what you do. Therefore, spend in-depth time in creating your Mission Statement, when you are stymied by what decision to make you go back to your Vision and your Mission Statements and make the decision that follows their path. If your Mission Statement says that your mission is to support women entrepreneurs to become multimillionaires, then when a male offers you a substantial amount of money to take him on as a client, although extremely tempting since the money will pay your rent for the next six months, you are able to be very clear on who your mission serves. Either that, or you realize you want to change your mission.

Your mission statement gives you a strong sense of your purpose, which allows you to be 100% committed to what you want to achieve. You need to believe totally in what you are doing or you won't be able to convince others to believe in you. Research shows that companies with meaningful mission statements are more successful than ones that are only profit driven.

When brainstorming ideas for your Mission Statement ask yourself the following questions: What values are most important to me? What value am I offering my community? Is it innovative or unique? How am I unique? What problem do I solve? Who does my offering serve? Who do I want to serve? What tangible benefit do I offer? What intangible benefit do I offer? Am I offering a service or a product? What business do I want to be in? What needs in the world do I meet? What single phrase would describe my offering? How do I want to conduct my business? How do I want to be perceived? Keep asking yourself WHY.

Your Mission Statement is the brains of your company that informs your heart and soul how to move forward. Involve everyone in the process. If you are a one-woman shop get input from people who care about you. Read other people's Mission Statements. Paint a picture that will inspire action and be meaningful to your customers.

Once you do the work on the Mission Statement you will have answered many of the questions needed for your business and marketing plans. **Research Date: Mission Statement**

# Passionate Mission Statement

*What you will do matters. All you need is to do it.*
*Judy Grahn*

# VISIONARY EXECUTIVE SUMMARY

*The Executive Summary is the compelling sales pitch for the rest of your plan, enticing the reader and summing up what you're all about.*

*The Executive Summary appears first but write it last, after you have done all the other pieces of your plan. The Summary is a one-two page, brief summary of your entire plan which should entice your reader to go further. One of its purposes is to enable prospective lenders to quickly obtain a sense of what you are all about, why they should be interested and whether they should read beyond this section. Include the following categories and take notes in the space provided:*

- Description of your business.

- Overview of the market for your offerings.

- Management expertise of your key dream team.

- Strategic directions you are taking.

- Visionary Executive Summary Notes:

# VISIONARY EXECUTIVE SUMMARY

# Company Summary

*The company summary answers the questions of who you are and why you exist.*

- What is the background of your company, its history and, if new, how did it come to be?

- What makes you unique?

- How do you create value and what will make your business successful?

- State core competencies: What you do well, what your customers rely on you for and address any pressing need they have on their wish list and how you are going to fulfill them.

- How are you organized? Sole proprietorship, Partnership, LLC, corporation.?

- Company Summary: Put it all together. Tell about the "you of it."
  Show how your business will impact for good.

# Company Summary

# Market Analysis

*Market analysis answers the questions of how external factors affect you, who is selling a similar product or service, who your potential customers are and why they will buy what you are offering.*

- Who are your potential customers?
- Why do they come to you – loyalty, good service, convenience?
- What is their motivation to buy your offerings?
- Include demographic information of your potential customers.
- How large is the market?
- Is your market a niche market?
- Identify and evaluate what's hot that may affect your market.
- What are the external market influences: economic, demographic?
- Who are your competitors? What is your advantage?
- Give statistics or researched data (i.e. news articles) to back up your information.

# Market Analysis

# Dream Team

*This answers the question of why you will be a success based on how fabulous you and the people around you are.*

- Describe your dream team: Who they are – their backgrounds, experience, education and strengths, as well as why you think they will be instrumental in making this business succeed.

- Describe other players involved in your company: consultants, advisors, directors and anyone to whom you outsource business that plays a key role in your company.

# Dream Team

*Who makes up your dream team? Hiring or partnering with someone because you like them or they "feel right" doesn't necessarily spell success. The people on your team need to align to your company values. You can teach people how to answer a phone – you can't teach them how to have values. Partners don't necessarily have the same livelihood objectives – be clear about each other's expectations. Having a contract with partners and employees is not about distrust or disrespect. Precise details establish clear expectations and agreement and avoid carelessness in our relationships.*

- Make a list of the knowledge and skills needed to make your company thrive:

- What skills are "must haves?" What are "nice to have?"

- What are you willing to teach/train? What you are not willing to teach/train?

- How will your staff be rewarded?

- How will you know they have achieved the results you require?

# STRATEGIC PLAN

*The Strategic Plan is the substance of your Visionary Business Plan because it shows that you know how you are going to proceed in order to achieve your goals.*

- Marketing Plan: How you plan to get your offerings to the market you have identified.

- What your offerings look like: packaging, logo, letterhead.

- How you will add value to your offerings over and above the competition.

- How you will sell your products and/or services.

- Measures you will be taking to realize Objectives.
  Example: Find 4 new retail outlets by _____.

- What Strategies you are taking to build this company/department/activity over time. Example: Build community networks.

- Statements of Plans being activated. Example: Contact potential distributors by June.

- Who will benefit/what will be improved?

# Strategic Plan

# Company Livelihood and Success

*In order for us to see the bigger picture and have better control of our lives it is essential for us as women to have an acute understanding of just how money works. You will need to do a realistic and specific projection of how much money you need for business start-up costs such as licenses, permits, insurance, equipment, office supplies; cost of production such as materials and labor; cost for rent, utilities, marketing, advertising, signs, bookkeeping and accounting, salaries and commissions. Don't let it scare you!!!*

- Describe how your company will make money and why you believe there is significant revenue opportunity.

- Do a break-even analysis—How much do you need to sell at what price to break-even? This will help you in setting your prices, along with what the market will bear. Do your research.

- You will need to complete a number of financial statements for 1-3 years.

- Balance Sheet—Assets/Liabilities: This shows what the company is worth at a specific time.

- Income (Profit and Loss) Statement—Income/Expenses: This shows whether your company is making a profit.

- Cash-Flow Projection: This shows whether the company has sufficient cash to pay bills.

- Appendices:
    - Resumes of key leaders
    - Bios of Management Staff and Other Key Participants (Consultants, etc.)
    - Letters of Reference

# Company Livelihood and Success

# THE FINANCIALS

Often, one of the big challenges for women is managing money. Research has shown us that women have less access to getting cash for their businesses then men do. Although there are over 10 million women-owned businesses in the United States only a very small percentage of those businesses earn over $1 million.

It can scare us to think about profit and loss statements, balance sheets and cash flow statements. We need to educate ourselves so we can make the best choices for ourselves by better understanding how money works. Even if you have hired someone else to do it for you, it is essential to have a working knowledge of the concepts. It gives you an advantage in business and allows you to understand where you are, where you are going and whether you can afford to go there. It gives you better control of your business, allows you to make smarter decisions and be a better manager. Also, in order to receive money from lenders you need to show them your financials in the present and at least three years out. You will also be taken more seriously with this knowledge. It would be a VERY good idea to take a basic accounting course. You can also get free help from SCORE (Service Corps of Retired Executives) through SBA (Small Business Administration.) Look for networking groups or a mentor who can help you understand the financial aspects of your life work.

First of all you need to invest in yourself. Here are some ideas that other women have used to get started. Remember to think CREATIVELY: Visit your bank and ask for a loan or get their advice on what you need to get a loan. Look for a woman banker who is innovative. You could use your mortgage as collateral. Investigate getting a micro-loan (anything under $25,000.) One company that does this is www.count-me-in.org.

- Get a partner.
- Use money you've saved for a rainy day.
- Barter your talents for something you need.
- Sell things you own – you could sell your new car and lease one.
- Get cash advances on your credit cards (although most financial people shudder at this solution although over 70% of women owned businesses finance themselves this way.)
- Borrow against your life insurance policy.
- Borrow from friends and family (another top way women finance their businesses.)
- Look at where you can save money – can you cut out one haircut a year – cancel a magazine subscription – forgo the latte – think of 5 ways you can cut expenses that can add up to you. being able to buy business cards or design a web site.
- Research the best prices.
- There are web sites where you can design business cards for free.
- Send out requests for quotes to get the best price on anything for your business.
- Go to garage sales to get a desk for your office.

- Keep your present job and build your business at night for a period of time in order to gain a long-term advantage.
- Talk to your vendors about giving you payment terms over a period of time.
- Work with your customers to get them to pay right away instead of giving terms.
- Find an angel investor - research on-line how to find and market to angel investors.
- Do your research on where the money is and how to go after it.
- Know what your start-up costs will be and then add 25% in case you run into unforeseen circumstances.

## Creative Ways I Can Raise Money

*What material success does is provide you with the ability to concentrate on other things that really matter. And that is being able to make a difference, not only in your own life, but in other people's lives.*

*Oprah Winfrey*

# Start Up Expenses List

I DEFINE MY OWN DOMAIN!

# REPORTS

Whatever you do to get your party started, here is a list of the four financial reports you will need to help you on the way and help you "talk the talk." Remember as well that you need to review your numbers on a regular basis, so put it on your schedule.

**Income Statemen**t (Profit and Loss): This is a basic format to show where your money is coming from, where you are spending money and whether or not you are making any money. This allows you to budget and forecast what your expenses. When reviewing your Income Statement you need to ask yourself questions based on the outcomes and variances;
I spent less money last month on advertising but did it reflect in lower sales the next month?

**Balance Sheet**: The Balance Sheet shows you where you stand at a particular moment of time based on your 1) assets (money, equipment and inventory) and 2) liabilities money you owe and 3) your equity is (assets minus liabilities.)

**Cash Flow Projection**: Shows you where you are getting your cash, how your cash goes out and how much money you will have at the beginning of the next week, next month or next year. Have a monthly cash flow statement for your business plan for year one and a quarterly one for years two and three. You need this to truly understand how much money you will need on a monthly basis to survive. For a bank loans officer, the Cash Flow Projection offers evidence that your business is a good credit risk and that there will be enough cash on hand to make your business a good candidate for a line of credit or short term loan.

**Break-even Analysis:** A break-even analysis is a simple way to determine how much of the product or service must be sold to generate a specific profit. After all costs attributable to bringing the product to market are deducted, each product or service yields a certain amount of profit. This profit contribution can then be divided into the "fixed costs" to determine how many units must be sold to break even.

Here's a simple example of the break-even model: The total costs of operating the business each month are $10,000. Each product the company produces can be sold for $1,000. Each product costs an average of $800 per unit to produce, sell and deliver. The profit contribution per unit is therefore $200 each. $200 is divided into $10,000 to determine the break-even point, so $10,000 divided by $200 equals 50 units. The company must therefore sell 50 units per month to break even, or approximately two units per business day. Only after the company has sold 50 units in one month does it begin to earn a profit of $200 per unit.

Conducting an accurate break-even analysis requires a careful examination and study of costs and prices in your business. You must know what your product or service costs in total to deliver to the final customer, as well as the price you can charge for the product or service. Include and deduct all miscellaneous expenses involved in operating your business.

**Example Income Statement for the Period Ending January 1, 2008:**

| | |
|---|---|
| Revenues from Sales | \$100.00 |
| Cost of Goods Sold (your productions/purchase cost) | \$ 25.00 |
| Gross Profit | \$ 75.00 |
| | |
| Operating Expenses (rent, salaries, advertising, insurance, computers, phones, marketing and everything else) | \$ 30.00 |
| Income/Profit (Gross Profit minus Expenses) | \$ 45.00 |
| Income Tax | \$ 10.00 |
| | |
| **Net Income** | \$ 35.00 |

## Profit Margin

Three other figures that you will need to know are gross margin, operating margin and net margin. They will help you talk to financial people. These numbers will show you and investors whether your company is financially viable and how much profit it can garner.

**Gross Margin:**
Divide your gross profit by your sale of offerings. In the example above (\$75.00 /\$100.00 = 75%) which gives your business has a 75% gross margin. This will allow you and investors to see your chances of growing into a profitable business. You can research acceptable national averages based on your type of business and use this comparison to both see how you compare and establish your ideal margin.

**Operating Margin:**
Take your income and divide it by your sales revenue (\$45.00/\$100.00 = 45%)

**Net Profit Margin:**
Take your net income and divide it by the sale revenue (\$35.00/\$100.00 = 35%) and this will give you your "bottom line."

The Profit and Loss Statement is usually done for a three-year period, so when are starting out, you will need to project the numbers.

*In all realms of life it takes courage to stretch your limits, express your power and fulfill your potential...it's no different in the financial realm.*

*Suze Orman*

# Sample Balance Sheet

As of December 31, 2007

| | |
|---|---|
| **ASSETS:** | |
| Current Assets (anything you can cash in for money within a year) | |
| Checking/Savings Accounts | $ 80.00 |
| Accounts Receivable ($ owed you from past sales) | $ 20.00 |
| Inventory (your saleable items currently in stock) | $100.00 |
| **Total Current Assets** | **$200.00** |
| Fixed Assets | |
| Automobile | $ 50.00 |
| Computers | $ 25.00 |
| **Total Fixed Assets** | **$ 75.00** |
| **Total Assets (Total Current Assets + Total Fixed Assets)** | **$275.00** |
| **LIABILITIES:** | |
| Current Liabilities | |
| Accounts Payable (unpaid $ you owe) | $ 30.00 |
| Credit Cards (the full balance owed) | $ 15.00 |
| **Total Current Liabilities** | **$ 45.00** |
| Long Term Liabilities | |
| Loan from Mom | $100.00 |
| **Total Long Term Liabilities** | **$100.00** |
| **Total Liabilities** | **$145.00** |
| **EQUITY:** | |
| **Retained Earnings (total assets – total liabilities)** | **$130.00** |

# SAMPLE CASH FLOW STATEMENT

For the Period Ending January 1, 2008

| | OCT | NOV | DEC |
|---|---|---|---|
| **Opening Balance** | **$ 30.00** | **$260.00** | **$150.00** |
| Source of Money: | | | |
| - Cash | $100.00 | $ 50.00 | $150.00 |
| - *Accounts Receivable | $100.00 | $ 25.00 | $100.00 |
| - Investment Income | $ 30.00 | $ 5.00 | $ 50.00 |
| - Loan | $100.00 | ----0---- | ----0---- |
| **Total Cash Received** | **$330.00** | **$ 80.00** | **$300.00** |
| | | | |
| Money Used: | | | |
| - *Accounts Payable | $ 50.00 | $ 50.00 | $100.00 |
| - Operating Expenses | $ 30.00 | $ 30.00 | $ 30.00 |
| - Income Tax | $ 10.00 | $ 10.00 | $ 10.00 |
| - New Inventory | $ 10.00 | $100.00 | $ 25.00 |
| **Total Money Used** | **$100.00** | **$190.00** | **$165.00** |
| | | | |
| **Cash Flow** (total $ received - total $ used) | $230.00 | (110.00) | $135.00 |
| | | | |
| **Cash Balance** ($ flow + opening balance) | $260.00 | $150.00 | $285.00 |

A cash flow statement is also a powerful forecasting tool that allows you to know how much cash you will have the following month, or how much money you need to come up with in order to cover your butt.

You need to understand that Revenue and Profit are different. You may be bringing in lots of cash (revenue) but not *making* money (profit). By understanding why you're not making a profit (expenses too high, not enough distribution channels, price is too low) you can then figure out how to fix it so you are bringing in a profit.

Go for it! Happy money hunting and creating! Thank you to all the women whose wonderful advice and mentoring has enabled me to understand just enough about the financial part of the business plan.

* Notes on terms and notation: (1) Accounts Receivable on a cash flow statement refers to any sales made in a previous period and paid for in this period. (2) Accounts Payable on a cash flow statement refers to any money you owed and paid to others (staff contractors, vendors) during this period. (3) Negative numbers are expressed by putting the number in parenthesis in your statement.

# Creating Revenue

## *Gross Profit Equals Revenue Minus Cost of Goods Sold*

**Dori Etter**

We've discussed at least one model for setting prices and there are others. But, once you are in business, how do you determine if your prices are enough to cover your on-going costs and what about discounting?

Setting prices can be confusing and scary…how do you ensure you can make money while still pricing to the market of consumers available to buy your products or services? A key indicator to measure is your Gross Margin. Gross Margin in often expressed as a percentage of sales.

The simple calculation is: **Gross Profit** divided by **Total Revenue** equals **Gross Margin**

Gross Profit is: **Total Revenue** minus **Costs of Goods Sold** equals **Gross Profit**

Let's start by looking at the elements of the gross margin calculation to get an understanding of how these numbers are calculated and relate to your business.

COGS stands for "Cost of Goods Sold" and is calculated as the materials and services necessary to get your product or service in "sale-able" condition. A simple example would be buying a product for resale. COGS is simply the amount of money paid for the item and the shipping to the sale point. If you are making or manufacturing a product, COGS includes all of the individual costs to do so. For example, if I'm baking cookies, it would include the cost of the ingredients and the packaging required to put it on display or deliver it to the customer. COGS for a specific period of time is best calculated by taking your cost for the beginning inventory plus the cost of any new inventory that you purchase in that period, and then subtracting the cost of any inventory that remains at the end of the period. Note: The 'cost' in this case refers to your cost not your customer's purchase price.

What COGS does not include is your "overhead" or "fixed" costs. Things like the rent on your building, the cost of buying the oven and utensils, advertising, or the cost of employees to sell the cookies.

This simple example gives you an idea of how to create your costs number for the gross margin formula. It really is up to you to decide what does or does not go into COGS, as there are grey areas. Some businesses do not include the shipping costs of raw materials (i.e., ingredients), while others do. The key is to decide your calculation and stick with it. You want to accurately reflect the difference between your beginning and ending inventory levels. (NOTE: If you are in a service industry, you will not have inventories, so COGS is as simple as the costs to deliver your service.)

The next element of the Gross Margin calculation is revenue, sometimes simplified into "sales." This is the total amount of money received into your business. This number is pretty straight-forward...how much money came in? You will, of course, have to take into account things like sales tax collected (this is NOT your revenue) and returns, but for the sake of this calculation, this total revenue number is "income" for a specific period of time. By taking revenue minus COGS, you get the first number in the formula, your "gross profit." This number, before dividing to create a percentage, is important in and of itself. This is the total dollars you have to "run your business"...to pay your employees, cover your rent & utilities and, of course, to pay yourself.

Now, one more comment about the calculation before we get to why gross margin is important.

Both your revenue and cost number should reflect the same "business" and the same time period. You could generate a "gross margin" for a day, a week, a month, a quarter, or a year. Most businesses calculate this at least monthly and if your business tends to be seasonal, you may want to calculate it more frequently.

In addition to the "time" of revenue and costs matching, you want to ensure the numbers reflect the same "line of business." You should always calculate your bottom-line gross margin, which is all of your business, but you may have different lines or brands with different cost & pricing structures and you would calculate these gross margins separately.

For example, I may bake cookies and package them for retail sale. But, I may also bake cookies for the three local catering companies. Those require different packaging and advertising, for example. For the most effective use of the gross margin calculation, I would want to know the GM of my retail line, the GM of my catering line and the overall GM of my business.

In this case, as my inventory is similar (but not the same,) I may need to allocate a percentage of inventory and purchases to each line to generate these numbers. I may have purchased 100 pounds of flour and estimate that I'm using about half for each of these lines, but my packaging costs would be separate.

Now, why is Gross Margin important?

The GM calculation is simple and quick and gives a great look at the health of your business. In addition, it can give you insight into pricing and discounting changes, as well as give you a mechanism for measuring future opportunities or generating pricing on new lines or products.

Let's use the example of the cookies again and assume these numbers for a month:

| | | | |
|---|---|---|---|
| Retail Sales: | $1500 | Retail COGS: | $850 |
| Retail Gross Profit: | $650 | Retail GM: | 43.3% |
| Catering Sales: | $3000 | Catering COGS: | $1200 |
| Catering Gross Profit: | $1800 | Catering GM: | 60% |
| Gross Profit: | $2450 | Overall business GM: 54.4% | |

If you've ever heard about Costco's Gross Margins, you would think these numbers are fantastic! Costco exists on a 2% GM. Pretty remarkable! But, most small businesses require at least 50-70% Gross Margin to survive. So, what do the numbers above tell us?

First, we generated $2450 new dollars to cover all the expenses of our business this month. That's simple and straightforward, but many businesses neglect to calculate this number for a specific time and focus only on "cash flow." Your daily inflows and bank balance may be covering your outflows, but without taking this "snapshot in time" you can't really know if the items you're selling today are covering your costs today. Calculating this number allows you to anticipate problems before they arise and most importantly, make changes that could make the difference between success and failure. By finding out now that your monthly outflows exceed your income generated, you can make changes for next month. These can include everything from reducing employee costs, managing unnecessary expenditures, or changing your pricing or product offering.

Second, there is a significant difference in the margins of these two business lines. The GM of the retail line is below an acceptable level and certainly below the target I would set for myself, while the catering business looks good both in margins and profit. These differences would have me looking at my business on several different levels.

So what questions from the above scenario will help direct business decisions or strategies?

- Is my monthly profit enough to cover expenses and continue the business?
- What costs could be reduced or removed in the short and/or long-term to improve my numbers?
- Are my pricing and discounting strategies creating the desired results?
- Is my inventory selling before it becomes old or stall? (Do I have a high enough inventory turn over?)
- What trends do I notice in my gross margin calculations over time? How do this month's numbers compare to last month's? Last year's? Are they trending towards my desired outcome?
- Should I shift the focus of business from one line to another?
- Are my costs properly allocated? Do my costs reflect the actual costs for a service or product line?

# Evolutions and Acknowledgments

*We are all so proud of you for getting to this point in your journey - how incredible! We would like you to take this page to list some of your break through thinking in regards to your business since you started. What realizations have you had, perception shifts, goals realized or created that YOU feel GREAT about!*

The duty we are called to is precise and personal—the fulfillment of our own authentic self expression—even though we may carry it out imperfectly. The imperfection is our growing edge. Reverend Ellen Grace O'Brian

Success
she said
Isn't something you do
It is someone you be
It is not somewhere you go
It is somewhere you live all the time
Oh, I said
So it is something I can choose
Even if I don't have a lot of money?
Even if I don't look great on paper?
But because....I have done good work?
Oh Yes, She said enthusiastically
You don't have to wait for approval or reports
You just have to start acting like a success
Oh, I said
You mean it is nobody's business but mine?
I can celebrate and create no matter what others say?
You got it! She said, smiling. And so, I became an overnight success!
Shiloh Sophia McCloud

# COMMUNICATION

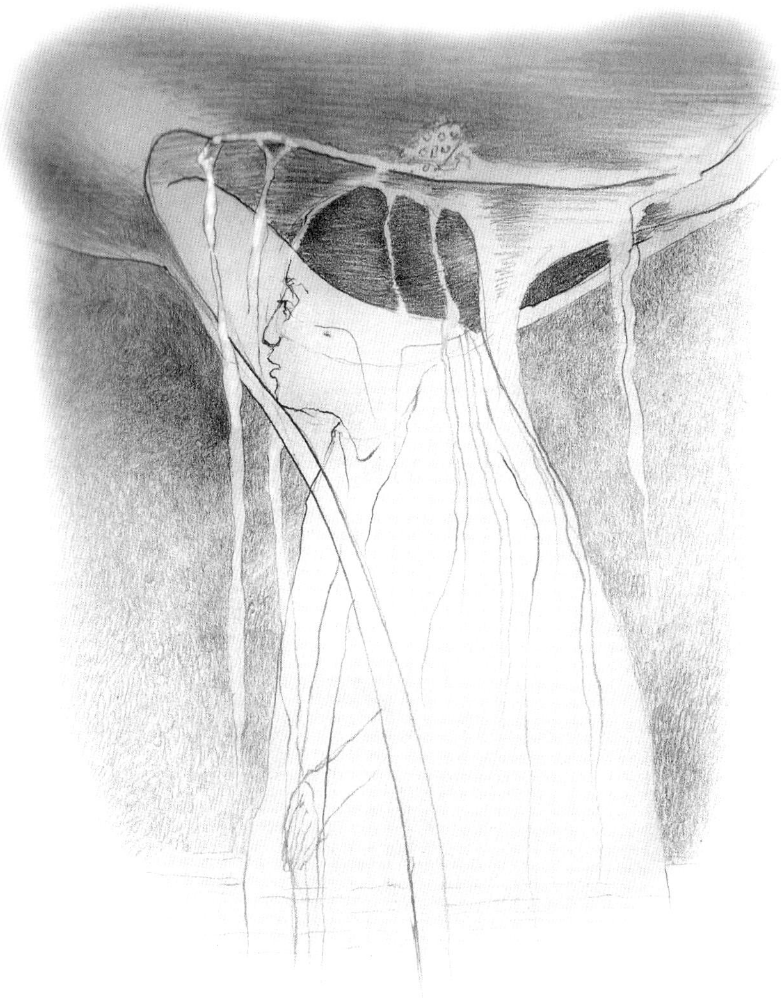

## The Power of Action

**elizaBeth Benson-Udom**

WITH

**Shiloh McCloud and Mary MacDonald**

**Illustrations by Shiloh Sophia McCloud and Sue Hoya Sellars**

# you will begin

**elizaBeth benson-udom**

you will begin
the dream will take root in your heart
and require your wings
and for a moment, 'til you notice
you're doing it
you will fly and then it's likely
you will remember you are human
and humans can't fly
cause they don't have wings
and even though YOU ARE FLYING
you will believe your eyes
and think you are not and you cannot
and you will fall
and you'll stay on the ground for awhile
using your arms as your arms
and your legs as your legs
and walking and working
cause that's what humans do
and in the quiet
of your cubicle
the seed of dream will sprout again
and then you will begin again
you will begin
and with the beginning, the seed
will swell and grow
the dream will take root in your heart
and require your hands and legs and eyes
and body and mind
and for a moment, 'til you notice
you're doing it
you will shine and then
with the first or the second or the third
or the thirtieth set back
it's likely you will want to fall apart
and so you will
and when you're done falling apart
you will begin again
you will set out on your heart's adventure
with a sure step, the right "stuff"
and every good and true intention
that accompanies every practiced adventurer
every life artist that begins from a place
of knowing
with a map and a bit of experience
some practice some learning
you will begin you will embark
and this time you will do it,
and you will know you did it
and it will not be it exactly
and you will offer your brilliance
to the cutting room floor
and mend and heal and lick wounds
and go shopping again
you will begin again
you will begin again and again
and maybe this time
you will wander the path with friends
and you will notice, especially when it looks
like you are not that you are still alone
and you will feel it and then you will stop
and then you will stop all that stops you
and you will begin again
and then you will see and then you will know
and then you will find and then you will BE
and then the dream that took root in your
heart will take root in the world
and then you can go you will begin
with as much promise as god sews
into his every sunrise you will begin
and if you spend every new day of your life
beginning well,
then you will be ready
for the new beginning
that marks the end of a life
well lived on this earth
now begin.

# heartvision: ten things you can always do

Often, when it's our heartvision we're trying to make room for in the world, we need a lot of dream time. We need plenty of incubation. We need a lot of holding precious and growing solid and making strong. That's why, I think, it takes many of us years to get to the moment of announcing ourselves to the world. And it's okay for it to take as long as it takes—and it's okay to never get "there"—the heaven you imagine for yourself and your business. But it's okay to get there, too. I think, sometimes, risking at the big stuff of soul we sometimes make excuses about holding back or put some aspect of ourselves in the way of getting on with it. And, without judging, I want to use this space here to do a little nudging. Even when it's daunting, there are always ten things you can do.

1. **Breathe.**

In and out, the deeper the better, every moment of every day.

**2. See.**

See your vision for yourself and your business in its final glorious state—imagine every detail—then let it go. Exhale as you do it. Let it go completely. Practice the seeing and letting go like breathing. Trust the vision. Let go of the dream. Get down to the basics.

**3. Start showing up for yourself.**

Just like you did when you had a "guaranteed" paycheck. Many people, who had regular paycheck gigs, got paid, primarily, to show up. If you were paid by the hour, had a time clock to punch, held a "salaried" position, then showing up was the first and most important thing you did Monday to Friday, week in and week out and that is, in fact, what you did to guarantee the paycheck. Your salary was based on a complicated formula that was a mere fraction of what value your work offered to the company as a whole. Working for yourself, your dream, your vision, is always a straight commission gig. For straight commission gigs, you are paid well, you make your own hours, you determine your strategies and ethics—but you have to show up for yourself.

**4. Cultivate consciousness.**

Which means notice, track, write down, collect, enter the ins and outs, the flow of your business and business activity. Write down what you do each day. What time you start and end each part of your project. Write down how much you spend and what you spend it on. Write down how much you earn and who you earned it from. Track. Write down. Collect (receipts). Enter data. Make it a mantra. Do it like you brush your teeth—every day, sometimes twice.

**5. Do what comes to you to do.**

When you're in the space of your business and you've envisioned your business, the unseen collaborators of your business will tell you what to do. Take a concrete action, a practical action, a physical action every time you feel their inspiration. Writing down the inspiration counts. Putting the stamps next to the envelopes counts. SARK calls these micro movements. Micro movements count.

**6. Give your dreams a birthday.**

Marry the goals for your business to a date on the calendar. Thinking of them as "life lines" instead of deadlines allows one the necessary space of anticipation and preparation for things achieved. Events, products, collaborations, exhibitions, books, conferences, businesses get BORN—they start something, they live in the minds and hearts and bodies and sensory memories of those that bring them into being, serve them or are served by them. The person or persons birthing them are forever changed for having done so. This "birthday" or "due date" for goals and dreams allows for all the natural cycles to take place. Thinking in terms of birth, even God needs 9 months and collaborators to bring a child into the world. Give your dreams a due date. Physically write them (in ink) on the calendar. Work backwards from the anticipated birthday party to determine what needs to be done to create your thing.

**7. Talk to strangers.**

Certainly, you will talk to your friends. You will talk to your neighbors, your former colleagues, the people in the parking lots you frequent, but make a point of talking to strangers. Meet people you don't already know. Tell them who you are, what you're about and what you do. Invite them to buy from you. Invite them to become your customer. Invite them into the secret society of ones who KNOW and SUPPORT you and your business because they have bought what you have to sell. Every single human being who breathes has the potential to (1) Be your customer or (2) Refer you to someone they know who will be your customer. Talk to every human being that breathes—especially the ones you don't already know.

**8. Allow yourself to be assisted.**

Help is a four letter word. So many of us are not good at asking for or allowing ourselves to be helped. It's something like charity or hand out or weakness or "they won't do it like I would do it" or something—something that brings up our control issues. Assistance, however, might be a semantic doorway that allows accompaniment. Rarely will we say no to the person who sees us struggling with boxes and offers to carry one of them for us. Rarely will we make a fuss if someone opens a door or holds the elevator or picks up something we drop on our rushing way to somewhere else. This is assistance. Allow assistance. Insist on assistance.

**9. Write joy descriptions.**

As you begin to insist on assistance, it will come to you—the kinds and qualities of collaborators you want and need. Write what comes to you. Not job descriptions, but joy descriptions. All of life is one seduction after another—not always culminating in romance, but we are all supposed to fall in love with each other and we are all supposed to spend our time on this planet following our bliss and doing what we love. Someone is called to work with you—to love what you do-to partner in co-creation of the miracles your business is designed to bring into this world. Get ready for them. Remember the Mary Poppins job description Jane and Michael wrote? Remember that golden rule, "do unto others" and offer the best, most creative comp plan you can imagine. State the comp plan with the joy description. Make sure at least part of the compensation offered is based on results you and your new partner create together.

**10. Rest.**

When you do these things—breathe, see, show up, get conscious, do what comes to you, celebrate birthdays, talk to strangers, allow assistance, write joy descriptions - you'll need a little rest. It is a dream you are making real, after all, and dreams speak clearest when you sleep. Make sure to take good care of yourself—eat, rest, relax, see friends, make meals, read good books, watch a little TV, partake of the downtime, spend time in nature and sleep. It's often that the greatest breakthroughs come when people take a breather. Be sure to make your mind available for breakthroughs by staying connected to the rest of life.

**11. Friendship.**

Spend time with your women friends. Cultivate relationships that last a life time.

Women are the real architects of society.

Harriet Beecher Stowe

# Ways to Get Started

1. Dream the biggest dream you can. Track it in this workbook. Join us at a *Heart of the Visionary* workshop.

2. Name your enterprise—doing this invokes the spirit of the thing you are beginning and immediately provides "help" in your collaboration and partnership with the named spirit.

3. Set benchmarks—we'll accomplish this by this date. Write them down and post them somewhere you can see them every time you sit down to work on your dream.

4. Determine how you will evaluate your success or failure. Give it considerable thought because what you think of it now may not be the measure you want to use. Invent a new measure.

5. Make a financial commitment to your idea. Determine what you have in personal funds to devote to it. Then, evaluate whether the spirit of your dream requires more than you have. If it does, determine how you want to raise money and from whom. Create a budget. Be real about money, including your personal money work.

6. Raise your money. Give up what you think you have to give up to get what you think you need to start to do your dream in the biggest way you can do it.

7. Evaluate your business or project from all angles. Who does it serve? What will it cost me personally? Is there an impact to earth or environment? Is it sustainable? Is it green enough? Is it "time" in terms of where the market is going? Is it for the highest good of all beings? What will it compromise? What are the challenges I may encounter?

8. Find the perfect place to do your dream the way you envision it. Do not compromise. Make the perfect deal for your perfect place. Do not compromise. Make it look like what it looks like when you dream it. Do not compromise.

9. Continue to work on your self development as you go along. Take workshops, join circles, attend conferences. Plan a self growth practice and stick to it. Also plan time for leisure, wellnessand resting.

10. Write **joy** descriptions for every person you see in your dream—including yourself. As you do this, think of how each person and position contributes to making your dream a success. Use these for determining "performance standards" and determine how you will evaluate each person's performance. What will you pay them? How will you reward them for doing a good job? How will you let them go if they need to be let go? Write it down. Interview your candidates.

11. Write down what you want by way of a personal support system. Determine how you want to be supported and by whom. Determine the ways people can demonstrate their support. Make a list of people you know or would like to know who you can interview to see if they are the ones.

12. Work continuously on your vision plan. Keep visioning and writing and sharing and creating around your vision to keep it juicy!

13. Consciously choose the energies you want to help you steer your ship and invite them onto the support team. (Traditional business organizations might call this support team a Board of Directors.) Let them know what you're asking them to do, very specifically. Let them know, in clear terms, what feels like support to you—and what does not feel like support.

14. Determine your agreement with your support team, write it down and ask that each signify their support by signing the agreement. Distribute copies to all.

15. Create affirmations and declarations for yourself and your team that you post around your work space. Keep yourself fired up through all that great positive thinking material!

16. Bring your teams together, dream your mission statement, write it down and put it where everyone can see it. Add images to text related items.

17. Determine your operating agreements—how each is going to work with each, write them down and give everyone copies.

18. Give symbols of trust to your team members (keys, passwords, etc.). Create acknowledgment opportunities.

19. Continue to practice your spiritual rituals, health commitments, family and self care. It is easy to get overwhelmed and it is of utmost importance to practice well being in order to navigate this incredible terrain.

20. Plan your first "coming out party" or group activity or event. Celebrate along the way! Invite! Have your party—a ritual to honor your success! ENJOY EVERY BLESSED MOMENT!

21. Plan mini-visionary vacations, for 24 hours, where you rest, dreamand vision the next steps.

22. Make a space to create art at home. A space to be creative. A room of your own.

***GO TO WORK. SHOW UP EVERY DAY. RECOMMIT TO YOUR DREAM. SHARE YOUR STORY. PUT YOUR WORK IN THE WORLD. DON'T LET ANYTHING STOP YOU!***

# 10 ways to increase press presence

1. **Send well crafted, succinct stories to the press about some aspect of your business every 4-6 weeks.**

Write about the people you hire. Write about product launches. Write about events you sponsor or participate in. Write about speaking engagements. Write about high profile customers. Write about the seasons and how your business adapts to them. Write about products or services you donate to local charities and causes. Write about your big wins. Write about your heavy losses. Write about your perseverance. Write about your dream. Write about yourself, your vision, your mission, your heart, your wisdom, your courage, your possibilities. Write about the mentorships and internships your business offers. Write about your business and its relationship to the wider community. In November of every year, write a dream list of topics for the press releases you will send for the following year. At a minimum, you need to send 8-12 releases each year and I recommend maxing out at no more than one/week. Write those topics on the calendar day you commit to sending the press release. When you get to that moment on the calendar, use a brainstorm topic, or adjust to the most important thing going on in your business at that moment. Tell a human story with lots of quotes. Include web links and phone numbers.

**2. Know your receivers.**

Read the paper. Do a little Internet research. Spend time noticing who writes your favorite columns, who's profiled as a contributing writer in your favorite magazines. Send your releases to people you know and respect. Notice the features editors, the business writers, the fine arts writers, the reporters on "your" beat. If you're sending blindly, then know and respect the magazine, website, newspaper, TV or radio station you're sending to. Align yourself with media that extends the vision and mission of your own business. Stay current with these vehicles and get to know the writers on the receiving end of your release. Remember to cultivate these relationships and notice, treasure and reward (with a nice note of thanks) the good writing done about you and your business.

**3. Cultivate your list.**

Keep track of what you send to whom at what frequency. Stay current with the comings and goings of reporters. Guard this list, know its value and exercise prudence when sharing it with others. Add to it with each new release sent. Set a goal to add ten new writers with every releaseand you grow your list by 80-120 names each year. New media is changing the nature of keeping, cultivating and updating lists—and if you can align yourself with constant contact or Icontact or other kinds of e-mail list management services, then you can track the responses and click thrus of the various human beings on the receiving end of your missives. Research free press opportunities in your local area.

**4. Pick up the phone.**

It's always harder to resist someone who makes an effort to connect. When you notice from your smart e-mail tool who is looking at what you send and clicking to find out more, then pick up the phone. Pitch your story. Ask for a spot on the front page. (The answer will be yes or no.) The writer also wants his or her stuff to be on the front page. It's a win-win for all parties.

**5. Send pictures.**

With e-mail, it's easy to attach a jpeg with your press release. Always send art. Sometimes the story will run with your picture and sometimes just your picture will run. It's better for you. It's better for the media outlet. Include color images. Head shots are fine, but pictures of the effect of your business in community is better. Where you can tell a story with a picture (always worth 1000 words), do. Show what your business does. Demonstrate its value. Do it with images.

**6. Keep clippings.**

Writers make an effort. Even if it seems all they do is cut and paste your release, if you made it into the paper, onto the television spot, it's because a writer, editor or reporter wanted you to. Make sure to make the effort to find the clippings and tape the spots. Keep everything that's written and put it in a press book of your own. Keep it where your customers can see it in the lobby, or make flip books for your sales team, or frame the clips and put them on your wall of fame.

**7. Send press kits.**

Once you have clippings, make photocopies. Post links to articles about your business on your website. Record TV spots to dvds and upload the spot to youtube.com. Put these clippings and copies together in the nicest folder and have a dozen of them with you at all times. As you get more press, add to the kit once a year, cull the mentions and keep the feature stories. Pass these kits out to big clients. Use them to document your successes for grant applications. Send them to higher profile news organizations or talk shows in an effort to gain a moment more in the spotlight. Press begets press. If someone else liked you enough to write about you, someone else will think they are supposed to be impressed. Keep rolling, ever forward. Tell your story until every human being on the planet can tell it too.

**8. Create client testimonials.**

Save every nice letter you ever receive from a client. Put customer letters together in a book. (I like the three holed plastic sleeves). Let these words you didn't write about your business serve as quotes for your various releases. Where you can, record the words of your clients and use podcast technology to send sound files to radio outlets. Use these love letters to spread the love for your company and what it provides by quoting them in releases. Take pictures of the letters and use the images of varied client handwriting in brochures and other advertising. I don't know why this is—but when someone else says it about you, rather than you saying it about yourself, there tends to be a greater reception and respect for what is being said.

**9. Spread the word.**

When someone writes about you, quote them. Mention the press you receive. When you win a certain magazine's award for something, tell every other magazine what happened. When you're reviewed favorably by a critic, quote the critic in the next release. Use the cache of those media outlets who feature stories on you to help open doors for your story at other media outlets. You're familiar with the "as seen on tv" products and the "as seen on Oprah" designations and the "Joel Siegal gives this film five stars." When you earn five stars or are seen on Oprah, send a press release about the experience and how happy it makes you.

**10. Make it a habit.**

Writing about your business isn't doing your business or being in your business or the only job you have in your business—but it is a job and an important job in your business. Make a press muscle. Decide, every Sunday night, to send a release. Get good at writing them. Don't lose your passion for telling your own story. Keep faith that your efforts are getting you somewhere. Stories are better than advertising. Stories are real and whole and true and bring some aspect of what you do and why it's important in the wider world for the reader and the writer. Write what's true. Keep a copy of your releases. The practice of telling your story succinctly on paper and then sending that out to other people in the culture charged with telling stories is a deepening and ingraining practice. Doing it regularly, each time with new folks, makes a difference in you and in the world. If you write about you and share what you write about you with others, others will write about you, too.
Don't farm this out if you can help it.
All great stories are always greatest when they come from the horse's mouth.
Use your voice. Make a muscle.
Form a healthy, true storytelling habit.
Your words will spread. The press will do you good.

# new media resources

New resources are being launched on the web each and every day. Just play—spend some time looking—maybe just 10 minutes a day. See where your search takes you and grow your own list of new media/marketing tools to help you. Here is a short list of my current favorites:

1. **Evite**: www.evite.com. It's more of a "party invitation" tool, but has many easy templates and formatting that allows you to say all the specifics and track responses and gives people the chance to say something to you.

2. **Constant Contact**: www.constantcontact.com. Constant contact is free if you're sending to less than 50 people and after that, not very much, it's a design tool that lets you make the look and feel of your communication look and feel like you and what you're looking for. It's not hard. Go to the site and play with it. I recommend constant contact because it allows you to see who looked at your flyer and it allows people to forward your flyer and add on to your e-mail list by sending that flyer to friends and giving friends the option to subscribe.

3. **You Tube**: www.youtube.com. This puts you in charge of your documentary, your advertisement, your message. Buy a video camera and make sure to use this tool. It makes it easy for mainstream media to pick up and use what YOU have to say about YOUR OFFERING.

4. **Visit** www.mamamillionairedesigns.com for printing as well as web hosting, graphic design and newsletter mailing services. Another source is Vista Print. Vista Print is FREE for business cards and 100 postcards and a bunch of other smart, professional looking marketing materials.

5. **Visit**: http://www.publicityinsider.com/release.asp for press release formats.

6. **Stumbleupon**: http://www.stumbleupon.com. This tool allows you to discover new sites. You download their toolbar, set up your account (free) and they create a blog of what you've looked at and liked. It's a social networking tool, too.

7. **Digg**: http://digg.com. This site allows you to "vote" on content you've found on the web--it allows people to earn notoriety that is "sponsored" by those that like it. Also free, it's a great way to bring what you love on the web into visibility.

8. **Blogspot:** http://www.blogger.com. allows anyone to set up a blog--a video blog, a photo blog, a blog of words to say what you have to say to the world. Also free, it's an absolute must. This is the place to work out what you're thinking about the importance of your work in visible words.

9. **flickr**: http://www.flickr.com. Flickr allows for easy sharing of photos on-line. You can

stumble these photos and digg them, too. This is a great "carrier pigeon" for your photos to find their way in the world.

10. **Lulu**: www.lulu.com. Lulu allows for the simple, cost efficient launching of your own press or creation of your own books. Through simple uploading of basic word files and a little money and lulu magic, you can make your words come together in book form and sell them from your lulu launch pad.

Each of these tools will lead you to a universe of other tools that will benefit your life and business. Be certain to budget the amount of time you're willing to play on the Internet learning new things and maximize your search results.

## Media Ideas for My Project

*It's never too late—in fiction or in life—to revise.*

*Nancy Thayer*

# websites, newsletters and mailing lists

## Shiloh Sophia McCloud

So we gotta get the word out about your stuff - what else is there to say really? It is about getting it in front of others, and these days, it is essential to work with things like e-mail and web-sites. The Cosmic Cowgirls have been working with our membership base over the past several years to do what we can to decode some of the challenges of launching things like web-sites as well as designing postcards. printing and more! We are launching our new web based business division that is focused on getting the word out about YOU!

**WEBSITES:** I am not exaggerating when I tell you it took me over five years to be able to update my own web-site - it was like another language I felt I would never be able to learn. I can do computer some - but I did not have what it took to do the programs like Dream Weaver.
I searched for years and finally I came across a template that actually seemed like it would work. We purchased a piece of the do-it-yourself pie and now we are offering and assisting women in getting their web-sites up! You can do it yourself - or we can help you with it and you can work with our designers - and then keep it updated on your own. Now that we have the basics figured out we want to share it with you. You can set up on-line stores, folks can request information, sign up for your e-newsletter and your communication with the outside world is happening, often while you are working on other projects. Think of your web-site as a part of building your own personal on-line legend.

**NEWSLETTERS or E-Zines**: Since you are going to go ahead and get the word out, may as well make it interesting and packed with value! Ask yourself, what is going to make the person on the other end of the document, interested, as well as engaged and blessed. Each month I include a new painting as well as a brand new letter or poem that corresponds with the painting. I offer free stuff, discounts, links, information and I literally spend at least 3 days working on it with the intention of it being a blessing for others. I sometimes ask myself if it is worth it - but the sales show that it is. There IS a learning curve but once you get used to it you will be inspired that you can communicate with hundreds and even thousands of clients sharing about your offerings. I am big on images, in case you didn't notice, and so I highly recommend using images to spice up your work. If you want to use some of mine, or another artist's work to spice up your look you can often get permission just by e-mailing and then offering to put the artist's name and a link to their site. (Note: there is a link on our site for a free newsletter program trial) Be diligent wherever you go in getting e-mails. Collect business cards, talk to folks and attend events where you think your customers gather. Cultivate and nurture your list! Have newsletter sign up easy to find.

**PRINTING**: You will need a business card and most likely letterhead and postcards from time to time at the very minimum. A brochure can come later. There are many sources for this kind of work and it cannot be a secondary item. This is of course part of getting the word out - but it is also about branding and making your mark. When picking images to represent you - draw some ideas out first. I recommend spending a few days just on your image/name heart storming.We can help you with ALL of the items on this list. This is part of our work, our ministry and our own income stream - to help women manifest their visions!www.mamamillionairedesigns.com

# web presence

Invent the beginning rough draft text for your first five pages. Start with the basics!

**Welcome**

**Bio**

**Vision**

**Location and Hours**

**Menu of Products or Services**

# how to write a press release

**Mary MacDonald**

1. Make your heading stand out so it is interesting to the reader. It should summarize the rest of the press release.
2. Media are inundated with press releases on a daily basis so try very hard to make your press release one page and definitely no more than two.
3. The first paragraph is the most important and should answer the questions: who, what, why, where and how. Answer these questions in the most creative way possible. Most media professionals only read the heading and the first paragraph so you must capture their attention.
4. Decide why you are writing the press release and keep focused on that. You can send press releases to: promote, educate, inform, update.
5. Find a hook: What's newsworthy about you or your offerings? What's unique about you or it? how will the reader benefit?
6. Be clear and concise and make sure you check your spelling and grammar!!!
7. Use simple language.
8. Think of the press release as a sales tool and appeal to what will interest your buyer.
9. Make sure you provide as much contact information as possible.
10. Use testimonials to give credibility to you and/or your offerings or use expert quotes.
11. Use an active voice as much as possible.
12. Tell the reader what the problem is and how your service or offering will solve the problem and why you are qualified to solve the problem.
13. Human interest stories sell – make your reader care.
14. Don't phone and ask if they got your press release unless you have a working relationship with the journalist.
15. Know your audience – send it to the right people at the right time. Don't send a press release about a new computer software to a sports writer.
16. If you use statistics make them accurate and make sure they are a statistic that will grab the reader's attention.
17. Don't forget local media – they are always looking for good news stories that will appeal to their local readers.
18. Prepare a fact sheet that you can make available to the press when they need more information from you.
19. Don't just send the one press release and then be disappointed when you don't get a reaction. Send them weekly for a period of time with a different angle on the same theme.

**On the next page is a sample press release and the page after that is for you to write your own. This is another great research date on the Internet.**

**FOR IMMEDIATE RELEASE**

**A New Book With A Feminine Approach to Visionary Business!**

Contact: Mary MacDonald or Shiloh McCloud
Phone: 1-888-385-6866
URL: www.cosmiccowgirlsink.com
Email: cosmiccowgirls@gmail.com

Mendocino California —July 1, 2008—Reverend Shiloh Sophia McCloud, famous for her illustrated journals and her vibrant woman centric imagery, collaborates with 22 other Authors and Artists to publish **Heart of the Visionary - A Workbook For Women's Work** which guides users to realize entrepreneurial dreams that are in alignment with their personal values.

The research for this book is based on over a decade of Shiloh's work guiding thousands of women in the realization and manifestation of their life work. Shiloh continues to see the power of putting tools into the hands of women and is sharing her process by inviting women to be Member-Owners in a publishing and production company, Cosmic Cowgirls Ink, LLC which she founded in 2006. This is the company's first book and the foreword is by best selling author SARK with writings from 21 other authors including Alice Walker and Jean Shinoda Boden. Primary Authors include Mary MacDonald, Elizabeth Benson-Udom, Shannon McCloud and Caron McCloud.

This exciting workbook is designed to be used through the lens of creativity, using right and left brain practices. The book features a fill-in-the-blank visionary plan, a business plan template, inspirational stories, affirmations, illustrations, teachings on abundance, bookkeeping, marketing, sales, and so much more, all done with a woman's creative flair and a heart for blessing others! Where else can you find traditional entrepreneurial wisdom combined with Art, Poetry, Laughter Yoga, Painting Days, Raw Food Recipes and the development of a woman's legendary self?

"I wanted to create a business know-how workbook for budding women entrepreneurs," says Shiloh. "Most of all, I want women to see that they CAN do business, that they CAN do it their way, that they do not need a ton of money, a lot of people, or even a traditional business plan to get started. They just need a focused plan of action that is written in a language they can relate to as women." Shiloh has sold two million dollars worth of her own work and has previously published five titles. Workshops by the same title are being offered in the Northern California area.

Cosmic Cowgirls Ink www.cosmiccowgirlsink.com is honored to partner with Girls Inc. www.girlsincislandcity.org and Women's Initiative www.womensinitiative.org and gift 10% of the net profits of each book.

Heart of the Visionary - 384 Pages - $39.00 - 9.25" x 11" - Wire-O.

###

# the missing piece

In the many creative businesses I've built on paper and in practice, there has always been the same missing piece: Me. See, when I was promised a paycheck every week, I would often work eighty hours. I would get up early, endure hours of commute traffic, stay late, work on e-mail after I got home, answer voicemail in the commute, constantly look for new ways of doing my company's business and write proposals into the night.

I would prepare for management meetings and department meetings and board of directors meetings. I would track the performance of my team and document to justify my own. I would quantify my specific smart goals and I would publicize my endeavors. It was easy. It was for someone else. About something else. An abstraction.

In my own creative practice and enterprise I have often failed to truly commit myself to a single course of action, to articulate any of the business "pieces" in my vision puzzle. And I have not shown up. Not eighty hours a week. Not in the same accountable ways as when I was guaranteed a paycheck. And my performance is reflected in the paycheck I can't write to myself.

Certainly, the eighty hour week thing was something to bring into balance when I traded traditional employment for creative enterprise—but for me, for so many of us who dream things, showing up in our own dreams seems to be the determining factor in understanding our mission, dedicating ourselves to bringing it to bear and committing, truly, to bring our piece of the world's puzzle to the grand table of humanity.

Now, this workbook is not about failure—but it is about telling the truth. It is about guiding to a mutual success. It is about accountability and action. And it seems so disheartening to me, that in my own creative practice, I have been remiss in doing the things needed to support myself. So this is what helps: Making myself accountable to others and to God. If I can remember that I am in the center of a perfect love, being pulled and pushed and guided and prodded into divine action at divine timing by a divine web of interconnectivity, then I can show up differently. If I can remember that my piece of the puzzle—the piece of the puzzle that is me—is required in my own vision and in the visions of others who are charged with appearing in my dream, then I can share myself differently. If I give myself a divine mission, I can show up for God. If I give myself a divinely sanctioned relationship, I can show up for my partner. If I understand and commit to my greatest purpose—my greatest potential—my divine calling, then I can show up with energy and joy and freedom about me. And the work itself can fuel me.

I have had my best job. Now there is only the job I create for myself—and this job is divinely ordained. This job is the job of a transformative artist alive and working in the world. This is a shaman gig. This is the building of the pyramids, the placing of Stonehenge, the creation of America, the dawning of new enterprise. This is my moment. And I am my own missing piece.

So now, with that knowing, there is a chance to commit—fully, just like I would if I had a "contract" or "employee manual." And so I have to show up for work. No, I get to. And aren't I blessed?! And aren't you?!

# pieces of your vision puzzle

A long time ago, in a Silicon Valley far away, I once passed out a very impressive business card that named me as vice president of human beings and corporate culture for a technology start up. Somewhere on the fast ride before the flame went out, I was profiled in *Fast Company Magazine* for our innovative hiring practices.

One of those practices included a game we played during interview day, where I asked aloud "What do we need in order to be a world class company?" and applicants would shout out their answers. If I liked their answer, they would earn a puzzle piece from me and when applicants earned their puzzle pieces, I put them "in charge" of the pieces in their possession. For purposes of the interview, they became instant managers of the projects in their hands.

Now the puzzle, not that it matters, was a 48 piece floor sized puzzle of the solar system I found at The Discovery Store at the mall. On each piece I wrote the names of things that I thought we would have in place when we were a world class company. While it was not comprehensive, or a well thought out analyzed list, it was a great tool and supported me in concretely naming some of the symbols for a fulfilled vision of business.

**Draw and write your puzzle pieces for creating a world class company!**

*And the trouble is, if you don't risk anything, you risk more.*
*Erica Jong*

# launching a workshop or event

1. Start dreaming on paper—write 3 pages, long hand, every day for two weeks about your dream. The words will give you a direction. Then you make a plan.

2. Make a business plan, a marketing plan, an implementation schedule. Do this by taking the words you've written, marrying them to an event on the calendar. Working backwards from that date to determine ten steps toward making that date/event possible, determining what day you take each step and WRITE IT DOWN. (See other sections of this book for ways to begin these various plans).

3. Think through, arrange the details of and create an invitation to your event—who, what, where, when, how, how much, who pays, driving directions.

4. Ask your friends to come to your event. Ask them to bring friends. Invite them to enroll, register, purchase their ticket, reserve their seat. (You can do this through invitation, phone call, e-vite, flyer.) The more personal and direct your invitation, the better your response will be.

5. Determine a way you are comfortable asking people you do not know to enroll, register, purchase their ticket, reserve their seat. Direct mail, e-mail, flyers in strategic places, advertising—find the details of each product and purchase the tools necessary to issue these invitations and SEND.

*SEND! DISTRIBUTE! HAND OUT! You know this already.You can re-write your flyer/invitation/ press release a hundred times, but it won't do you any good until you hand it to someone. A flyer is a flyer is a flyer. I like to pick them up, 'cause I think someday I might want to do what's being offered.*

a. You can hand it to them directly—this is the best way—accompanied by a look in the eye and a "please take my class and bring a friend" message.
b. You can hand it to them by leaving it in places people might find it. For these places I encourage you to pick up a copy of "the groovy paper" in your neighborhood and take your flyers to every business that advertises in that periodical.
c. Have a bunch in your purse and in your car and hand them to people who look interesting when you're in line at the grocery store, the bank, the the Department of Motor Vehicles.
d. Take them to all your classes everywhere you already teach and invite your students to invite their family, friends, caregivers.
e. Take them to your neighbors.
f. Take your flyers to local colleges and community colleges and high schools and adult schools and traffic school venues.
g. Take your flyers to all the local libraries.

6. Write a testimonial about yourself and your "expertise." Write why people should get this experience from you and why you are the *best* one for people to spend their time and money with. The bottom line is that you have to talk about yourself. The fun way to do this is to make an exhaustive list of all the things you are good at and then PLAY with them—really, it's important to remember that by writing it down and putting it on a piece of paper intended for a public audience, people can read it. Put as much of yourself on the page as you can! Use this testimonial along with the specifics of your event to create a press release and send it to ten media sources you, yourself, use, watch or read.

7. Make a list of benefits people get from spending time with you at your event. It's a habit now, for people to want to list the benefits of doing a particular thing and to articulate the outcome. This is a fun exercise, too—and like with all things written, the more specific you can be, the better picture your words can paint and the more likely you'll be able to connect with someone. Specifics. Specifics. Specifics. Keep going with this concrete, specific list. You may not tell the whole story on a flyer or a post card, but when you are interviewed, or pitching your stories to the press or writing press releases you have to have the hook of good stories. So you write down the specifics and then you talk to people and they will ask for the stories. And once they ask you for the stories they either WILL take a class from you and tell everyone they know to take a class from you or they will NEVER take a class from you. Either way, you win.

8. Ask everyone who's ever taken your class to list specific things they got from their time with you and what it did for them in their lives. Keep a growing list with tally marks behind the things people say over and over again. Then you can make a "testimonial" space on your flyer and brochure and website and other marketing material. The point is to write marketing materials you yourself would read and enjoy and connect with and take action on. And amuse yourself - let it be good for YOU.

9. Oh and the action thing—you have to tell people EXACTLY what you want them to do by when in what way. You have to say, "Register for this class by August 1, by calling me directly and interviewing for a place in the class," or whatever you want to be the thing you want them to do. How can they pay for the class? Are the fees the fees, or is there a sliding scale? What do they need to bring? Where is the place they're to come? Try and think like the most afraid person in the universe and answer all the questions they would need answered before they could feel safe enough to ask the questions, let alone, safe enough to come and play. Give them their safety through your complete answers to what you can anticipate as their questions. This becomes your FAQ (frequently asked questions) and will go on your website. Then, on your day, you'll be DOING IT! And you will be entering a whole new phase of your development, where your experience becomes your teacher. Keep these steps close to help you begin again and again and again as needed for you to keep showing up. Keep moving through it. Keep true to your vision.

10. No matter what—Keep SHOWING UP to DO your dream.

# playing well with others

I was recently in a room with Mildred Howard. She, at 62, an accomplished, museum-collected artist, having worked passionately in the various revolutions of her life, was talking about her art. Instead of talking about it, really, she spoke poetry that said it all. And she showed some slides. And she presented a powerpoint. And she answered questions. And she said things—really important things that apply to all of us as women of vision and artrepreneurship. She said, "APPLY FOR EVERYTHING" and "BE NICE TO EVERYBODY" and she added, "cuz you never know…"

And with these pearls dripping from Mildred, I began to contemplate what you have to do to apply for everything and be nice to everybody. You have to:

1. Know what's going on in your part of the world.
2. Believe yourself worthy of entering, applying.
3. Get over yourself enough to apply and actually do i.t
4. Believe in yourself, your mission, your possibilities and your work beyond rejection and keep believing through to the moment you win.
5. Document your successes and toot your own horn in language that doesn't sound "of the ego."
6. Understand you are in relationship with every other human on the planet.
7. Honor that relationship by being fully who you are in person and on paper all the time.
8. Honor that relationship by encountering others with respect and dignity all the time.
9. Remember who you've met.
10. Remember who you are.
11. Never think you "know" it all…or are the only one who knows it.
12. Share your Heart.

*Never doubt that a small group of thoughtful committed citizens can change the world. Indeed, it is the only thing that ever has.*
*Margaret Mead*

# i live in pursuit of creating the idea

*i live in pursuit of doing my part of it right.*
*i live in pursuit of creating the idea,*
*the confidence, the company*
*that can capture the imaginations of talented amazing people*
*who join together in creative pursuit*
*of an ideal working experience*
*and profitable enterprise*
*that provides all those who work inside that dream*
*and are affected by that dream*
*with the resources to make our lives*
*and by extension the whole world work*
*the way the creator of the world envisioned and intended*

***elizaBeth Benson-Udom***

# WELLNESS

## The Power of Awareness

Shiloh Sophia McCloud, Nikiah Seeds, Ananda Wildflower,

Alisa Franzone-Davis, Mary MacDonald and Gennifer Mountain

Illustrations by Shiloh Sophia McCloud and Sue Hoya Sellars

The Journey

One day you finally knew
what you had to do, and began,
though the voices around you
kept shouting
their bad advice --
though the whole house
began to tremble
and you felt the old tug
at your ankles.
"Mend my life!"
each voice cried.
But you didn't stop.
You knew what you had to do,
though the wind pried
with its stiff fingers
at the very foundations,
though their melancholy
was terrible.
It was already late
enough, and a wild night,
and the road full of fallen
branches and stones.
But little by little,
as you left their voices behind,
the stars began to burn
through the sheets of clouds,
and there was a new voice
which you slowly
recognized as your own,
that kept you company
as you strode deeper and deeper
into the world,
determined to do
the only thing you could do --
determined to save
the only life you could save.

~ Mary Oliver ~

# Wellness for Women

*True personal wellness includes living on the awareness continuum between our health and caring about the health of our environment and all the other beings on this green earth.*

Write a wellness self-care poem to your body and heart.

# Wellness and Creativity

*Being Creative is Good Medicine for the heart, soul and body!*

**Shiloh Sophia McCloud**

Have you read the slogan: 'Art Saves Lives?' Every time I see it, I go: YAHOO - that's right. Then a second later, I go, does it really? Then a second after that I go: YES!

There has been much documentation on the ability of art, writing, dancing and other creative practices to show that healing occurs through creative mediums. So why did we stop? And why are they taking it out of schools? Art can and does save and change lives. And businesses. Creativity can help us learn new ways of being. Especially in business, which is profoundly creative!

We replay our negative scenarios over and over, until they just run without pressing play - they are just on when we get a moment to ourselves - running us. They then affect our ability to make healthy choices. Am I saying I think we can change this pattern? Yes, I am. I do believe it, I must believe it and have done it and taught others to do it. BUT it must be backed up with creative practice, which is regular disciplined creation.

That is why this is called a w-o-r-k book. Because it is work to start thinking you are awesome - and that you have a contribution to make. It doesn't come easily, we have to create it for ourselves. Will you believe with me? We have to take responsibility for working on designing who we will show up as in our vision. To get your mind, body and heart moving along different pathways of discovery. There are missing pieces to your puzzle that creative expression may be able to reveal to you.

In terms of forging the paths, in the case of learning to sew, play music or make art - sometimes it takes a bit more effort as we age. But often with children, it is so fresh they can just do it, and haven't learned negative associations yet (we hope and pray they won't either.) But in the case of adult women and teen girls, we already believe all this "we can't" stuff so that it is hard to get through to the juicy stuff of I CAN and WILL. Being Creative Is Good Medicine For ME! And when we start getting this, chances are, you won't want to stop because you will be so inspired about what you have to say!

**When we create with a healing intention we activate and awaken our personal transformation.**

Some schools of thought say you must first know the cause to end the suffering. I am not in this school. I have worked with many folk who think they know the cause of why their life isn't working and their life still isn't working. I think if we create - what needs to be known will arise naturally within a platform that can deal with the information. Our own brain, our conversations with therapists and family, cannot seem to stop the suffering caused by the whatever. We MUST ACT - physically and spiritually. We must find ways and patterns that bless us, excite us and make us feel proud of who we are.

This book is infused with the hope of bringing some of that to you. We need these positive pathways to be more powerful than the negative ones. When I speak to people about the voice of self love and honor - they sometimes don't even know what I am talking about. But when I bring up the voice of the critic, they go - oh my! They know her well! So why can't we cultivate the good guide to tell the critic where to put it?!

Practicing creativity is the most powerful way I know to actually make change happen at the personal and transpersonal level. We can interrupt the patterns that are ingrained and the best way is to quickly and consciously introduce new wholesome patterns. This book is a part of making that transition.

If you want to, write some of the bad things that you think are preventing you from doing your work on another piece of paper. Then tell what or whoever it is that you don't want those things anymore and that they do not serve you. Now, throw it away. Just throw it away. Don't keep it. Rip it up if you want. Part of being creative is making small meaningful rituals all throughout your process. Then on the next few pages, invite the transformation you are looking to create as a woman free of the critic. Just a business book written in this way is a radical shift. Join the revolution!

Write from the voice of the liberated woman. Use "I am" sentences. Lead with the positives. And gather wellness support and community from your women friends.

# Self Care Basics

If you can only do a little bit, don't miss adding these basics to your schedule!

Drink at least three full glasses of filtered water a day.
Stretch at least 5-15 minutes a day.
Walk for 15 minutes a day.
Spend at least 5-15 minutes in prayer or meditation.
Read for 10-15 minutes about something enlivening and educating.
Vitamins: Find a good multivitamin.
Breathe consciously two times a day.
Work on something that is all about you - at least 15 minutes.
To activate right brain left brain activities do the cross crawl action.
Draw with both hands at the same time!
Get a water filter for your shower.

Don't eat fast food if you can help it.
Get organic when you can.
Buy green when you can,
especially get a green mattress.
Don't install any carpet but organic.
Love yourself as much as you can.

Pedicures can be equal to therapy,
only they cost less.
Take long baths by candlelight
with rose petals.
Take a journal and go sit under a tree
and draw leaves. Bring your dog.
Take a girlfriend to go buy new lipstick
or perfume or sparkly earrings.
Buy red cowgirl boots.
Write correspondence to loved ones.
Turn music on and dance your cares.
Have a spa day - all day.
Take a vacation at home.
Laugh and sing out loud.
Continue this list for yourself....

# Self Care Commitments and Ideas

# Hormones, Hot Flashes and Hot Tempers

**Shiloh and Friends**

When you are having PMS, or even just the week before your period, try not to make major decisions or schedule critical meetings, at all. And remember that no matter how many times you tell yourself, this is how I really feel and the rest of the time I am just glossing it over, it is not true. While there are truths to be realized during PMS, it is not the whole truth and should be used as a viewing tool, not as a tool to dismantle things.

Since you probably work with other women, know their cycle too, put it on your calendar. And if they call you and start ranting and raving, gently remind them that it is their cycle time and you'd like to talk next week. This is not silly girl stuff. This is wisdom. How many times have we regretted things we have done or said? And what if our friends, family and associates knew us well enough to say, let's talk later. No judgment. Just, this is not a good time to have this kind of conversation.

Also, know when your BEST time of the month is—usually, right after ovulation for me. And schedule BIG things and meetings and planning during that time. When I have PMS, I simply do NOT schedule workshops and important meetings during that time. I schedule other things that are GOOD for me.

An important note: The whole week before and during the days of your period, do not stand in front of the mirror too long. Just don't do it. Look later. And, have a few of your favorite outfits ready to go, matched up and dry cleaned. So that all you have to do is put them on without thinking too much about it. Prepare for your best times and your challenging times.

And please, please (if your periods are challenging and painful) try to schedule a two-three day window to take time off, lay in bed, eat ice cream and stay in a fluffy pink robe watching old movies and calling your grandmother to tell her you love her. I like to have one rest day and then one day to leisurely do things that are important to me that I don't give myself permission to do. Like research health websites on the Internet, paint a painting just for me, or just paint my toe nails, write letters, take baths, braid my hair, gaze out the window, make a bouquet from my yard, cuddle with my cat, make an alter, make soup for my guy—homey kinds of things. Then you are not only rested, but nourished and ready to go when you get to the other side. And if you feel good enough, going out with girlfriends can be truly nourishing even if you drink a martini. Olives are vegetable right? My grandmother Davis always used to say, while eating pie a la mode for breakfast,

*Everything in moderation....*

## *Additional Words of Wisdom from other women on this subject...*

**Nancy Ballard**

I went through all the craziness at 35, never imagining that menopause could hit at such a young age... if you are feeling crazy, having periods that flow like rivers, want to divorce your husband (which I almost did) and can't stop crying or find any joy, wonder, happiness or delight in your life... you might want to look into the possibility of early menopause...who knew? Save yourself from the horror of losing your mind.... you may just be going through, what they called in the olden days, "the change." PS - once diagnosed, I was given what I needed to subdue the horrible unknown. It was given a name and a cause. I was able to salvage my marriage and get on with my life, assured that I was NOT crazy, was not a worthless, horrible, terrible waste....that was catalyzed by the craziness of hormones run amuck.

**Caron McCloud**

I would not trade my old age for youth if that youth included periods and all that comes with them, like PMS and bleeding. Though I tried to get with the glory when, during the 70's, feminists were romanticizing all things female, including menses, I just couldn't get there. But maybe it's just me, since after two years of jogging I never got the "joy of running" either. I feel that those who do have a hard time with periods or menopause should, if possible, follow the good advice to take a break instead of breaking our butts trying to pass ourselves off as sane (or by trying to jog) during these attacks. As for hot tempers, with or without flashes and hormones, I get a lot done when I'm angry. I once took part in a seminar where we had to role play a personal situation while coming from a specific emotional state (such as joy, irritation, depression, love, enthusiasm) that was written on a slip of paper that we drew from a basket. The emotional state I drew was anger. Hey! Right up my alley. I was so compelling that I got a standing ovation.

**Mary MacDonald**

I remember the day my stepdaughter Mercede got her period and she phoned me in tears - in pain - and scared. not knowing how this "curse of womanhood" would affect her life, and angry about the unfairness of it all. Being the wise sage I counseled her about the wonders of being a woman and how that began with your menses and the strength it gave us, the joy of being able to welcome new life – yada yada yada. How could I justify telling her this crap when for most of my life I suffered pain, anger and the indignities of bloating, blood and overflow on a monthly basis? The fear when my period was late, the anguish when it wasn't. Men's crass comments about "you must be on the rag" and their assumption in the workplace that you couldn't make rational decisions "at that time of the month." And yet when I looked into her beautiful face, tense with the anxiety of this new world being thrust at her, I was so happy to be with her in that moment, reveling in our "sisterhood."

**elizaBeth Benson**

I think I was 24, living on Catalina Island (as an earth day performance piece that wasn't sponsored by Shell or Chevron), when I realized that something gets born every moon cycle. If it's not a baby, it's a new born part of yourself. At least that's how it seems to me.

And being a woman means having a menstrual cycle. It means managing the vortex one becomes in the space of being used (by spirit? by God?) for the bringing forth of new life. And being a powerful woman means having a space and grace about one's moon time. You remember how much you loved The Red Tent when you read it—and the idea of having a place to go off, away from everyone, to experience the rush and flow of bleeding woman? Even though we often can't escape our surroundings to take ourselves away from our lives, we can move consciously and prayerfully through this gift of time. This requires a presence of mind, a consciousness of time, a space for being kind and good and thoughtful of one's self. I like to curl up with "chick flicks" and let myself cry. I like to indulge in chocolate as medicine for the duration. I like to take LOTS of hot baths and read some precious book I savor for these kinds of moments some delicious, self-indulgent fiction—not self-help. I like to put the top down and drive through forests or find a favorite rock and sit on it—thinking of how women in centuries past would have spent their week bleeding onto a rock—and their sacred cycles would have been honored as such. I like to color in Shiloh's journals and coloring books, or draw like I did in high school—simple black line drawings that fill the page with hearts and eyes and rainbows. I like to sleep deep and indulgently—knowing that my dreams and the rest they provide will get me to the other side. When I remember to notice, or feel the swell of uncomfortable emotions, I like to warn my beloved—just mention that my period is coming. It helps when we both know what is going on....

**Shannon McCloud**

For me, the challenges of menses and its uninvited participation in my breakdowns and breakthroughs wasn't about the heavy periods, intense pain and other major discomforts that many face. My challenge was feeling that I was in vivid high-definition technicolor via IMAX screen EMOTIONAL PMS for about three weeks out of each cycle. I agree that we need to adjust our schedule in order to align with our cycle, but this wasn't an option for me working in the corporate world and primarily with men. In reflection, PMS was even worse than "The Glass Ceiling." I am surprised that I was able to become successful. Maybe it was through my "Denial Serving Its Purpose" program that I was able to appear present and intelligent while faking some semblance of sanity. A woman has to compensate on the outside so that the guys they work with don't know what's going on in the inside. Actually that's not so hard cause they never know anyway. Where did that term menopause originate anyway? Because they paused in shock and had nothing to say? When PMS or womopause comes into play, you gotta jive to survive and stay alive and keep others out of harms way. Wait! I think I just wrote a poem! My main recommendation for both PMS and ?-opause is to write poetry and spend as much time with women as possible. Women aren't impossible to be with in the first place. No even during PMS. Also, focus on "Strong and Brave, not Weak and Afraid" with every breath you can take. If you actually find time to breathe—let me know about that. Are we ever free from horror-mones at any point in our lives? I still, thank you Pasty Cline, feel like a "Kitten Caught Up a Tree." I also feel "Crazy." I love you Pats. You make me feel normal. Speaking of normal, when I hit menopause, or should I say it hit me, I never did go back to meet with the boys. So in the end, I guess I did adjust my schedule.

# Hot Hot Hot Flash

*Write about your own experience with pms, hot flashes and hormones!*

# TOO TALL, TOO THIN, TOO OLD, TOO...

**Mary MacDonald**

After years of thinking I was too tall, too old, too poor, too scared, or too late, I had run out of excuses. I wanted to sing, dance and shout my music to the world, but my dilemma was identifying what that music looked like, smelled like, tasted like. I read every book and magazine article that remotely dealt with finding your bliss, understanding your intuition and how to figure out what you want to be when you grow up when you are already grown-up. I combed the bookstores searching for stories about people who had set out on a similar pilgrimage that culminated in a successful outcome - aside from Luke Skywalker that is. All I found were people who had left six figure income jobs with hefty savings accounts - so it appeared I was on my own. I read books that tell us to look back to when we were children and what we loved to do. Well, I tried that too but couldn't really figure out how skipping and playing hopscotch could play a big role in my life's work. If any of you out there have the answer, please, I urge you to call me as I would love to find out and maybe we can make a million or two skipping together.

I had bought into all the negative stories that I and others told me about myself. I believed that if I followed the "rules" everything would work out. I needed to look at what role I played in the drama I called my life. And God knows I loved a good drama. As my friend Sandra said, "You never just had a yeast infection, it had to be a raging yeast infection." I forgot who I was because I was too busy being what I thought everyone else expected me to be and playing out the 'story' I told about myself. Much of how I behaved and reacted was based on these stories of the negative I Am's - I am: selfish, unworthy, abandoned, unappreciated and never enough. I needed to acknowledge, feel and then release these beliefs and stop blaming others and myself and stop giving my power away. When I was able to see my part in what I had created and took responsibility for it, I was able to release the old stories. I found out that once you do that you can never go back there for very long. Sometimes I really, really wish I could go back because at times it would feel great to blame someone else! Accepting what is and then taking action from there frees me to create what it is I truly want.

In my late 40's I was compelled to make a change in my life. I didn't know what that change looked like, only that I HAD to make it. I needed to find out who I was apart from my roles and my history, except I didn't even know how to tell what I wanted, what I liked, even what I didn't like. At that age I was terrified to leap into the unknown - I thought I was too old and how could I possibly manage financially, what would people think? But it was like two hands on my back pushing me. It didn't feel courageous as so many said - it just felt that unless I jumped off the cliff I would lose myself completely.

So when I asked my friends for the trillionth time what I should do with my life they barely rolled their eyes. They are loving and beautiful, funny and wise, wild and brash, demanding and talented, judgmental and kind, compassionate and always there when I need them and even when I don't. They let me know I am never alone but let me alone when they know I need to be.

So when, at the ripe young age of 50, I took a leap of faith, although some would perhaps call it a leap of folly, quit my well paid job and sold all of my possessions, they bought stuff they didn't need at my garage sale, stored the stuff they didn't buy, shared copious bottles of "see ya later" wine, assured me I am well loved, packed me up and sent me on my way.

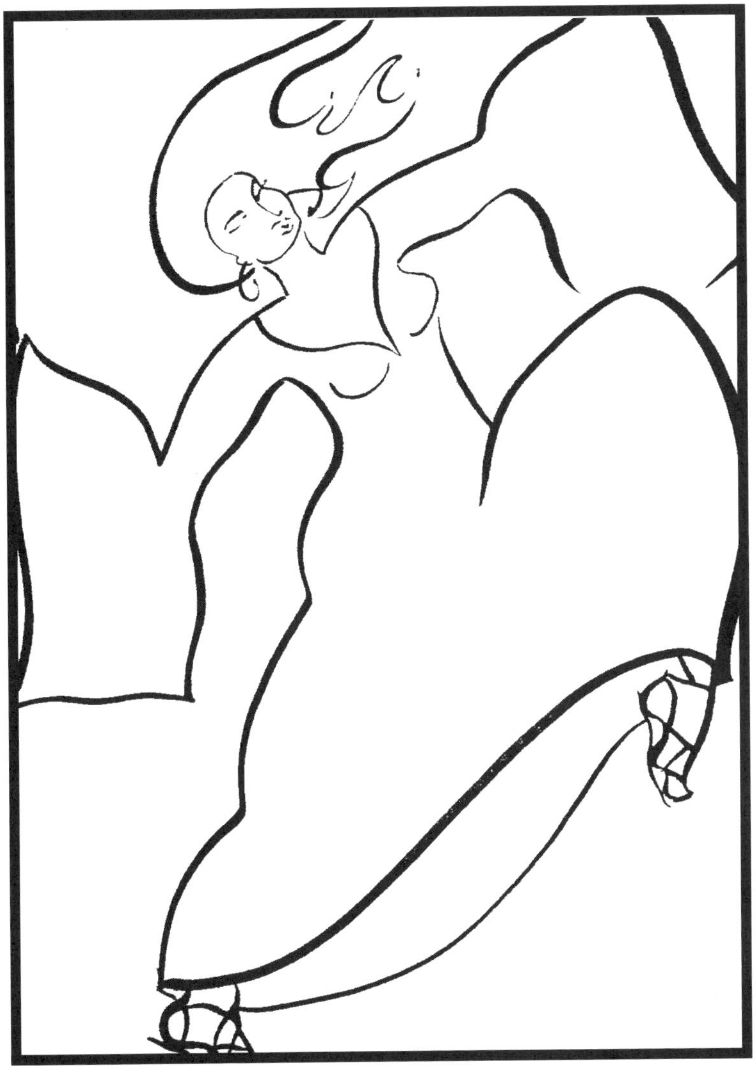

So I got into my car and began my solo road trip across the country, minus the Thelma to my Louise. So as I continue to navigate the yellow brick road I am guided and prodded every step of the way - at times vigorously talking back to who or whatever is doing the prodding. Although it is still sometimes terrifying when late at night the "bag lady blues" fills my head and I still don't know where I'll land - at this moment I am dancing as fast ***as I want to*** in this magical, mystical world. Although deep inside I have always been a security hound I am finding out that living with less can be a blessing and where there is a will there is a way. So don't let anyone tell you that you are too old, too short, too blue. Claim your truth and live life as large as you want to be! And be on the look out for a book called *Living Large on $10 a Day*.

TO BE CONTINUED…

Sometimes your only available transportation is a leap of faith.
Margaret Shepherd

# The High Road

**Navigating Challenging Exchanges and Responding With Grace!**

## Shiloh Sophia McCloud

**In a situation where you feel reactive**

stop --- breath --- pray --- inquire --- imagine --- wait --- choose --- respond

1. Stop – do not respond now. If you can, tell them you will get back to them. Ask for time. You can just say—I really need some time right now. Can I get back to you? It may take profound discipline to not react. Honor the large context by choosing in advance that you will not react.

2. Breath – sit down, drink some water, reflect, go ahead and feel mad/sad or whatever you are feeling. Experience it as fully as you can, alone. Write in your journal if you have to. Write a letter or e-mail and do not send it!

3. Pray or Meditate – get guidance from within, or from a non-related party. Try to get grounded. To feel connected to you. To the greater work and greater issue. Use your own spiritual practice to basically chill out. Then try to get your mind off of it for a while. Read an inspirational text.

4. Inquire – Ask yourself: What do I want the greater outcome to be from our exchange? What did they mean? What did I make it mean that it might not have meant? How can I make this work? Does it matter who's right? Is my ego informing my behavior? Am I responding this same way with other issues, so, is it one of my hot points? Do I really think this person meant such and such or could they have meant something else? Is it important enough to address? Does it need to be confronted? Can we move on gracefully? How can I make this work, no matter who I think is right or wrong? What is my part?

5. Imagine – see yourself creating the solution. See the low road option, see the high road option. Imagine the conversation and the outcome. Imagine how you could bless them in this situation. Imagine acknowledging your part powerfully. Imagine what you really want to happen.

6. Wait – do not take action yet. Go about your business. Let it sink in. And if after all that – you still want to get mad at them – then perhaps it is appropriate. But if not, perhaps you are ready to take the high road!

7. Choose – Set up a time-space to talk. I do not recommend processing emotionally via e-mail. Tears, quivers and half smiles will be missed and our words cannot speak for you unless you are a master wordsmith, in which case, even more so, wait. Request a phone call or even better, a face to face.

8. Respond – Okay, this is it. Remember all the work you have done to not ruin this relationship, this bond, this ally. Whether she was right or wrong does not matter, the relationship is what matters. Keep remembering your HIGH ROAD decision and keep responding from that place instead of the victim place. Make sure they feel heard. Listen to them first. Just a note: If this person continues to act out, be abusive or manipulate you after doing this two or three times, then do it one more time and use it to exit the relationship gracefully and ask for a "time out." You do not need to tell them it's because they are such a jerk. It can be about you.

# Mompreneur

**Nikiah Seeds**

Something happens to women after they have children—a softening occurs and regardless of whether or not they choose to go back to the work they did before having children, it suddenly becomes of great importance that time spent away from their children be fulfilling.

Following one's life path is not easy when you have bills to pay, but women who, after childbirth, are fortunate enough to have some time off from their "paying" job, often find themselves day dreaming about things they left behind. If you are one of these, who, along with the consuming task of raising children, are longing to create a life for yourself and make money on the side, then perhaps you have it in you to become a "Mompreneur."

Mompreneur? Why the heck not! Women have long fought for the right to have jobs, to be equal in the workplace and to show the world all the amazing things that woman can do! However, it is still not a perfect world and women are still not paid as much as men in many business settings and it is really hard when you are trying both to work your way up the ladder and take care of your children. For some of us the solution has been to go into business for ourselves.

Most of my friends who are mothers and have chosen to stay home with their children are just not willing to give up that part of themselves that gave their lives the depth they desired beyond grass stains and paint spills. As a Mompreneur myself, with two children and a thriving small business that I run from my home, I know all too well what it takes to juggle diapers and deadlines, stomach flus, runny noses and a messy living room that needs to be cleared of kids homework and snacks and cleaned in time for an important business meeting.

Our role from the days of our mothers and grandmothers has changed so fast and is so far removed from the pressures and choices even our mothers had. Add to all these challenges two other factors unique to women: the constant feeling of Guilt about time spent or not spent with our children and/or our business, and Guilt's best friend, the feeling of Unworthiness. Many women, whether mothers or not and whether they are creating knitted scarves or jewelry for sale from their homes or are working outside the home in full fledged corporate consulting firms, suffer from these afflictions. While most of us share these same problems, we often feel alone when it comes to the unique types of stresses and issues that modern women face today—particularly with regards to our children and business and money!

Besides being driven to find our life's work, we deserve to make money at it without feeling guilty. Two things seem to help: Creating networking and support systems and journaling in order to process and gain clarity. This is what "Heart of the Visionary" is all about!

# No Need To Re-Invent the Wheel!!!!

**Gennifer Mountain**

**So you want to start your own business?**
I did! I had my business plan, business cards, office supplies, a scented candle that smelled like lemon grass for inspiration, a symbol to light my path, to blaze my trail to doing the work I really wanted to do. I also had thoughts of what suppliers to work with, how much inventory to invest in, for sales tax information. Would I get myself health benefits? Will I have the staff of my dreams? Would those people I chose to work for me/with me, have the skill set to do the job as I envisioned? Could I do all the work by myself if needed? Should I really RE-INVENT THE WHEEL?

During my college years, in a million of my Public Health classes I heard time and time again, "DO NOT RE-INVENT THE WHEEL!" I have used this notion time and again while building curriculum, or thinking about strategic program planning, so why on Earth was I about to do it here, with this business? Did I really have all my bases covered? While I was about to conduct surveys to find out what women's interests and needs were pertaining to my entrepreneurial idea, did I pause and take the time to conduct a survey with myself? How would I go about this? I thought about it for a couple of days and then decided to scour the phonebook and skim over the web, until I found a business that was already established, to see if I could become a part of it. And I did!! And I learned a whole lot about wanting to start my very own business!!

Original Plan: To provide women with a safe environment to learn, to discuss, to share their experiences, their laughter and their curiosities about sexual and reproductive health. I am such a huge advocate for women's health and had my share of employment where I worked with groups of women to help them make the best choices regarding their sexual and reproductive health. What I loved were the conversations, the learning and the eye opening experiences that women had in these groups, the craving they gained to know themselves better and to make healthier choices.

I was going to take it on the road, open up space for women to have home parties, to discuss these issues, to purchase literature, to discover massage oils, to gain a better knowledge of just how many massagers and vibrators existed for their pleasure.

I even had my MOM involved. She created a beautiful logo for the business and a name to go with it. She agreed to hand design and make each piece of sensual sweet lingerie that would go with me on my journey to home parties. We had ideas to market a - Design your own 'Goddess Robe' made of the finest fabrics and velvet trims one could find and she was going to profit as well. We even went as far as to design themed vibrator bags for the special toys!

What I learned, is that my MOM loves me, is proud of me and would go to great lengths to be in team with her daughter and her whimsical ideas. This idea, while not whimsical, had a huge air of romance to it and so we dreamt together.

What I do now: Not far from the vision, I am a consultant with Oh You Naughty Ladies home parties. They have been in business for over 20 years and are a very reputable and successful business. I am a consultant; I have my own business license, business name, business cards and a resale permit. I get to pay sales tax and I even have lemon grass scented candles. What I do know is that by not Re-Inventing the Wheel and taking on this space in my life to be a consultant for this company, I have discovered that while I love being a part of this business, I certainly would NOT want to be the owner of the company.

## DISCOVERIES

WHAT I LOVE:
I love getting together with groups of women and sharing what I know about health and sexuality. I love that we can get together and create a space to celebrate ourselves as sexual human beings. I love helping answer those questions woman usually do not ask and I love hearing and making women laugh! I love getting ready for a party in perfectly professional princess wear, showing up and meeting new gals! I love sharing my box of toys and listening to the giggles. I love the money. Wait, I said, I LOVE THE MONEY$$$! I love creating my own hours, doing parties when I like, I love knowing that I am a part of a business that I can grow how I like it, that I do not OWN the entire business and that I will never have to do it alone!

I DO NOT LOVE:
Paperwork, orders that are backed up, people who flake on parties, worrying if I can live off this career path, advertising, the actual logistics and all the details that linger on well after the party is over.

THE LESSON:
In thinking that I wanted to start my own business, I was choosing to do work that pleased me, that fed my soul, that nourished me on some level. My Grandfather told me several times over the course of his life that I should find a job to do that I would do for free. I took his encouragement very seriously. Most of my life, outside of the waitressing and bar-tending jobs I had during college, I have done exactly what my Grandfather advised. I have made choices to do the work that I like, that gives me a sense of accomplishment, that makes me feel like I have a purpose and that connects me to the people of this planet.

# HO!HO!HA!HA!HA!

## The Practice of Laughter Yoga

**Ananda Wildflower**

*The Wonderful Work of Laughter For No Reason!*

Laughter Yoga is an innovative breakthrough exercise which combines Unconditional Laughter with yogic breathing (pranayama). Anyone can laugh without relying on humor, jokes, or comedy. Laughter is initially simulated as a physical exercise and promoting childlike playfulness. This quickly leads to real and contagious laughter. Science has proved that the body CANNOT differentiate between simulated and real laughter. Laughter Yoga is the only technique that allows adults to achieve sustained hearty laughter without involving cognitive thought. It bypasses the intellectual system that normally acts as a brake on natural laughter. It is modeled after children's play because children laugh naturally 300-500 times a day and this reflects our authentic state of joyful and ecstatic state of bliss.

The physical benefits of Laughter include lowering the effects of stress hormones, releasing endorphins and feel-good hormones, boosting the immune system, detoxification, massaging the internal organs, flooding the body's cells with oxygen and increasing circulation, making the heart healthy with cardio-aerobic exercise, producing natural anti-depressants and painkiller hormones in the brain and lowering blood pressure. It also helps the skin with anti-aging! Because Laughter Yoga is based on the science of Neuro Linguistic Programming, we can affect our mind through our body by teaching our body to laugh. From laughing we initiate powerful positive changes in behavior, body, mind and emotions, which serve as anchors that create new brain connections conditioned to the joyful anchor action in the body. "Motion Creates Emotion" is a proven scientific fact that there is very little difference between thinking about doing something and actually doing it. This makes Laughter Yoga a very easy and powerfully effective tool for personal transformation and empowerment of the values and attitudes we want to have. Laughter Yoga was founded in 1995, in a public park by Dr. Madan Kataria and his wife, Maduri Kataria, a yoga teacher. It is now a worldwide movement in over 63 countries, with over 6,000 laughter yoga clubs meeting for Unconditional Laughter.

### Laughter Yoga Practices

For each exercise, chant the Laughter Yoga chant, HO! HO! HA! HA! HA! in a rhythmic pattern and sound repeatedly as you get going! Don't worry about feeling silly. You will! Just embrace silly - and the power of laughter to dislodge blocked passages in your mind, heart, body and soul! Warning: You might want to try this when you are home alone, or with a really good girlfriend or group of girlfriends. Sometimes it is challenging for us to let out our belly laughs when someone is listening!

**Living Gratitude Laughter**

Gratitude is at the heart of the Visionary! This exercise in gratitude creates a powerful merging of your visionary self, the laws of attraction and your experience of living in gratitude! What you act out and feel in your body opens the way to experience more gratitude for your life!

Stretch out your arms, lengthening and feeling open and light in your body. Breathe deeply from your belly, with an inner smile coming from your heart. Close your eyes and turn your attention inwards to your heart experience. Fill yourself with the emotion of Gratitude. Begin to laugh as you celebrate all the good that is coming to you all the time and how GREAT you feel because you are so in gratitude. Increase your excitement and intensify your expression of Gratitude with Laughter louder and louder! Act out the body experience of celebrating getting what you want! You might even do a little gratitude dance. Look up at the sky with your face and chin and eyes and your arms and hands outstretched to reach the sky! Radiate your inner joy and smile to all your cells and organs and expand your energy body with this blissful consciousness, full of living gratitude and celebration for all the beauty and gifts you have been blessed with already and that are on their way to you now! End with 5 deep belly breaths.

**Emotional Freedom Laughter**

Often times, what keeps us from manifesting our dreams into action plans is our conflicting emotions. When we are clear on what we want and we practice that emotion and way of being then it keeps the conflict at bay. This exercise encourages us to release the emotional energies that are often keeping us stuck, that are not in alignment with who we are. As much as you are able, give yourself to this emotional release to free up your energy! The ability to manifest is a tool and abundance is available all around us! Let's ask for it!

Begin to think and feel the emotion that you suspect might be keeping you from manifesting the highest dreams of your extraordinary self. You are healed, healthy, whole and wealthy just as you are! Be in touch with the energy of anger, resentment, hurt, sadness, shame, fear, the undeservingness and the story that came along with it. Don't worry that this is taking you into some negative place, we go there all the time anyway - we are accessing it so we can release it. Go deeper into the intensity of that feeling which you are ready to release. When you are ready to let go and become emotionally free of it, breathe in from your belly, fire breaths of intensity, scream and shake and move your body and let the energy out of your body, stomp your feet and then bring your entire body and arms down to the ground, yelling out, even crying might come up - if it does, express it! Let it all be released into the gentle nurturing earth which will receive this prayer and compost it into beautiful blossoms of fresh new life. When you are completely ready, and have exhaled as much as you can, let the feeling and visual presence of divine golden light pour in. Then begin to laugh, giggle a childlike, girlish, shy giggle. It may feel silly at first, but once you get started you will feel the joy of this practice. Begin to move your body upward, again. Move your arms up, slowly bringing your spine up straight and roaring with laughter! Breathe in your peace and wholeness and your ability to access the tools of manifestation to turn ideas into actions! Breathe the inner smile for 5 deep breaths before completing. Anticipate your highest good flowing towards you!

**Inevitable Abundance Laughter**

This is an easy and fun exercise to do because its about receiving showers of Money! Enact the laws of attraction in the universe by feeling the joy and celebration of your bounty in your body and spirit. The more you allow yourself to feel it, and get into it, the more it will become real for you as a way of being. We can experience inevitable abundance all the time when we are ready and willing to laugh it on in! Of course, abundance is not always money based, but in this case, our focus is indeed money. And Abundance sounds so much better than finances!

Imagine Gold Coins are showering you like snow flakes falling from the heavens, falling gently all around you into piles of gold that belong to you. All you have to do is receive it because its coming to you personally! Laugh and Breathe in the reality of 'having enough' - and then more than enough! See the Gold Coins turning into whatever you want to create with it, buying a new wardrobe or feeding the hungry children of the world, or starting your own company with the money you have now. Realize that YOU are so much abundance, you deserve to be taken care of. When you are ready and sure it is yours, and feel the emotion of possibility and confidence, then give some away, scooping it up into baskets and distributing it to those you love and charitable causes you want to help - including using your resources to empower other women and girls! End with laughter and breathing gently, seeing that you are always in the flow of wealth and have a lot of money and resources to share! Breathe 5 full deep belly breaths and add the inner smile in your pause in between inhalation and exhalation as you penetrate and expand your energy body with inner blissfulness! See all your cells and organs and body expand and be full and radiant with the bliss nectar of wildflower abundance that is your true nature!

# In wellness we thrive

**Alisa Franzone-Davis**

Who is a powerful leader? You are! We are! Presently, if you are not feeling or living like a leader, it is because your leadership may be dormant. Now is the time to bring it forth; to develop it from within; to help it grow and flower through daily practice. Now is the time to become the woman that you were meant to be! Are your ready!? Of course you are! Even if you weren't before, you can start right now!

A powerful woman looks within to make decisions, to make choices and to find the answers. She trusts herself, her heart, her intuition, her soul. The light lives within her. The power lives within her. Her leadership is at the core of her being. It allows her to stand tall in the light and in the dark. She makes choices and decisions that are in the best interests of herself (the individual), her business, the world and the universe, in any given moment, no matter the circumstances.

What does this have to do with health and wellness? When a woman experiences health and wellness, she is supported to develop from within herself, to become and be the woman she was meant to be and, once this occurs, she can choose happiness, harmony and peace, regardless of the chaos around her.

So, how do we attain health and wellness? There are key daily practices we can undertake that will help us reach the health and wellness which will support us in drawing out the powerful woman that lies within all of us and is just waiting to be set free. Most often, she has called out to you already. Now it is time to invite her more fully!

- PLAY toward your vision, dream, purpose. It will become a reality.
- EAT AND DRINK organic, vibrant, whole foods and beverages - the ultimate eating lifestyle would include 80% raw organic whole foods and 20% cooked organic whole foods. Nurturing the body nurtures your vision, dream and purpose. The harmony of organic whole foods plus the harmony of fulfilling one's life work and purpose brings forth health and wellness
- EXERCISE your physical self a minimum of 3 days per week. It stimulates the body, mind and soul!
- SLEEP get plenty! Make time for rest, relaxation and healing.
- BREATHE fully throughout the day. This practice may seem obvious, but the majority of people do not breathe properly and therefore are lacking in oxygen.
- TAKE TIME for meditation, silence and/or reflection. It is a time to watch, detach and let go of the mind chatter, the self criticism, the complaints, gossip, sarcasm, excuses and/or whining. Write down all that you are grateful and thankful for! This workbook can help with that!

- JOURNAL your thoughts, ideas, visions, and/or dreams. It is a crucial tool that helps to bring forth the creative powers that lie within you just waiting to be unleashed!
- CONNECT Make time for your family and friends! Give love to those you cherish.
- LET NATURE NUTURE YOU Get sunshine, take in fresh air, observe the beauty that surrounds you. Commune with nature, connect with the earth, the world, the universe.
- GUARD YOUR INTEGRITY Make sure your thoughts, words and deeds are in alignment.
- CHOOSE Everyday, throughout the day. Consciously choose health, balance and harmony. Choose to see the truth and reality. Choose honesty and love.Choose your life. Choose to be a powerful woman!

When it is time to eat, simply ask yourself, "Is this going to enhance my health, wellness and overall well being or deplete it?" When it is time to make a decision or a choice, ask yourself , "Is this going to enhance my health, wellness and overall well being or deplete it?" In the moment, ask yourself, "Am I being true to myself?, Am I choosing health? Am I letting circumstances dictate my emotions? Am I creating my life or am I giving that power away to others?"

This list of key practices is not exhaustive but it is complete enough to get you started on your journey toward total health and wellness. We can recapture our true selves. and become the women we were meant to be.

Practice daily and you will be rewarded in ways you've never dreamed. We can be at peace. We can have balance and live in harmony. We can be gorgeous, powerful and wear a #*@^ eating grin!

# JUICY RECIPES FROM ALISA

Use organic ingredients (grown without pesticides, herbicides or genetic engineerings) whenever possible.

**THE GREEN GODDESS**
2 handfuls of baby spinach
2 handfuls of sunflower sprouts
8 stalks of celery
1/4 bunch of parsley
1/2 organic cucumber
1 1/2 organic apples
You may add lemon juice, ginger juice, cayenne and/or crystal salt to taste.

If you are using a juicer, place all ingredients through the juicer and enjoy. If you are using a blender, place all of the water based ingredients in the blender first (cucumber, celery) and then add the rest of them one ingredient at a time until all have been added and fully blended. If the mixture will not blend you may add filtered water - a little at a time so you do not "water down" the drink. You want just enough water to get the ingredients to mix. If you wish not to use water at all, add some fresh apple juice instead of using whole apples (4-6 oz or you may use 4-6 oz coconut water). Once the mixture is fully blended place the mixture in a nutmilk bag and squeeze out the juice into another container. Add condiments to the juice at this time.
Compost the pulp and enjoy the juice.

**RAINBOW SMOOTHIE**
14 oz fresh apple juice
1/2 cup frozen blueberries
1/2 cup frozen strawberries
1/2 cup frozen mangos
1/2 frozen banana
4 oz young thai coconut meat
1 T Vitamineral Green (or other superfood green powder of your choice - optional)
1 T Blue-Green Algae, such as Spiralina (optional)
1 T Rainbow Smoothie Supplement - I like Bright-Earth (optional)
1 T Hemp Seeds (optional)
1 T Bee Pollen (optional)
Place all ingredients in a blender and blend well. Pour and enjoy!
Serves 2
Note: You can purchase a young thai coconut at any health oriented food store and sometimes at your local supermarket - unfortunately, usually, they are not organic - the young thai coconut will be found in a white husk - it is not the coconut that you find in the brown hairy hard shell.

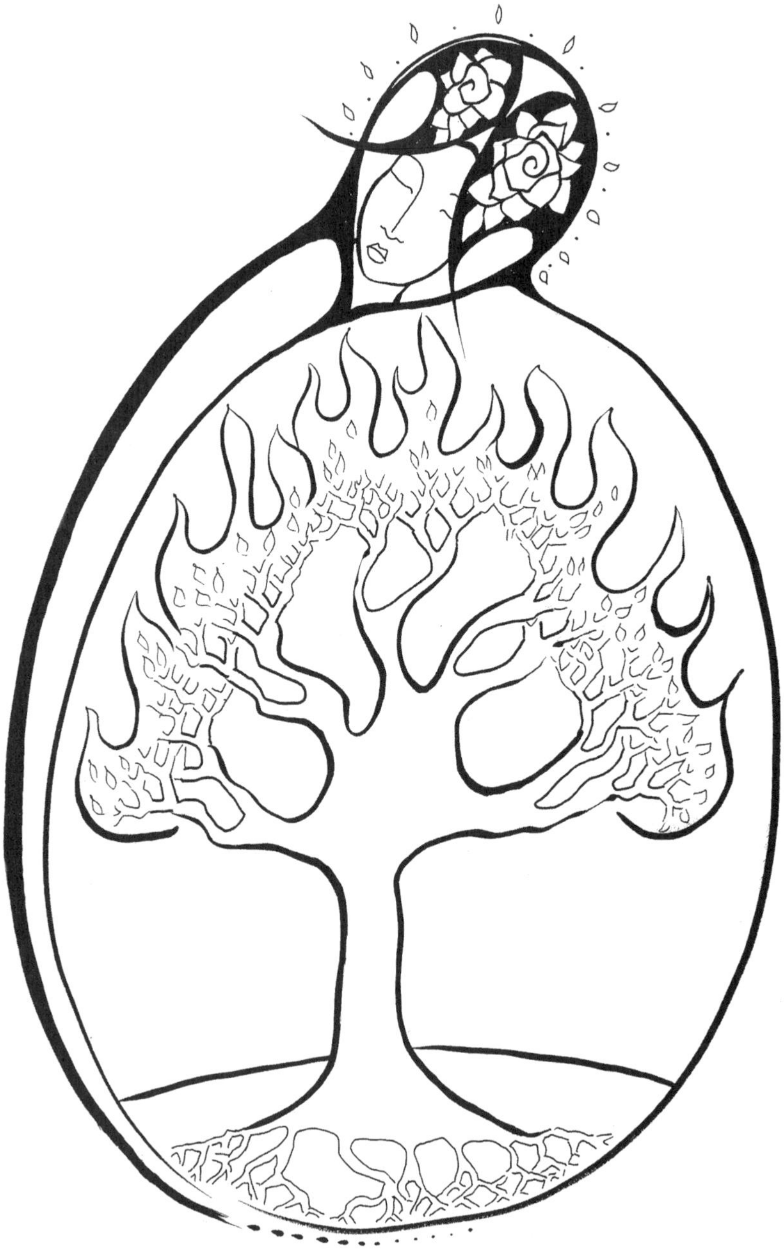

When I care for myself, I care for the World.

When I love myself

I am more lovable and more able to love others.

# Write a Love Letter To Your Body

# DECLARATION OF INTEGRATION AND INDEPENDENCE

FOR

## Visionary Entrepreneurs

### Shiloh Sophia McCloud

**We hold these truths and realizations to be self-evident, that all women and men are created equal, that we are endowed by our Creator with unique gifts and a Life Purpose that is specific to us personally. Among these gifts are life, liberty, love, wellness, the pursuit of happiness and sustainable life work. That to realize these gifts and fulfill our life purpose, relationships, businesses and governments are instituted among men and women, deriving their just powers from the consent of those participating. We hold that whenever any form of relationship, business, paradigm, belief system or government becomes destructive of these ends, it is the right of the people to alter or to abolish it, and to institute new systems and pathways in alignment with life giving moral standards. The foundation of which shall be formed on such principles and organizing its powers as to us, shall seem most likely to create our safety and happiness and abundance. To show our faith in this declaration and in our work let the fruits of our labors be submitted to a candid world. We shall go forth and create our independent works of profound beauty that have lasting impact, are good for all concerned and create a sustainable livelihood thrive, clothe, feed and house ourselves, our endeavors and our families, and to give to those causes which we see fit.**

I give thanks to the Declaration of Independence, which can be easily viewed in it's entirety on-line at www.ushistory.org/declaration/. I do not in anyway intend to defile it's perfection or the beauty of that occurrence. I hope to use it as a tool to inspire us to create our own declarations. The Declaration of Independence was a part of creating the United States and getting the folks who wrote it clear on why it was needed in the first place. We too need to do that for ourselves. And much of the document is articulating the injustices that have occurred. There is not a thing wrong with naming what has been holding us back in an effort to move forward.

# MY DECLARATION OF INDEPENDENCE

## The Vision Re-Visited

*Re-write your Vision Statement based on what you have learned since you started. The vision is different than the mission because it includes more of what inspired you to do this work and what the big picture and impact will be on the well being of others or the planet. Go back and take a look at the Feminine Business Paradigm questions and answer some of them with your vision. Share it with a friend and continue to refine until if feels so totally good to you!*

## *Every Woman Is the Queen of Her Own Heart*

*Shiloh Sophia McCloud*

*She must decide how to govern her own domain.
She seeks friends and allies that honor who she is now
and who she is becoming.
She has the power to create miracles.
Her prayers and intentions manifest in right order.
She does not know how or when her needs will be met,
but she trusts the will of the Divine.
Being the Queen of one's domain is not about being
the ruler over anyone else's life or ideas.
And it isn't even about calling herself a Queen.
It is about self honor. It is about choice.
It is about knowing her limits and setting her boundaries.
And about encouraging others to live their possibilities.
It is about learning how to live with what comes her way,
with as much grace, majesty and justice as she can.
And sometimes, yes, she has to have her own way!
She claims her unique destiny and recognizes she has a calling.
A calling to greatness within her own life.
And within her own heart.*

*The Queen of Her Own Heart invites others to join her there -
in the middle of the awakened sacred heart.
She invites others to love powerfully - unconditionally -
while at the same time practicing discernment and wisdom.
She is forgiving. And she believes healing is at hand.
She leads her own life as grand experiment in happiness,
in creativity and in abundance.
She offers her gifts to others, but not to her own detriment.
She rests as she needs to, ruling one's own life takes energy.
She chooses to embody wholeness
even when she feels fragmented by all there is to do.
She holds the prayers of the world within her
because she cares what happens - with everyone -
even though she cannot reach them all. She reaches who she can.
She often feels like she is not pulling it all off,
and sometimes she isn't. But she keeps reaching anyway.
She keeps opening her heart and being in her own power.
Knowing and Sharing her heart is ecstasy.
Sharing the heart of her beloved is absolute and perfect joy.
She lives in gratitude.*

# COMPASSION

## The Power of Caring

**Shiloh Sophia McCloud, Alice Walker, Jean Shinoda Bolen, Marilyn Nyborg**

**and Kelly Takunda Orphan Martinez**

**Illustrations by Shiloh Sophia McCloud and Sue Hoya Sellars**

## *Give It To the People*

*Song By Kelly Takunda Orphan Martinez*

*In this time of uncertainty*
*The question is who's really free?*
*Scales tipped over to one side,*
*too many people to survive.*

*So they dig a hole and call it home,*
*But there's not enough to go around*
*And nobody's warm.*

*But I sit here comfortably.*
*Maybe a palace fit for kings.*
*Wondering what is my place*
*In this life we lead.*

*When I stop and think about*
*How much has been given*
*I gotta turn around, pass it on*
*And keep on livin'.*

*CHORUS*
*Give it to the people What's been given*
*Give it to the people Keep on Living*
*Give it to the people What's been given*

*Gotta keep on walking, keep on talking, keep on moving on.*
*Give it to the people.*

*Fallen into a sleep that doesn't want to see*
*Broken lives and shattered dreams.*
*Greed has clouded so many eyes.*
*Some of them fail to recognize:*

*The brother pushing the cart, growing old, collecting cans*
*My sister trapped in jail, she's just trying to make amends.*
*If fate would have it, if it was my time around,*
*It could easily be me who's lost and never found.*

*CHORUS*
*Give it to the people*
*What's been given*

# *The Awakened Heart*

*Waking Up to the World Soul*

**Shiloh Sophia McCloud**

An Awakened Heart happens when a person is awakened through compassion to an awareness of the collective beauty and suffering of the world soul. The people that compose that world soul, which is all of us, then become a part of the visionary landscape of our individual experience, informing how our love manifests in the world. We are now called to a way of being that includes the lives of not just our immediate circle, but the greater circle of the whole world. This experience contains within it the absolute bliss of connectivity, the crushing pain of our separation from one another and from the Divine. To remain awakened to it and receive the gifts that come from this kind of profound caring, one must act on behalf of other lives, somehow working to relieve even a small part of the suffering. This action arises not out of an attempt to be a good or holy person, but rather so we can awaken to what is happening in the heart of the world.

The weight of the knowing causes many to become inspired to their greater life purpose! But it can also be thoroughly depressing and cause one to feel hopeless, Sometimes its a combination of both. This is understandable based on the circumstances. However, when important information is revealed to us, to not live into that knowing is not an option. When you know, you know. If we choose not to respond we may become resentful about what appears to be the meaninglessness of our existence. The blessings that accompany designing a life that brings healing to the heart of the world are immeasurable in areas of insight, access to information, personal relationships, community action, creative expression and connection to the divine fruits of life. And when we dedicate our efforts to our life purpose, instead of spending our precious time dwelling upon what has hurt us in the first place, then greater strides towards wholeness can be made.

When one can also learn to harness the power and flow of abundance in order to ensure that they can do their work, focusing on thriving instead of just surviving, then it is truly something to celebrate! Both in the past and present there are beliefs indicating that ministers of heart work should give their work away for free. While that may be the call of some servants of good, it is certainly not the call of all who are doing the work of Spirit on this earth. The nature of reaping and sowing ensures that the sower must collect the harvest in order to continue to sow the next season. Some saints may have escaped this process, but most folk have immediate cares and they cannot cease to create actual income in order to pursue a holy vision. There has also been an insidious collective misunderstanding about the value of visionaries, artists, musicians, poets, healers as agents of change and servants of the Holy One. While the work is considered important, it is still marginalized by the status quo and constantly in question regarding how these kinds of positions are to be compensated, if at all. May we all be awakened to the beauty, power and abundance that comes from answering our life calling!

**Entrepreneurs are agents of change** who through their chosen independence, ideas and fierce determination set out to create a value which they hope to define for themselves. They seek to provide a product or service that meets a need or a want that can be created independent of corporate origins. As with any powerful tool, entrepreneurs can use their gifts for good or ill, but there is no question that entrepreneurs are redefining how business is done. Their businesses have the flair and branding of the individual, but are designed to meet the needs of many.

Just think, if entrepreneurialism was focused entirely on creating what many have been calling, "the highest good for all." We are calling for a continuous flow of conscious entrepreneurs to enter the marketplace and change the way we "consume" through providing healthier choices and options! Many new businesses, like hemp and bamboo fabrics, organic mattresses, organic farming, green building and so much more, are doing just that. The trend towards information going green and environmentally stable is educating us far and wide about caring for our planet. And this in turn means caring for our people.

Much of the "caring" of the people of the world is being negotiated by incredible teams of heroes who work for non-profits. What a blessing it is to have a business entity that can operate on this premise. And still, the words non and profit connected with the people and companies continues to create a devaluing of care for the people model of living. A new business structure is called for. One in which the benefits of the non-profit can be received, while the opportunity to grow financially for the folks running the business is operative. Conscious Entrepreneurs are the first tier of this new business structure and are paving a way to do good works for good money and not have that be contra-indicated.

For example, our publishing is visioning and living that model in three ways:
*Giving:* We align with non-profit companies to collaborate on projects and financial gifts.
*Working:* We pay women authors and artists to work with us to create our projects and materials.
*Offering:* We sell products and services that are designed to empower and provide healing tools.

Through this book we are inviting you to join us in this revolutionary movement! When we find our purpose in life, live it and are able to sustain it, that is the surest and most prudent way we can transform the current system from greed based to care based. And it is the happiest, most rewarding. And the funnest too. Welcome!

# Note from Shiloh regarding Alice Walker's
## In Search of Our Mothers' Gardens

*Alice Walker graciously gave me permission to print excerpts from this powerful piece from In Search of Our Mothers' Gardens: The Creativity of Black Women in the South from 1974.*

*I have been working with Alice on projects over the past several years and I continue to be stunned by the beauty, heart break, poignancy and hope present in her works. This writing, with its focus on creativity and black women who were oppressed, seemed like the ideal complement to begin to bring our book to a close in our final chapter, Compassion. Through our yearning to create beauty and balance in our lives against all odds, our struggle is transformed into art. And our Grandmother's would be proud.*

*Some might ask, what a chapter on compassion is doing in a book on women's business? I trust that by now, you know the answer to that question and will be able to inform others that our work as women is informed by our compassion and care for others. That does not mean that to run an organic farm is any less or more important than to be a painter or a dancer. I tell my students that they can march in the streets and that they can also go to their art studio and both are affecting change in the world. I believe the world needs for women to live and express our creativity in all of its forms. Business is one of those forms that also stands the chance of bringing livelihood and transformation to our communities and our world.*

*In this book we have focused primarily on the good, the inspirational, the hope of living a life in alignment with who we are as women. We have chosen not to highlight the oppression and suffering that women have endured throughout the centuries, whether it be from misogyny or unfair wages, harassment, the lack of equal opportunity, the edict to bear children or our own internal oppression. But the reality remains that all people are subject to the tyranny at work in the world, no matter what belief system or tradition one practices. We are at a critical time in our world when the lives of every single particle on earth are at risk. So as women, we might ask: How then can I do "my work" when so many are suffering? Instead of doing my own thing, should I be doing more to help others? Asking this is easy, answering it is not so easy.*

*Alice, Sue and I spoke of this one day - the value that women's creations have on earth. Our conviction that to be joyful, to be artists, writers, dancers, entrepreneurs, to create beauty when there is so much need and also so much needed. We spoke of the audacity it takes to be a happy woman and agreed that those who are privileged enough to be in a position to create should create. For herself and for all those who cannot create. For our Ancestors who struggled to create. And create they did, because here we are. Let us shine our lights wherever we are able. I cannot think of anything more healing for the world than for women to rise in their endeavors and bring more beauty and peace on earth through our creations.*

# In Search of Our Mothers' Gardens
## Alice Walker

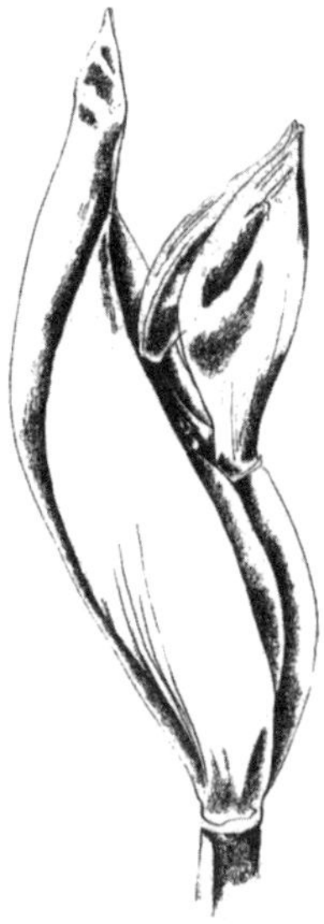

*Speaking of Mother and Grandmothers, Alice shares their story of moving to a "music not yet written"*...They waited for a day when the unknown thing that was in them would be made known; but guessed, somehow in their darkness, that on the day of their revelation they would be long dead.

For these grandmothers and mothers of ours were not "Saints," but Artists; driven to a numb and bleeding madness by the springs of creativity in them for which there was no release. They were Creators, who lived lives of spiritual waste, because they were so rich in spirituality—which is the basis of Art—that the strain of enduring their unused and unwanted talent drove them insane. Throwing away this spirituality was their pathetic attempt to lighten the soul to a weight their work-worn, sexually abused bodies could bear.

What did it mean for a Black woman to be an artist in our grandmothers' time? It is a question with an answer cruel enough to stop the blood. Did you have a genius of a great-great-grand-mother who died under some ignorant and depraved white overseer's lash? Or was she required to bake biscuits for a lazy backwater tramp, when she cried out in her soul to paint watercolors of sunsets, or the rain falling on the green and peaceful pasturelands? Or was her body broken and forced to bear children (who were more often than not sold away from her)—eight, ten, fifteen, twenty children—when her one joy was the thought of modeling heroic figures of Rebellion, in stone or clay?

How was the creativity of the Black woman kept alive, year after year and century after century, when for most of the years Black people have been in America it was a punishable crime for a Black person to read or write? And the freedom to paint, to sculpt, to expand the mind with action did not exist. Consider, if you can bear to imagine it, what might have been the result if singing, too, had been forbidden by law. Listen to the voices of Bessie Smith, Billie Holiday, Nina Simone, Roberta Flack and Aretha Franklin, among others, and imagine those voices muzzled for life. Then you may begin to comprehend the lives of our "crazy," "Sainted" mothers and grandmothers. The agony of the lives of women who might have been Poets, Novelists, Essayists and Short Story Writers, who died with their real gifts stifled within them.

And if this were the end of the story, we would have cause to cry out.

But this is not the end of the story, for all the young women—our mothers and grandmothers, ourselves—have not perished in the wilderness.

When we have asked for love, we have been given children. In short, even our plainer gifts, our labors of fidelity and love, have been knocked down our throats. To be an artist and a Black woman, even today, lowers our status in many respects, rather than raises it: and yet, artists we will be.

Therefore we must fearlessly pull out of ourselves and look at and identify with our lives the living creativity some of our great-grandmothers knew, even without "knowing" it, the reality of their spirituality, even if they didn't recognize it beyond what happened in the singing at church —and they never had any intention of giving it up.

And so our mothers and grandmothers have, more often than not anonymously, handed on the creative spark, the seed of the flower they themselves never hoped to see: or like a sealed letter they could not plainly read.

But the telling of these stories, which came from my mother's lips as naturally as breathing, was not the only way my mother showed herself as an artist. For stories, too, were subject to being distracted, to dying without conclusion. Dinners must be started and cotton must be gathered before the big rains. The artist that was and is my mother showed itself to me only after many years. This is what I finally noticed:

My mother adorned with flowers whatever shabby house we were forced to live in. And not just your typical straggly country stand of zinnias, either. She planted ambitious gardens—and still does—with over 50 different varieties of plants that bloom profusely from early March until late November. Before she left home for the fields, she watered her flowers, chopped up the grass and laid out new beds. When she returned from the fields she might divide clumps of bulbs, dig a cold pit, uproot and replant roses, or prune branches from her taller bushes or trees—until it was too dark to see.

Whatever she planted grew as if by magic and her fame as a grower of flowers spread over three counties. Because of her creativity with her flowers, even my memories of poverty are seen through a screen of blooms—sunflowers, petunias, roses, dahlias, forsythia, spirea, delphiniums, verbena . . . and on and on.

And I remember people coming to my mother's yard to be given cuttings from her flowers; I hear again the praise showered on her because whatever rocky soil she landed on, she turned into a garden. A garden so brilliant with colors, so original in its design, so magnificent with life and creativity, that to this day people drive by our house in Georgia—perfect strangers and imperfect strangers—and ask to stand or walk among my mother's art.

I notice that it is only when my mother is working in her flowers that she is radiant, almost to the point of being invisible except as Creator: hand and eye. She is involved in work her soul must have. Ordering the universe in the image of her personal conception of Beauty.

Her face, as she prepares the Art that is her gift, is a legacy of respect she leaves to me, for all that illuminates and cherishes life. She has handed down respect for the possibilities—and the will to grasp them.

For her, so hindered and intruded upon in so many ways, being an artist has still been a daily part of her life. This ability to hold on, even in very simple ways, is work Black women have done for a very long time.

Guided by my heritage of a love of beauty and a respect for strength—in search of my mother's garden, I found my own.

And perhaps in Africa over 200 years ago, there was just such a mother; perhaps she painted vivid and daring decorations in oranges and yellows and greens on the walls of her hut; perhaps she sang in a voice like Roberta Flack's—sweetly over the compounds of her village; perhaps she wove the most stunning mats or told the most ingenious stories of all the village storytellers. Perhaps she was herself a poet—though only her daughter's name is signed to the poems that we know.

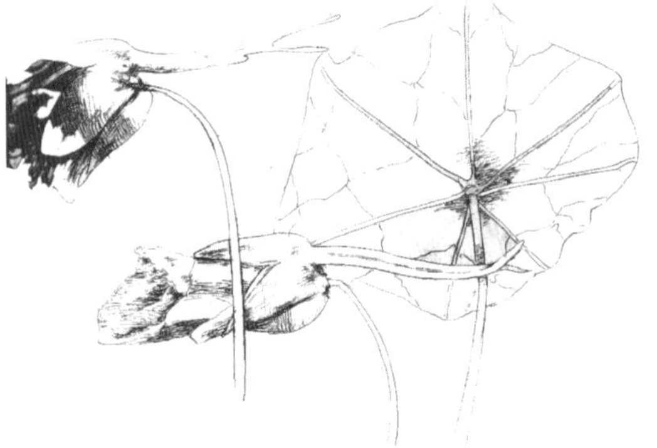

Guided by my heritage of a love of beauty
and a respect for strength—
in search of my mother's garden,
I found my own.

Alice Walker

*Note: Alice Walker and Shiloh McCloud collaborated with Palm of Her Hand to publish a line of greeting cards. The above statement is quoted from what Alice wrote for the back of the cards.*

I believe women know what we need. It is a matter of looking deeply into our lives, our dreams, failings and successes and understanding ourselves, our deepest selves, in relation to them. We guide ourselves by following an invisible thread that grows from the very center of our Being. So that I may lie dreaming for a long time, lost in a fog of sadness and confusion and one day awaken knowing that I must dance. It will be clear to me that: "No one can end suffering, except through dance!" By the time the dance is over the community and all my friends are exhausted along with me, we have moved ourselves to another plateau. We find again art and lust and love and satisfaction, great meals and wide rivers. Such is the aliveness of life. Alice Walker

# A Letter to Grandmother

# *The Millionth Circle and The 5th Women's World Congress*

**Jean Shinoda Bolen**

Bishop Desmond Tutu wrote,"Our earth home and all forms of life in it are at grave risk. We men have had our turn and made a proper mess of things. We need women to save us." Some recognition of this may be reflected in the increasing number of countries that have women heads of state: there were twenty-one in 2007.

Women are the empathic gender, which doesn't mean every woman, but it does mean that women collectively have this as a distinguishing quality. Empathy is the understanding that what hurts me would feel the same way to you. It is the foundation upon which moral decisions are made.

In 2006, research on the female brain got widespread media attention and was the subject of a best-selling book. These studies found that there are four parts of the brain that are usually larger and more active in women than men. These parts have to do with self control, patience, intuition, empathy, ability to weigh options, worry and emotional memory.

The message contained in this book's subtitle,"Gather the Women, Save the World," is about the need for women to participate in peacemaking at every level and has to do with feminism, spiritual activism, mother power, women in circles with a sacred center and three to the nineteenth power. If three women heed the message and if they tell three other women, there would be nine. If each of them then spread the word to three others, there would be twenty-seven. If each of these twenty-seven passed this along to three of their friends, there would be eighty-one. If these eighty-one women talked to three others, in just four steps—there would be 243. In nineteen steps—three to the nineteenth power—this idea would reach over a billion women (1,162,261,467). This is how geometrical progression works, this is how a virus spreads and becomes an epidemic, this is how consciousness-raising groups became the women's movement. This is how a call to gather the women could bring women together in villages, cities, in corporations, in governing bodies everywhere, to do whatever it is that is their assignment from Mother.

Full equality between men and women is one of the most important prerequisites for peace. Without full equality, there is injustice and the promotion of harmful attitudes in boys and men which is carried from the schoolyard and family to the workplace, to political life and ultimately to international relations. Without full equality, qualities associated with women are suppressed in boys and men.

I believe that a 5th United Nations–sponsored international women's conference would be a giant step toward a tipping point—in terms of numbers attending, connections made and a ripple effect. Only a U.N.–sponsored conference would allow women to attend who otherwise would not be able to get visas and support from their countries. Women would share information about what has worked, they would find role models, mentors and allies.

The principle that women's rights are human rights and the Twelve Critical Areas of Concern that constitute the Beijing Platform for Action were the accomplishments of the 4th U.N. International Conference on Women in Beijing in 1995. Half the NGOs that exist now were not in existence in 1995. For there to be a 5th women's conference, we need to create grassroots advocacy for this in the countries that belong to the United Nations and at the UN Commission on the Status of Women meetings.

Excerpted with permission from **Urgent Message From Mother Preface** with permission from Jean Shinoda Bolen www.jeanshinodabolen.com. More info can be found at: www.5wwc.org and www.MillionthCircle.org.

*Without leaps of imagination, or dreaming, we lose the excitement of possibilities.*
*Dreaming after all, is a form of planning.*
*Gloria Steinem*

# *Gather the Women*

## Marilyn Nyborg

*Note: The following article is written by Marilyn Nyborg of "Gather The Women." Marilyn and I have been in touch over the years about what we are both doing in our work with women and she graciously agreed to allow us to print this article as a way for women to learn about the collective gathering that is happening. Thank you Marilyn for calling us together!*

In 1888 a very wise man, ahead of his time said: "If ever the world sees a time when women shall come together purely and simply for the benefit of mankind, it will be a power such as the world has never known." Matthew Arnold.

This is the call Gather the Women (GTW) has responded to and this is the call she has in turn made to women in the world at large. We believe in the importance and value of a woman's perspective. We know men and women think differently, approaching issues and problems from different angles. Women's approach was long ago relegated to family and home. Many of those who have brought their voices to bear have had to assume masculine perspectives to be heard. We believe it is the time now to bring the voice of the Mother out beyond our personal families and into our communities, regions and the world at large. Buoyed by the power of our own internal masculine with the wisdom and compassion of the feminine we seek to contribute to our world and to enter a balanced partnership with men.

Gather the Women avoids specific issues that might be considered divisive so that we might attract women from all religious or political persuasions. We focus on a variety of forums in which women can come together in a safe environment, an environment of beauty and harmony which offers inspiration and encouragement. However, women ARE encouraged to discover their passion and interest and above all to move beyond the personal family to the greater family of humanity. We encourage her to create or join the many opportunities in the community to serve other women, to bring her opinions, skills, time, money and energy to the issues that call her.

For those already doing that and for those who do not know where to begin, we invite you into on-going women's circles. There the gifts and value each woman brings to the circle can be witnessed. Each woman in a circle is nurtured and supported for her work in the world. Gather the Women offers networking with local and national organizations to involve her more deeply in the issues of our day. We urge women to create other initiatives that will bring more influence and value to feminine perspectives.

Women are hungry for deeper, more meaningful, conversation. We love to connect with other women who share our experiences as women. When she can come together with others to make personal connections in a safe space, when the environment is safe enough to speak from her authentic self, when EACH WOMAN is witnessed for her unique gifts, she will be strengthened and empowered to bring her voice to the table…from the kitchen table to the board room table.

NOW is the time for women to gather to activate the incredible power of our wisdom on a planetary scale. It's easy to sit up and take notice. What's difficult is to get up and take action.

# *Calling the Circle*

## Marilyn Nyborg

How to gather a diverse group of women: If we are EVER to get beyond our differences we have to start somewhere to explore our commonalities. The following suggestions are those Gather the Women hold as a container for bringing women together.

• You might begin with your own circle of friends. Would they be interested in gathering women – and would they each bring one other friend?

• Reach out for balance. i.e.: Invite groups representing all major political parties, both sides of an issue, all faiths.

• Encourage, initiate or join on-going women's circles that incorporate circle principles. www.millionthcircle.com that will support and strengthen one another. This can also be project oriented.

• Using methods like THE WORLD CAFÉ to work with questions that build on what is working in your community or organization. www.theworldcafe.com

• Invite women to your home for salons around a subject using a variety of DVDs, or "experts." Deepening the conversation.

• Create a Chautauqua: Invite representatives of other organizations either specific to the issues you are working on or in general to meet. Find out what is working for them? What is not working? And how can you work together to create an event and attract women to join you in your concerns and actions?

• Approach your local newspaper (the more local the better) ask if you can initiate a column for Women's Voices to add their perspective on issues.

• We love festivals, picnics, potlucks. Keep it personal, relational and educational. Give women an opportunity to be heard and appreciated for their unique perspectives.

• Encourage women in education and business to underscore a women's responsibility to the world around her and her unique role.

• Speak from the heart of compassion and do not rely on your frustration and anger with what's wrong with the world to activate women.

• Avoid meeting the energy of anger and war with the same energy and assume it is for peace.

Gather the Women is part of a growing world wide movement, a new feminine wave of energy, of women seeking to bring reverence, respect AND empowerment to all that is feminine. When I speak of the feminine, I am not referring to our makeup, fashion or women's sexuality. I am speaking to our innate capacity for relationships, global thinking, compassion, nurturing attributes, our ability to multitask and even our different way of thinking and problem solving. The recent book *The Female Brain* has documented what most of us already knew....we ARE different from men. And this difference has for centuries been considered less than, the weaker sex, diminished and holding less value outside of the home. This belief is held consciously and unconsciously in the culture by BOTH men and women and has served to rein women in. JUST imagine what that would mean if we lived from respect, reverence and empowerment of all that is feminine?! This is our message. Now....HOW do we communicate this? How do we raise awareness? www.gatherthewomen.org

# Heart of the Visionary

Shiloh Sophia McCloud

She is unreasonable about loving.
At the center of her being
Is a heart as big and bright as the world.
She doesn't know how it got that way.
She knows a lot of women who feel like her.
They want to save the world.
They want the suffering to end.
What is she to do with all of this Love?
How can she love people she doesn't even know?
The lady at the supermarket.
The man at the gas station.
The little boy with dirt on his face.
The little girl with a flower in her hand.
The teenage boy who works a night job.
The teenage girl who feels like she is not enough.
The old woman who drove off the cliff after work one day.
The old man who walks his dog every day.
Uninvited guests of despair and hope and possibility.

She remembers a time before they came.
A time when her days were filled with objectives
And not with the burden and bliss of an open heart.
In her life she has been called a rebel.
A bitch. A mover. A shaker. A revolution maker.
The guests of her heart call her
To the road less travelled.
She walks between the worlds of the yellow wood.
Along the path she sees what must be done.
Sees her part in the great unfolding.
Sees how she can soothe the
suffering with living water.
Sees the other visionaries on the path beside her.
Sees where she can go to make a difference
And be true to her own vision in her own unique way.
It isn't just the soup kitchen or the volunteering.
It is about sharing Art. Beauty. Possibility.
Vision. And good times.
Love is at the center of all her choices.
Love for herself and love for others.
It isn't just about giving - because to the visionary
Giving is getting. And getting causes more giving.
At the heart of the visionary
is the soul of the world.

# COMMUNITY

## The Power of Legend

**Sheroes, Author's Bios, Cosmic Cowgirls Ink, Resources and More!**

**Illustrations by Shiloh Sophia McCloud and Sue Hoya Sellars**

Every woman is the sheroe
of her own story.
She makes it all up
as she goes along.

She must respond to her past.
Navigate her present moment
and design her future.

She is the sheroe
of her own story.
Whether or not
she lives her life in that context.

She works hard. Loves Large.
And dreams BIG DREAMS.
She saves the day,
on so many days,
for so many others.
She solves problems.
Reaches out. Makes plans.

And

she still suffers
and cares too much.

She does not always ask for help.
and she has to continually refine her intention.

What can make the difference is for her
to realize and claim that SHE IS
the sheroe of her own story!
She can live her life within the context of
LEGEND.
It changes things. Gives one a wider view.
It is a permission slip to be a great and powerful woman.

When we choose for life to be a celebration no matter what
we encourage those around us to do the same!
Why not be Legendary?

Shiloh Sophia McCloud

**OUR SHEROES ARE THE WOMEN WHO HAVE GONE BEFORE US.
WHO HAVE MADE IT POSSIBLE FOR US TO DO OUR WORK.
FOR US TO BE WHO WE ARE.**

*All of our lives are made possible by those who have created a way out of no way. Their work, wisdom, inspiration and path-forging spirit will guide us as we move forward with our dreams. You may be a sheroe for someone, or for many people. Write below your own personal sheroe legend. What you want to be known for.*

# COSMIC COWGIRL AUTHORS THANK AND BLESS THEIR SHEROES

**elizaBeth's Sheroes**

thank you, queen of talk, Ms. Oprah
thank you, visionary art maker, Susan Seddon Boulet
thank you, bandit queen, Phoolan Devi
thank you, for overcoming your pain to paint your dreams, Frida Kahlo
thank you, for running with wolves, Clarrisa Pinkola Estes
thank you, for *The Color Purple*, Alice Walker
thank you, for reproductive freedom and education, Margaret Sanger
thank you for your living example of christ's love, Mother Teresa
thank you for your dinner party, Judy Chicago
thank you for your holding power, Karen Sjoholm
thank you for every american girl, Pleasant Rowland
thank you for your painted yard, Gina Wilde
thank you for the taste of calm, Rheem Rahim
thank you for doing it your own magic marker way, SARK
thank you for your body shop, Anita Roddick
thank you for your seeds, Lynne Franks
thank you for findhorn, Eileen Caddy
thank you for beloved, Toni Morrison
thank you for you good things, Martha Stewart
thank you for cookies, Mrs. Fields
thank you for all your make-up, Estee Lauder
thank you for sitting down, Rosa Parks
thank you for standing up, Jane Fonda
thank you for going first, Shirley Chisholm
thank all of you for paving the way.
thank you for your example.
thank you for making our lives possible, our dreams practical, our reaching from a place on a ladder you have left us to climb.
thank you for opening us to what is possible, for believing so fiercely in your own dreams, that ours could catch fire from the light you shine.
thank you for blazing the trails, finding the way, sending word of the twists and turns.
thank you for getting all the way there—safely and intact—and for sharing your stories of powerful dreams and unlimited possibilities.
thank you for being my sisters who did it.

**Shiloh's Sheroes**

Blessings to you for writing the truths, Gloria Steinem
Blessings to you for showing us the chalice and the blade, Rhiane Eisler
Blessings to you for making me draw, Sue Hoya Sellars
Blessings to you for loving beyond reason, Mother Teresa

Blessings to you for illuminating the hard places, Pema Chodrin
Blessings to you for *The Secret Life of Bees*, Sue Monk Kidd
Blessings to you for the birth of Jesus, Mama Mary
Blessings to you for folking it up, Ani Difranco
Blessings to you for reminding us not to be small, Marianne Williamson
Blessings to you for bringing us wisdom, Mother Sophia
Blessings to you for being yourself, Dolly Parton
Blessings to you for music I love, Lucinda Williams and Gillian Welch
Blessings to you for being beautiful, Marilyn Monroe
Blessings to you for your image, Virgen de Guadalupe
Blessings to you for winning no matter what they say, Marion Jones
Blessings to you for being a best friend to me, Bridget Mermaid McBride
Blessings to you for teaching us about blood, Judy Grahn
Blessings to you for telling us the stories of how to run with wolves, Clarissa Pinkola Estes
Blessings to you for encouraging my creativity and individuality, Mama Cloud
Bless you, all midwives, all natural dentists, all healers, all lovers, all single mothers
Bless you, all men who support women
Bless you, all women who love whole heartedly and who are rebels
Bless you, all check out girls, waitresses, nurses, receptionists, latte makers and cookie cutters
Bless you, all abundant ones, who share your fruits
Bless you, all oppressed ones who refuse to stop reaching
Bless you, all women artists and dancers and writers
Bless you, all female politicians and judges and lawyers
Bless you, all women whose names we do not know or remember
Bless you, all women of all colors and countries and cultures
Bless you to all my students, who taught me to teach
Bless you, all Cosmic Cowgirls! And all the women and girls said YAHOO!

**Mary's Sheroes**
Thanks Sojourner Truth for "Ain't I A Woman."
Thanks Buffy Sainte-Marie for "My Way."
Thanks Eleanor Roosevelt for not caring what they said about you and letting your beauty shine.
Thanks Wilma Mankiller for being first woman Principal Chief of the Cherokee Nation.
Thanks for all the women who came before me and paved the way.
Thanks Melissa Ethridge for rocking it out and being there for me through it all.
Thanks Kate Hepburn for doing it your way – and in pants.
Thanks Joni Mitchell for defining a moment in time.
Thanks Shiloh Sophia McCloud for creating beauty that I can relate to.
Thanks Valerie and Elizabeth for being my sisters and my friend.
Thanks Elizabeth Cady Stanton for standing for all women.
Thanks Alice Munro for writing the stories of women.
Thanks Janis Joplin for being the voice of wild women everywhere.

Thanks Rheta-Helen Hermolin for showing me that it's possible to do it differently and never knowing a stranger. I miss you wildly, madly, deeply.

Thanks Jess, Mercede and Sam for coming into my life and being my wise teachers.

Thanks KD Lang for being a cowgirl with the voice of an angel.

Thanks to young women everywhere who are doing it your way.

Thanks to my girlfriends, one and all, for the power of your friendship.

Thank You Maya Angelou for the Sheroe word!

**Caron's Sheroes**

Thank you to my three granddaughters for being gorgeous, smart, and funny: Kirsten for being so cool and for my beautiful and good great grandsons. Morgan, for your powerful dancing and for my huggy bear great grandson. Haley for your excellent writing, and for being so faithful about staying in touch with me.

Thank you to my three B's: Brenda, who with my son Brent, has done a great job of staying together and raising incredible daughters. Bridget, my niece, for your unique beauty and style, your commitment and approach to education, your dancing, and for making me feel like I get to be a sheroe too. Brigitta, my beautiful and truly brilliant friend, for surpassing all that one hopes for in a friend and for your phone messages which say all the things I want my friend to say to me, and for your great story telling, and for making me laugh.

Thank you to my perfect D: Dori for being exactly who and what we needed. I love you like my very own.

Thank you to my number one L: Lillian, my step-mother who taught me about Jesus, truly loved my father, and gave me my Sheroe Sister, Janet.

Thank you to my four M's: Eden McCloud for being my Mama. You never taught me to worry about what the neighbors think, you never told me something couldn't be fixed, you showed me how productively and lovingly women, in spite of conflicts, can live and work together. Thank you for your incredible dancing. Mary for giving birth to, raising and teaching Jesus. Marilyn Cotton for being gorgeous, a brilliant musician and vocalist, a great story teller, very funny, and a very good woman. Mary Stella, for your wildness and wisdom and for coming to be with us just in time.

Thank you to my four S's: Janet Seaforth, my sister, who embodies the meeting of East and West and whose intelligence and 'Sing it again!" enthusiasm continues to engender the conversation that I most love. Thank you for your dancing and all your great moves. Sue Sellars for giving me perspective, and the courage to walk my own path, which is the science and metaphysics to which you introduced me braided with my theology and faith, and for helping me raise my children. Shannon, my daughter. Your beauty, loyalty, understanding, courage, strength, perseverance, gentle heart and touch continue to blow me away, to say nothing of your dancing! Shiloh, my daughter. Your incredible talent for art and writing, your commitment to ministry and healing, and to Jesus and Mary, your beauty and wisdom continue to blow me away. Thank both of you for loving me, forgiving me, and making me laugh.

Thank you to my first Sheoes: Wonder Woman and Sheena, Queen of the Jungle, and Brenda Starr for impacting my life with "The Right Stuff" before I was even old enough to read.

**Shannon's Sheroes**

Blessings to those Sheroes who are longing to be born.

Blessings to Bonnie Raitt for telling them I was with you when my fake I.D. didn't pass inspection and inviting me onstage to sing. And for remaining in my herstory so I could always feel safe to listen, learn and sing and dance with you. Thank you for sustaining me throughout the years no matter how lonely, happy, sad, sentimental, drunk or sober I was.

Blessings to the old black woman I sometimes see who, when I ask her how she is, replies, "I am blessed and highly favored and so are you my dear child!"

Blessing to that old white woman who endlessly rings her bell with her little wrist everyday. Even when someone contributes just a penny she expresses gratitude and a sense of abundance.

Blessings to Elizabeth Sunday for your passion, images of meaningful work and inspiration.

Blessings to Denise (Indigo Owl) for standing by me and with me 24/7.

Blessings to Pamalula (Red Hot Flamingo) for staying alive and loving me so.

Blessings to Joan Muira for taking care of me and our clients with beauty and grace.

Blessings to Mary Magdalene for being a strong fortress and for taking care of Jesus.

Blessings to Pink because she is so HOT! And brave, real and gorgeous and a rockin' WoMan!

Blessings to Chaka Kahn because she is so Chaka. BeautiFULL and courageous and remarkable. She has truly been blessed in fighting her demons and the press. I am addicted to her music.

Blessings to Sandi T. of The Lesbian Mafia. She calls me her confidant and ally because I make her laugh. She thinks I am so funny and I know she is!

Blessings to Jill Abrams for her listening, her brilliant writing and her book "The Myth, The Muse, The Meshuga" and for being Meshuga.

Blessings to Miss Lola Rose, Jill Abrams mother, for being HER, for not holding back, for her humor, her opinions and "who gives a crap" attitude, for how she feels about sex and her ex. And for wanting to meet "Witty, intelligent, talented, open-minded, honest, loving people."

Blessings to Tina Turner for surviving, being sexy and being Tina!

Blessings to Annie Lennox for her complete dedication to fight for the cause of saving and healing women and children with AIDS.

Blessings to Patti Smith for courage, poetry, songs and dedication to the arts and human rights.

Blessings to Susan Carlson for caring for me and my gramma when so in need of care herself.

Blessings to Salma Hayak for being a fortress and for creating the movie about your sheroe, Frida, through intense research, brilliant directing and acting. Thank you xoxo-ing me.

Blessings to Janis Joplin. Need I say more?

Blessings to my women friends and family for reminding me I am a Sheroe and that you need me to remain on Earth when I wanted to take flight to the Celestial Heavens before my time.

Blessings to my sister and mother who have patiently awaited my return to my origin, and who have embraced me in their wings with soft warm, clean and fluffy feathers.

Blessings to our flock of Cosmic Cowgirls who are worthy women and are supporting and enabling one another to become Sheroes through serving and inspiring others.

Blessings to those who live in poverty but find a source of wealth through love and caring.

Blessings to my Sheroes that are not listed here by name but are worthy and not forgotten.

Blessings to those women who take action everyday to make Sheroism happen.

# NAME YOUR SHEROES

# Meet The Women Who Made This BOOK!

*These women made this book happen. Whether they wrote one page or twenty, they were behind the scenes working, editing, heartstorming, writing, visioning, praying and being revolutionary!*

## PRIMARY AUTHORS and ARTISTS

**Reverend Shiloh Sophia McCloud, Minister of Sacred Arts** is a visionary artist, gifted teacher and writer whose work focuses in the transformational arts movement. Believing that we can experience healing by accessing our deepest knowledge of our desires and ourselves through our creativity, she has represented, marketed and coached thousands of women. She also works with women entrepreneurs to support them in accessing and implementing their vision. She has published five illustrated journals for women's creative development, which are featured in over 350 stores and galleries throughout the United States and Canada. She became a Reverend through a Christ Sophia mystery school in 1998 and has made working with women and creating art her ministry. Shiloh is a Christian woman, who also explores the relationship of the Divine Feminine in relation to the scripture and Mama Mary.

Shiloh was raised and still lives in Northern California and shares her life with her beloved husband of the past 14 years, the musician and poet, Isaiah McCloud. She continues to work in her studio daily and she owns a gallery, runs a school for women and girls and she is the Founder of Cosmic Cowgirls Ink (CCI). " I feel that I work for the needs of the collective woman soul. My heart is filled with unreasonable love for others and it is my work to express that Love." Shiloh is known as Chief Laughing Cloud and is the President of CCI. She was born on the full moon in June 1970 in the fair county of Marin, California. www.shilohsophia.com

**Artist Sue Hoya Sellars** was born in Prince George's County, Maryland, where she was mentored while in her early teens by renowned sculptor, Lenore Thomas Straus and also studied biological illustrating with Jan Roemhild. She attended the Corcoran School of Art in Washington DC and the San Francisco Art Institute under the instruction of Wayne Tiebaugh. At age nineteen, she became the youngest person to hold the position of head illustrator for the George Vanderbilt Foundation at Stanford University. She studied anatomy at the San Francisco School of Physicians and Surgeons while illustrating with Dr. Forbes and biological engineer, Hugh Hinchcliff. She was an illustrator for Janet Bollow and Associates for three decades, illustrating college text books covering Anthropology, Biology, Geology, Psychology and Sociology. She attended the School of Electronic Art in San Francisco. Sue opened her first studio in the early sixties, producing illustrations and Object D'art in porcelain and stoneware. Her work was handled by a number of galleries throughout the country and has been showing in Shiloh McCloud's gallery since 1999. Sue is and has been Shiloh's mentor since before Shiloh was even born! Sue defines her inspiration in terms of questions. She says: After illustrating biological structures for over 45 years, my questions shifted from "What does life do in these structures, to how did life get into these structures?" and "Who is it that is even doing this wondering?" Sue is a key illustrator and graphic designer for Cosmic Cowgirls projects and back at the Rancho she is known as Bayou StarButch. www.suehoyasellars.com

**Mary MacDonald**, is a proud Canadian and has worked in the corporate, non-profit, educational and retail business worlds as a communications, marketing, public relations, publishing and fundraising professional for the past 25 years. One of Mary's passions is to support women and young girls to be cognizant of their innate value and how their contributions make a difference in the world. "I feel strongly in the power of storytelling as a way to affect positive change and the need to preserve these stories in order to grow, heal and understand the world." She is in the process of writing her first novel. She feels proud and blessed to be the step-mother of three, the sister of three, the aunt of Emily and Daniel, the sister of Richard who left us far too early and is eternally grateful for her, "community of women who hold her up with their love, laughter and wisdom." Mary is a "Founding Mama" with Cosmic Cowgirls where she is known as StellaMac and has been working with Shiloh McCloud and the Cosmic Cowgirls for a year and a half, as well as working at Wisdom House in Mendocino. www.stellamacproductions.com

**Caron McCloud**, after having lived most of her life in the San Francisco Bay Area, now lives with her partner, Jim Wilson, in Port Townsend, Washington. She creates clothing, quilts and wall hangings which she calls "McCloud Covers: Coverings for Body, Bed and Wall," and writes and performs poetry. She recently published "Rachel's Bag, In Search of the Qabalah of Our Mothers," a book about the radical actions of Old Testament women. She is working on a book to be used in a Qabalah workshop. Along with her oldest daughter Shannon, she is involved in projects with her youngest daughter, Shiloh, including producing the Shiloh Sophia wholesale line. She also has a son, Brent, three granddaughters and four great-grandsons. Caron is Assistant Chief Editor for Cosmic Cowgirls, known as Mama Cloud. www.caronmccloud.com

**Shannon McCloud** is an expert negotiator, sales woman and consultant whose success is entirely measured in terms of "The Bottom-Line." For nearly two decades she was responsible for supporting her employers and their clients, who were world-wide key business leaders, in achieving their goals to "Build and Enhance the Company's Corporate Vision, Improve Profitability" and "Increase Shareholder Value." Shannon is currently a consultant for people facing challenges requiring critical negotiation strategies and implementation in both their personal and professional lives, with her main focus on counseling women who are challenged with adversities in their life issues. "I write fairy tales for grown ups who are recovering from being grown up." Shannon, also known as The Cinnamon Cowgirl works in outreach and communications with the Cosmic Cowgirls team. www.myspace.com/thecinnamoncowgirl

**elizaBeth Benson-Udom**, is an award winning poet, writer, blogger, photographer, visual artist, suburban arts activist and creative community builder who starts stuff: artescape studios, san ramon artswalk & festival, saturday afternoon live open mic series, san ramon community theatre and most recently, elizaPress—a theme based anthology press. "My big work," says elizaBeth, "is to live in a constant state of invitation—open to the collective collaboration of the magnum opus: a human world and wanting, always, to play a part in making a space for the art that is LOVE MADE VISIBLE while I am in the world." She is a happily married wife, mother, daughter and sister. www.writressworder.com

# CONTRIBUTING AUTHORS

**Nancy Ballard**, born on May 3, 1951 in San Francisco, California, is an artist whose work has been shown internationally in hotels, restaurants and galleries. She portrays both children and adults in what she calls "essence portraits" offering them the opportunity to see that they are just fine no matter what. Some experience her work as "medicine" providing healing through gaining a new outlook on an old situation. She also writes and illustrates books, including "Loving You: Celebrating the Body Through Art." She is currently working on a journal for those caring for loved ones with Alzheimers. She is a wife, mother, grandmother and sister. www.nancyballard.com

**Jean Shinoda Bolen, M.D.**, is a psychiatrist, Jungian analyst, clinical professor of psychiatry at the University of California San Francisco, a Distinguished Life Fellow of the American Psychiatric Association and recipient of the Institute for Health and Healing's "Pioneers in Art, Science and the Soul of Healing Award." She is a former board member of the Ms. Foundation for Women and the author of ten books. www.jeanshinodabolen.com

**Alisa Franzone-Davis**, earned a Bachelor of Arts degree from Columbia University and graduated with honors. Her Juris Doctorate was earned at The University of Miami School of Law. After 13 years of practicing law she was diagnosed with a debilitating illness. During her search for healing modalities, she was guided to heal herself by changing her eating habits to the Whole, Organic, Raw Foods Diet, after 3 months, her health was restored. She retired from the law and vigorously pursued an education in this exciting, progressive culinary field. She earned certifications in the preparation and instruction of living, raw, vegan foods and their nutrition from The Ann Wigmore Institute, The Tree of Life Rejuvenation Center and The Living Light Culinary Arts Institute. Alisa is the Wellness Chair for Cosmic Cowgirls Ink and teaches workshops with CCI. She currently, resides in Northern California with her loving husband, Michael and amazingly magical son, Ian. www.iamempoweredllc.com

**Dori Etter**, holds an Honors degree in Economics and Business from Indiana University. She started her career as a computer specialist in the US Navy, has owned a restaurant, worked for city governments and most recently was an international business consultant to Fortune 500 companies. She also paints, quilts and teaches. Dori has just recently returned from traveling Around the World and has settled in California's wine country. Dori is 37 years old, grew up in Indianapolis, IN with her older brother and two younger sisters. She is Director of Operations for the Cosmic Cowgirls leadership team, partners in a wholesale business and is committed to bringing the message of the value of women's legends to women of all socio-economic classes and to truly transforming the value society places on the work of women. www.doriwyota.com

**Kelly Takunda Orphan Martinez**, a vocalist, percussionist, songwriter and dancer and a native of the San Francisco Bay Area, has performed music on three continents and in both hemispheres. She draws that musical experience into her songwriting. In 1994, after recording and touring with Babatunde Olatunji and African Rain, Kelly studied music and dance in Zimbabwe and performed for such luminaries as Nelson Mandela with The University of Zimbabwe Choir. Kelly is the founder of her own band, the KTO Project and tours regularly. She works with The San Francisco Symphony's "Adventures in Music Program," performing for over 100 elementary schools in the San Francisco area. Kelly has also served as a Minister of Music at First Congregational Church of Oakland since 2002. www.kellytakundaorphan.com

**Jenett Miller**, is a proud mother of a new son and she is a happily married woman. She lives in Northern California where she works with clients on bookkeeping projects. She is also a wonderful chef who makes amazing food for the people she loves. Jenett is a woman of the Christian faith who loves God with all her heart! She has been working with Shiloh and the Cosmic Cowgirls for over a year. www.myspace.com/jenettmiller

**Sherri Cassady Morris**, born in Bowling Green, Kentucky, now lives in California with her husband and best friend, Larry, whose three children she feels blessed to have had a part in helping raise. She enjoys a unique career as a successful makeup artist which has afforded her much opportunity for creative expression, travel and the privilege of working with many talented professionals, celebrities and political dignitaries in film, television, fashion and commercial print. Her core belief and mantra (once spoken by an unknown source she would like to one day thank with a champagne toast) is "Live the life you love and love the life you live." www.brushworxmakeup.com

**Marilyn Nyborg**, has been a spiritual activist for over 40 years ("I started VERY young!"). Socially, politically and spiritually working for that which enhances all life and empowers women and gives voice to all diversity. The last 30 years she has done personal coaching, retreats, public speaking and workshops. She is co-founder and current president of Gather the Women Global Matrix, a national and international movement to bring women together to inspire, connect, collaborate to bring positive change to our communities and to the world. Marilyn is a mother of four, grandmother of two. She has owned and managed a technical recruiting firm in the bay area and the past 20 years has tele-commuted to Silicon Valley. She and her partner of 27 years live in Grass Valley, California, in the foothills of the Sierra Mountains. www.gatherthewomen.org

**Caterina Rando**, MA, MCC, coaches women in direct selling to book, sell, recruit and lead their teams with ease. She is the creator of the popular tele-courses Direct Selling with Ease® and Recruiting with Ease®. She is an international speaker, master certified coach and author of the national best-seller Learn to Power Think. She is a co-author of Build It Big—101 Secrets from Top Direct Selling Experts and More Build It Big. She is also the Success Center Director of The Direct Selling Women's Alliance and the featured entrepreneurship expert at Staples.com. Her clients include: Warm Spirit, Mary Kay, Creative Memories, Artful Decor and Weekenders www.directsalescoaching.com

**SARK (Susan Ariel Rainbow Kennedy)**, is the author and artist of 15 bestselling books and creator of hundreds of products. An acclaimed speaker and transformational teacher, she is the CEO and founder of Planet SARK, a thriving business that promotes empowered living. She is featured in the PBS series; "Women of Wisdom and Power." SARK lives in San Francisco. Visit her at www.PlanetSARK.com or call SARK's Inspiration Phone Line at 415.546.3742.

**Nikiah Seeds**, lives in British Columbia Canada with her two children. With ten years in the birthing and holistic field, she started mom-preneur of Mama Goddess Birth Shop.com{TM}, an on-line store specializing in birthing and midwifery supplies, natural baby care and unique gifts for mothers. She began training as a Herbalist and Reflexologist and then moved into the birthing field as a professional Birth Doula. She is a childbirth educator and Certified Birthing From Within mentor, working with hundreds of birthing women and loving her role within her birthing community. www.mamagoddessbirthshop.com

**Julie Lampros-Trad**, has been in the sales and customer service industry for 20 years. Outside of work, she spends time in her garden, listening to music, painting and with her friends and family. She currently resides in Portland, Oregon with her husband and their dog Buddy.

**Alice Walker**, is one of the significant voices in American letters. She was born in Eatonton, Georgia, the eighth child of a sharecropper family. She attended Atlanta's Spelman College on full scholarship, enrolling in 1961. After transferring to Sarah Lawrence College, she wrote her first book of poems and graduated in 1965. Inspired to activism as well as to a creative life, Alice joined the civil rights movement. In the same year she graduated from Sarah Lawrence, Walker met and later married civil rights lawyer Mel Leventhal. The couple registered voters in Mississippi, endured harassment by the Klan and bore a daughter, Rebecca, in 1969. Ms. Walker has lived in northern California since the late 1970's. www.alicewalker.info

**Gennifer Mountain Weaver**, has worked with many non-profits, serving youth and women from all walks of life. She lived outside the country for three years serving in both the Peace Corps Honduras and Crisis Corps Ecuador, working on creating systems for HIV/AIDS Education and helping women access services and knowledge to reproductive health information. Even with many travels under her belt, she has yet to have found a place more serene as a trip to Mom's house in the mountains. "I am creating my next legend in service to Cosmic Cowgirls as the Membership Diva, 'Diva-G!' I have always been filled by sharing resources and passing on information to other women, so that they can make better informed choices in their lives. I am passionate about using creativity as a therapeutic outlet and love being with my new husband, family and friends, Cosmic Cowgirls and drinking coffee in the sun!"

**Ananda Wildflower**, is a High Priestess who has been blessed with the gift to empower women and girls to express their childlike joy and playfulness and manifest their highest dreams through Laughter Yoga, in the Wildflower Way. The Wildflower Way is her own creation of a beautiful blend of mystic spiritual traditions and with her love of Laughter Yoga and breathwork in Ancient Yogic and the Taoist traditions of energy healing. She is a certified Laughter Yoga Instructor and her spiritual calling is to guide others to experience their Divine Bliss, which is our true Authentic Nature of Ecstatic Bliss Consciousness. Her work is transformational, healing and powerful on all levels for the body, mind, heart and spirit. HO! HO! HA! HA! HA! www.laughteryogawisdom.com

**Ama Zenya,** was the Pastor of the First Congregational Church in Oakland, a speaker with the national Network of Spiritual Progressives and a leader in inter-faith community organizing and serves on Oakland Mayor Ron Dellums' Network for Interfaith Action. She grew up in Kenya, East Africa, the daughter of a British-Kenyan father and an Irish-American mother. She received her Bachelor of Arts degree in Religion and Women's Studies from Wesleyan University in Connecticut and both her Master of Divinity degree and her Master of Arts in Biblical Studies from the Pacific School of Religion in Berkeley, CA. Pastor Ama lives in West Oakland with her wonderful husband and baby boy. www.amazenya.net

# Color of Woman Illustrated Journals

## By Shiloh Sophia McCloud

Women all over the world have been enjoying Color of Woman Coloring Book and Journals for the last decade, finding self-expression within these pages. They have written that they have used them as tools for personal transformation. The miracle is that somehow these books can contact women wherever they are! Color of Woman Journals are my first series - they are creative sanctuaries. A sacred space to express and explore and evolve! Each woman has a story to share, a poem to unravel, a dream to realize, a song to sing, a plan to craft, a wound to unwind, a vision to manifest, a journey to take, a prayer to dance, a life to live out loud, an image to reveal and these journals are made for just that!

These books are 9" x 11" with 30 illustrations of inspiring women to color, 90 blank pages on thick, creamy 110 lb. card stock. The paper accommodates pens, pencils, watercolor and acrylic paint. All of them include the artist's wisdom on the creative journey!

**Color of Woman - Journey to the Sanctuary Within**
This journal explores reclaiming our bodies and our natural cycles, a healthy self image, the journey of feminine spirituality, creativity as a conscious form of healing, choosing yourself as a creative being, matriarchal roots and sacred pathways.

**She Moves To Her Own Rhythm - A Guided Exploration**
This journal explores creativity as a journey to the self, expressing your wild-woman, breaking out of "boxes," finding your true voice, expressing your vision with passion, permission to play and be outrageous, learning to think like an artist, giving up guilt and choosing life!

**She Dances Between The Worlds - Exploring the Language of the Heart Through Word and Image**
This journal explores the challenges and joys of living in spirit and matter, relating to our internal voices with humor and creative expression, considering what is possible for our lives when we nurture all aspects of who we are, claiming our identity and transforming tragedy into triumph!

**Her Evolution - A Woman's Workbook for Personal Transformation**
This workbook explores the healing path, creativity as spiritual practice, writing and drawing as tools for self awakening, listening to our inner guidance, connecting with the spirit of life, the power of women as creators, self honor and acceptance, breaking through to your WORK!

**Heart Wings - A Book About Real Friendship**
This Journal honors the sisters of our heart through illustrations and quotes about the joys and challenges of really being there for someone. It celebrates the bond of women, risk taking and standing for each other's truths. This is also a good book for a woman to get for her own self! 5.5" x 8.5" - 33 Pages of illustrations - 70 blank pages

**Published by Cosmic Cowgirls Ink, LLC**

# Sacred Art Statement of Shiloh Sophia McCloud

I believe that art is a Spiritual Practice. I believe that art is a Path of Healing. I am an artist who performs my work as a Spiritual Practice. I think of my paintings, which I call Sacred Art, as: Prayers for the world; Offerings of love and hope and rest; Alignment with wellness and beauty; Devotions of gratitude and praise to the Divine; A most delicious outpouring of my soul.

Everything I create is rooted in my desire to ease the suffering of the world. Some of us serve in soup kitchens. Some of us are marching. Some hold the hands of the dying. Some of us teach. Some fight. Some pray. And some of us, create art.

Artists touch the suffering through our creations. Some say that art is not as important as other works and that to paint or sing or write a poem is not of the same worth as planting and digging carrots or volunteering at the (fill in the blank). But I believe that when the artist is committed to art as a form of service and devotion, it is as important as any and every other form of service and devotion.

I am not speaking of all art. I am speaking of Sacred Art. Art specifically and consciously committed to revelation, to inspiring healing and wholeness. Art—like a hearty soup cooked with love, a garden planted and tended with care, a song that raises one's spirit—art that is intended to lift the soul of humanity. Art in which we FEEL the soul of the work, speaking to us. This, I call Sacred Art.

I began creating Sacred Art over thirteen years ago. I had one of those mountain top experiences in Northern California. My heart had belonged to Jesus since I was a kid, but as a young adult, I felt that I desperately needed to speak with my Mother—my Divine Mother. Although I am not sure if I even knew there was one at that time, my earthly mother recently recalled to me that when I was a child, I had asked if Jesus came from a broken home. She said I wanted to know where his mom was since people always talked about his father, but not his mommie.

Some might call my mountain top encounter an awakening. Surely it was, for it was when the Mother, in the form of Mary, revealed herself to me that I truly became me. I was twenty-two at the time and had been seeking my art form for some years, but with very little fruit. As a result of becoming me, my art was also born. It is no surprise that the very first art I created that I KNEW was my life work was a Madonna and Child.

My call to create rang out from the heart of the Divine and I answered, YES!! I have not ceased to create since that time. This work is informed by something that is always challenging to put into words. Before I did not know what to create and for whom, so my work lacked vitality and originality. But with the coming of the Mother Mary—my precious Mary Ma—came information about the suffering of the world. With that, came responsibility. I knew of the suffering and tragedy, but I had been removed from it. It was "out there," not "in here." It was as if parts of my heart had been veiled and had suddenly became illuminated. I had access to more of my feeling, my seeing, my loving. I also felt profound agonizing emotional pain. This awakening was one of the most mystical experiences of my life—almost a third "birthing." First was entering the world, second was connecting with Jesus Christ and third was this awareness of my Divine Mother, her relationship to her children and my call to art. I prayed to her about what I was supposed to do about all of this newfound pain. Art was her answer. In order to contribute to the healing of our world I was to create and teach others to create. I have not stopped since!!!

As soon as I began to paint, the pain transitioned into knowledge, knowledge transitioned into wisdom and wisdom informed not only painting, but teaching. Clearly, my gift was to be, not only the products from painting, but the sharing and teaching of the process and to prosper the work itself. With the love, encouragement and support of my life long mentor, Sue Hoya Sellars, my beloved husband, Isaiah, and my wise mother, Caron, my career was launched. I had my first art show exactly one and a half years later. I sold everything. I went to seminary in Boulder Colorado to become a Reverend in the mystical Church of Grace of Sophia. Through my training there, the depth and breadth of my artwork as my ministry blossomed. I had ongoing shows at local cafes and galleries and I published my first journal book, Color of Woman, at Kinkos.

Now, twelve years later, I have consistently made a living through my sacred practice of creating and teaching art. With the continuing help and support of my family, I opened a gallery about ten years ago. I began having workshops and events designed to raise awareness around important issues. For example, we worked with Parsa, to connect with women artists in Afghanistan (pre-9-11) to create prayer shawls for women in our community. We educated people regarding these women and the conditions under which they lived and labored. They risked their lives to create those shawls for us. Their work arrived that November following 9-11.

I believe that all of us are creative beings with stories to tell and gifts to share. Art may be a natural talent, coming more easily to some than others, but I now know that it can be learned. Trying to make images look like something that already exists is what thwarts our efforts. If we invent from the soul, with our focus on the good, what comes out will be true and original. It cannot not be so. I have taught hundreds of women to paint who did not think that they could. But they did! And they loved it! And they learned that art can be a sacred practice. Being in possession of the peace, bliss and fulfillment that comes with finding one's life work, I cannot cease asking others these questions: What is YOUR vision? YOUR life work? What did YOU come here to create, birth, reveal, transform, fulfill? Until we have found what it is we REALLY care about, how can we know what to attract, what to focus on, what to manifest? It is with a heart full of love, gratitude and endless prayers, painted and yet to be painted, that I leave you with these questions.

**www.shilohsophia.com**

## *Our Visionary Sisterhood Partnerships*

Personal health and wealth does not occur in isolation. It happens in our work with others. Working with other women and women's organizations is an important part of the work we are doing! The following two organizations are doing POWERFUL work with women and girls in the world and we are honored to sister with them to bring education and resources to those in need of them. We are sharing 10% of our net profit with these two groups as a thanks to our teachers and mentors who are doing this good work.

women's**initiative** Inspiring High-Potential, Low-Income Women Entrepreneurs since 1988. Women's Initiative is a not-for-profit agency. Our mission is to build the entrepreneurial capacity of women to overcome economic and social barriers and achieve self-sufficiency. Women's Initiative has proven that women create jobs for themselves and others, access the mainstream economy and increase their economic self-sufficiency when they are given business planning and financing support.

By assisting women-owned businesses throughout the San Francisco Bay Area at our seven training sites, Women's Initiative directly contributes to the economic growth of communities. Our graduates have started and expanded over 1,600 businesses from photography studios to catering companies and mechanic shops. Our graduate created 301 new jobs in 2006.

www.womensinitiative.org

**girls inc.** Girls Incorporated is a national nonprofit organization that inspires all girls to be strong, smart and bold. With local roots dating to 1864 and national status since 1945, Girls Inc. has responded to the changing needs of girls and their communities through programs and advocacy that empower girls to reach their full potential, understand their value and assert their rights. Girls Inc. public education extends the values of girls' rights to adults as well, giving them the tools they need to assist girls' efforts to access their rights. Inspiring all girls to be strong, smart and bold.

www.girlsinc.com www.girlsincislandcity.org

**Do you want to collaborate on a project with us?**
**For a growing on-line list of resources and connections for visionary women go to: www.cosmiccowgirls.com**

# MAMA MILLIONAIRE DESIGNS

## Marketplace for Visionary Entrepreneurs

*Mama Millionaire is a brand of Cosmic Cowgirls Ink, LLC*

**Graphic Design**
**Web Hosting and Design**
**Promotional Printing of Postcards & Business Cards**
**Print-On-Demand Book Services**
**and Visionary Coaching**

Mama Millionaire was born out of our desire to provide affordable printing promotional services to the Member Owners within Cosmic Cowgirls - as well as to provide work for the Cowgirls themselves. We have many women who are stay-at-home moms, who have full time jobs, or women who are just getting their business started who want to create additional income on a very part time basis working with MMD projects. The services are available to the general public and we are focusing on marketing our services to women in business and women's organizations.

In addition, there are many of our Members who want to write or publish a book. Cosmic Cowgirls focuses on journals and workbooks for transformation, but women have lots of other book ideas too. So we have begun the MMD print-on-demand division to enable women to print their books through us with help navigating the rough terrain of the POD world.

We also have expert graphic and web designers on staff who can help women get their business presence out to the world - and get their promotional materials printed through MMD. We also have very seasoned business and visionary coaches who can guide women to create their own visionary business plans that they can take to the bank.

Don't let a technology challenge stop you from launching your brand simply because you don't know about printing or graphic design! MMD can build you a website that comes with our own on line web hosting program, so that you will learn how to update your own site once it's set up. The exciting news is you don't have to be techno-savvy to build your website - you are guided all the way through with templates - did I mention the word EASY - yep it's true and we have techno-phobe happy customers to testify to that! MamaMillionaire is here to help make it happen! All that being said, we are just getting this started, with a handful of happy clients who have already used our services, we are ready to get the word out. Share it with your friends!

**www.mamamillionairedesigns.com**

# UPCOMING PROJECTS

## FROM THE PALM OF HER HAND

*Palm of Her Hand is a brand for Cosmic Cowgirls.*

**IN THE WORKS**

Speaking My Truth: A Girls Rights of Passage Journal
The Caring One Journal: Caring for People With Alzheimers
Mending Invisible Wings: Healing from the Loss of A Child

**ON THE WAY**

A Journal for Women In Prison
Giving Birth - Pregnancy Journal: From Conception to Delivery
Recovery Journal from Drugs and Alcohol
Recovery Journal - Surviving Sexual Abuse
And Loss of A Loved One, Breast Cancer, Cancer Recovery,
The Red Thread - Women's Crafts: Knitting and Quilting
Women's Wellness Workbook
and about 100 more!

**www.palmofherhand.com and www.cosmiscowgirls.com**

***Are you are writer, or one who is just budding? Are you an artist, or one who is just starting? You can participate in our projects no matter HOW talented you think you are! Join us at the rodeo of the soul with the other Cosmic Cowgirls and share your story!***

# ABOUT THE COSMIC COWGIRLS!

COSMIC COWGIRLS is a revolutionary woman and girl powered production and publishing house committed to transforming lives into legends. We are a membership based collective that produces workshops, films, music, publish art, books and cards. Women from all over the world are joining us as members who are committed to creating positive revolutionary media.

Our organization was established by twenty-five Founding Mamas on January 23, 2006 in San Francisco, California. This vision was born out of a ten-year project of art and publishing called Color of Woman. Founder Reverend Shiloh Sophia McCloud has worked in the Sacred Arts Movement for the past thirteen years. She has published five journals and taught thousands of women about creativity as a path of personal transformation and spiritual practice. She brings her passionate work and research in this field to the platform of Cosmic Cowgirls, with the intention of expanding this ministry to include the voices and visions of other women and girls who are committed to this work.

We believe that each of us has a story to share that can empower and bless other women. Cosmic Cowgirls is the arena in which our stories, challenges and victories can be expressed and shared.

What if the suffering we have experienced could be transformed into medicine and healing for other women? What if our experiences could be used to ignite and support the success and prosperity of other women? What if women were actually able to financially support themselves through their creativity and teach others to do so? What if we have done enough healing work to enable ourselves and others to get on with the work of the visionary within each of us?

Guided by the spirit of love, wisdom, truth, abundance, compassion, justice and celebration, we are gathering our tribe and creating a legacy for ourselves and for future generations. We create, celebrate, shine and have a grand time! The collaborative creation of our work is designed to illuminate, inspire and inform the journey of a woman's life. A Cosmic Cowgirl is a woman with her feet in the grassroots and her head in the stars. She is both grounded in reality and continuously dreaming about what is possible, for herself, and for all people.

***www.cosmiccowgirls.com*** ***www.palmofherhand.com***

# DECLARATION

**On this day we do hereby offer this book**
**on the altar of wisdom books.**
**May this work serve as the blessing for which it was made,**
**to empower women to do the work they are called to -**
**And in so doing, bless the whole world with the fruits of their labors and**
**the radiant beauty of their gifts.**
**This book is given in the spirit of healing and transformation**
**with the knowledge that when women are able to be**
**who they truly are, all are blessed.**
**Amen and YAHOOO!**

## See You At The Marketplace!

*Well, Blessings to YOU Dear One*
*As You Go Out Into the World Shining!*
*We give you our absolute blessings to go and do your work!*
*We hope this workbook has been a gift to you on your path.*
*And that it has helped to empower you to do what you are HERE on this planet to DO and to BE! We know that it is often hard. And often seems impossible. And that we can wonder if it is worth it to keep going when there seems to be so many odds against us. Just because we are doing everything the best we can with the most positive attitude does not mean it is all going to go our way. We can learn to see the obstacles as teaching tools - but whatever we do - whatever you do - do not quit. Keep on working on your vision even if it is a little bit at a time. You never have to NOT be doing your life work again. You can claim that you are ON THE PATH and make that integral with your identity. You are a legendary visionary woman!*
*Be true to you. And do your good work. Love yourself first. And play hard. Make enough money. Feel like you are enough. Share your gifts with others. Be creative. Practice the parts that challenge you. Get help when you need it. And as my mother always says:Love. Trust. Dare. Create. Pray. Dance. and her newest is: Rest.*

*Never. Ever. Give up on your dream. It is living in and through you.*

*Blessings, from deep within my heart. I am sending you a big joyful HUG! (Did you feel it?)*
*Reverend Shiloh Sophia McCloud, June 2008*

# NOTES

# JOIN THE
# 25,000
# Woman Challenge
## Be A Part of Founding A Visionary Fund for Women!

One of our goals at Cosmic Cowgirls is to provide funding, scholarships and micro loans for women to start or improve their own businesses and to support them in projects dear to their heart.

A part of our plan to make that happen is for women to either contribute anonymously and or to add their business in our on-line advertising directory.
The cost is $10! Half of that will go towards the our fund for women and the other half to setting up a sustainable structure.

When 25,000 women sign up, we will have $125,000 to start giving from our fund.
We will continue to partner with not-for-profits and other service based organizations to make this happen!
Join us!

FOR DETAILS and TO JOIN US:
www.mamamillionairedesigns.com

*Many persons have a wrong idea
of what constitutes true happiness.
It is not attained through
self-gratification
but through fidelity
to a worthy purpose.*

*Helen Keller*